Police Law Primer

Police Law Primer

Fourth Edition

Kenneth Sloan
Legal Editor, Police Review

Butterworths
London, Dublin & Edinburgh
1992

United Kingdom	Butterworth & Co (Publishers) Ltd, 88 Kingsway, LONDON WC2B 6AB and 4 Hill Street, EDINBURGH EH2 3JZ
Australia	Butterworths Pty Ltd, SYDNEY, MELBOURNE, BRISBANE, ADELAIDE, PERTH, CANBERRA and HOBART
Belgium	Butterworth & Co (Publishers) Ltd, BRUSSELS
Canada	Butterworths Canada Ltd, TORONTO and VANCOUVER
Ireland	Butterworth (Ireland) Ltd, DUBLIN
Malaysia	Malayan Law Journal Sdn Bhd, KUALA LUMPUR
New Zealand	Butterworths of New Zealand Ltd, WELLINGTON and AUCKLAND
Puerto Rico	Equity de Puerto Rico, Inc, HATO REY
Singapore	Malayan Law Journal Pte Ltd, SINGAPORE
USA	Butterworth Legal Publishers, AUSTIN, Texas; BOSTON, Massachusetts; CLEARWATER, Florida (D & S Publishers); ORFORD, New Hampshire (Equity Publishing); ST PAUL, Minnesota; and SEATTLE, Washington

A CIP Catalogue record for this book is available from the British Library.

ISBN 0 406 00879 5

Printed by Thomson Litho Ltd, East Kilbride, Scotland

Preface

Much of this book has had to be revised since the last edition and a number of chapters have had to be rewritten. The new legislation includes the revised Codes of Practice, the Road Traffic Act 1988 as amended by the 1991 Act, the Firearms (Amendment) Act 1988, the Licensing (Amendment) Act 1988, the Children Act 1989 and the Criminal Justice Act 1991, plus a considerable quantity of statutory instruments.

I originally wrote *Police Law Primer* to provide a reasonably comprehensive coverage of the law of interest to police officers of all ranks in a compact form. Many modern textbooks simply sit on the shelves gathering dust because they are too bulky to be readily usable and I wanted mine to be read. Judging by the comments I have received over the years the book has fulfilled its purpose of providing a basic knowledge of the law and acting as a quick reference work. In respect of the latter purpose, all sources are quoted throughout so that more detailed research may be undertaken if necessary.

I have also discovered that it has been found to be of assistance to promotion examination candidates and I hope that it continues to help those taking the OSPRE examinations. Most of the new syllabus is included and is in a form which can be studied at odd moments.

As always, I thank all those who have offered criticism and suggestions for improvement. I welcome any contact with readers and will willingly answer any queries that may arise (but please enclose a stamped addressed envelope for a reply).

Ken Sloan
37 Macauley Road
Stockport
SK5 6JR

March 1992

PS Many thanks to my daughter, Mrs T A Geer, for her efforts in compiling the index.

Contents

Part 1
Evidence and Procedure

Chapter 1
Courts of Justice

MAGISTRATES' COURTS (PROCEEDINGS, FUNCTIONS, COMPOSITION AND JURISDICTION)

Magistrates

Magistrates or Justices of the Peace, are appointed on behalf of the Crown by the Lord Chancellor, or the Chancellor of the Duchy of Lancaster in Greater Manchester, Lancashire and Merseyside. Appointments are for a particular commission area, ie any county, any London commission area or the City of London.

Their services as magistrates are unpaid and legal qualifications are not required. The appointment is for life, but they may resign or be disqualified. Magistrates may be placed on the supplemental list and no longer sit in court as a result of age or for other reasons.

Their functions are:

(a) Judicial; ie to try certain offences and act as examining justices in other cases.

(b) Executive; ie to issue summonses, warrants, etc.

(c) Administrative; ie overseeing licensed premises, visiting prisons, etc.

Stipendiary magistrates are barristers or solicitors of not less than seven years' standing, who are appointed by the Crown to certain magistrates' courts, mainly in large cities. They are paid and have the same power as a bench of lay magistrates (Justices of the Peace Act 1979).

The courts

Magistrates' courts are held as and when required in the following circumstances:

   (a) Magistrates' or petty sessional courts;
- (i) To enquire into indictable offences as examining justices and either discharge the prisoner or commit him for trial by jury. A single justice may act in such a manner.
- (ii) To try offences triable any way (ie offences listed in Sch 1 to the Magistrates' Courts Act 1980).
- (iii) To try summary offences.
- (iv) To deal with certain complaints such as dangerous dogs or affiliation, etc.

   (b) Juvenile courts to deal with children and young persons charged with offences, or in need of care or control. They should consist of not less than two and not more than three justices.

   (c) Domestic proceedings courts; to deal with guardianship, separation, maintenance, etc.

   (d) Occasional courts; these are courts which function in county areas only, at places specially appointed to be used as an occasional court house. They deal with matters which cannot await the regular sittings of the magistrates' court. The maximum penalty which can be imposed is the same as that for a single magistrate.

   (e) Licensing committees.

Open court and prohibitions

As a general rule, with the exception of juvenile or domestic courts, proceedings must be in open court. However, children under 14 years, unless infants in arms or involved in the proceedings, must not enter the court.

A court can hear proceedings in camera (ie in private) only on grounds that justice would manifestly be defeated, or it would be contrary to public interest (eg proceedings under Official Secrets Acts) if the case were in open court.

It is an offence to take photographs in a court or the precincts of a court building, or make portraits or sketches of a judge, juror, witness, or party to the proceedings (Criminal Justice Act 1925, s41).

Appeals

A person convicted by a magistrates' court may appeal to a Crown Court:
- (i) if he pleaded 'guilty' generally against sentence only;
- (ii) if he pleaded 'not guilty' both against conviction and sentence.

Any aggrieved party may appeal to the Queen's Bench Divisional Court on any point of law by way of 'case stated'.

Progress of a 'not guilty' summary case before a magistrates' court

The accused is identified to the court, the charge is read out to him by the magistrates' clerk and he is asked to plead. After a plea of 'not guilty' the prosecutor may address the court outlining the facts of the case. The prosecutor then calls the witness or witnesses for the prosecution to give their evidence. These witnesses are examined by the prosecutor and they may then be cross-examined by the defending solicitor or counsel. If there has been a cross-examination the prosecutor may re-examine the witness on new facts elicited by, or to explain doubts raised by, the cross-examination. Entirely new evidence cannot be introduced except by leave of the court.

At the conclusion of the case for the prosecution the defending solicitor may address the court with a submission that there is no case to answer. If the court is not satisfied that a prima facie case has been made out they may dismiss the case at this stage.

If the case continues the solicitor for the defence may then either: address the court and call his witnesses, leave the address until after the defence witnesses have been called, or make an address without calling the witnesses.

When he calls the witnesses to give sworn evidence for the defence the defendant may be called and may make an unsworn statement instead of giving evidence on oath. If so, he cannot be questioned on this by the prosecution.

When the defence witnesses give evidence on oath they may be cross-examined and may also be re-examined. At the conclusion of the evidence for the defence the prosecution may call evidence of rebuttal. Such evidence can, however, only be admitted if it is confined to matters which have arisen unexpectedly in the course of the case for the defence.

After all this evidence has been heard either party may, with permission, address the court. If the court grants leave to one side to address the court for a second time it shall not refuse leave to the other side. Where both parties address the court twice the prosecutor shall address the court for the second time before the defence does.

After hearing the evidence and the speeches the court may then reach and deliver a verdict, and may retire from the bench in order to deliberate if necessary. If the court finds the defendant guilty it may hear evidence of character and antecedents before proceeding to sentence or otherwise deal with him.

Progress of an indictable case before a magistrates' and a Crown Court

The accused is brought before a summary court or examining justices, either by arrest or summons.

If the case is to go for trial to the Crown Court, examining justices record evidence in the form of depositions, or tender the submitted written statements in accordance with the Criminal Justice Act 1967. The justices consider whether there is sufficient evidence to commit the case for trial, or may, under s1 of the Criminal Justice Act 1967, send it for trial without consideration of the evidence. In either case the court may commit the accused on bail or in custody, and secure the attendance of prosecutor and witnesses at the trial.

At the Crown Court, an indictment is preferred, witnesses give evidence and a jury decides whether the accused is guilty or not. If guilty, the judge hears antecedents and pronounces sentence.

Offences triable either way

In the case of offences triable either way (ie summarily or on indictment) the mode of trial has to be determined by the magistrates. This is done by considering the nature of the case; whether the circumstances make the offence one of serious character; whether the punishment which a magistrates' court has power to inflict would be adequate; and any other circumstances which appear to the court to make it more suitable for trial in one way rather than the other.

If it is decided that the case should be dealt with summarily, the accused must be asked if he consents to this or wishes to be tried by jury and his is the final decision. Where there is a finding of guilt on summary trial the accused may be committed to the Crown Court for sentence (Magistrates' Courts Act 1980, s17 and Sch 1).

Offences under s1 of the Criminal Damage Act 1971 may be dealt with summarily if the damage is valued at less than £2,000 (Magistrates' Courts Act 1980, s22 and Sch 2).

CROWN COURTS

Crown Courts were established by the Courts Act 1971. They are the courts to which indictable cases are committed for trial or sentence by magistrates' courts.

Crown Courts may sit anywhere in England and Wales, and county boundaries have no significance in determining where a case should be heard. For administrative purposes the courts are grouped into six circuits, each circuit consisting of:

(a)   First-tier courts which are presided over by High Court and circuit judges and deal with criminal cases and civil cases.

(b) Second-tier courts which are presided over by High Court and circuit judges and deal with criminal cases only.

(c) Third-tier courts which are presided over by circuit judges and recorders, and deal with criminal cases only.

Recorders act when the need arises as part-time judges of the Crown Court. Justices can sit with a judge, as members of the court, when dealing with appeals and committals for sentence. They may also sit in other specified types of proceedings; eg appeals against a decision of the licensing justices.

The jurisdiction of Crown Courts is:

(a) To hear and determine all trials on indictment, with a jury.

(b) To hear appeals from magistrates' courts and pass sentence when cases are committed by magistrates' courts for that purpose. In these circumstances a jury is not required.

(c) To hear original proceedings in certain civil matters.

Different types of proceedings are heard by High Court judges, circuit judges and recorders respectively: and for this purpose offences are divided into different classes, as follows:

(a) Class 1 offences are triable only by a High Court judge. These are: any offence punishable by death; misprision of treason and treason felony; murder; genocide; offences under the Official Secrets Act; and inciting, attempting or conspiring to commit those offences.

(b) Class 2 offences are triable only by a High Court judge, except where a particular case is directed to be heard by a circuit judge or recorder. These offences are: manslaughter; infanticide or abortion; rape or intercourse with a girl under 13 years; sedition; mutiny or piracy; offences against the Geneva Convention Act; and inciting, attempting or conspiring to commit any of the above.

(c) Class 3 offences, which include all indictable offences other than those in Classes 1, 2 and 4, are normally tried by a High Court judge, but may be heard by a circuit judge or recorder.

(d) Class 4 offences are normally tried by a circuit judge or recorder. They are offences triable either way; conspiracy to commit an offence triable either way; death by reckless driving; burglary in a dwelling following forcible entry, etc; and any offence in Class 3 if it is so directed in a particular case.

Note: An indictable offence is an offence which is triable on indictment, whether it is exclusively so triable or triable either way. An indictment is a written or printed accusation setting out the crime for which a person is to be tried.

COURTS OF APPEAL

Crown Court

Hears appeals from decisions in magistrates' courts by re-trying the case, without a jury.

Queen's Bench Division

A division of the High Court composed of the Lord Chief Justice and other High Court judges. Its appellate functions are exercised by two judges sitting as a Divisional Court and they hear appeals on points of law by way of 'case stated' from a magistrates' court or Crown Court.

Court of Appeal (Criminal Division)

An uneven number of not less than three judges of the Queen's Bench Division sit in the Criminal Division of the Court of Appeal to hear appeals on matters of law, fact or sentence from the Crown Court. The Lord Chief Justice or the Lord Justice of Appeal may preside.

House of Lords

The House of Lords is the highest and final court of appeal and only hears cases where points of law of general public importance are involved. A quorum of three sit, comprising the Lord Chancellor, ex-Lord Chancellor and Lords of Appeal in Ordinary.

VENUE

The venue is the place of trial.

A magistrates' court may try any summary offences committed within the area of jurisdiction for which the justices are appointed. It may also try such offences committed within 500 yards of the boundary of its area, and those committed on journeys starting in one jurisdiction and ending in another.

Indictable offences committed within the court's jurisdiction may be dealt with by a magistrates' court acting as examining justices and they may also try indictable offences which are triable either way. A court may deal with such offences committed anywhere if the accused resides within its jurisdiction, or if it is considered to be in the interests of justice to try him jointly or at the same time as another person already charged within its area.

Other offences may be committed for trial to any appropriate court, having regard to the convenience of the defence, prosecution and witnesses and with a view to expediting trial.

CORONERS AND INQUESTS

Coroners' Court

It is the coroner's duty to investigate all cases of sudden, violent or unnatural deaths, and his enquiry is known as an inquest. It is also his duty to enquire into treasure trove. A coroner's actions are governed by the Coroners' Act 1988 and the Coroners' Rules.

A coroner's inquest is a court of law, although no person is accused before it. The functions of an inquest are to ascertain who the deceased was; how, when and where he died; and if any persons are to be charged with murder, manslaughter or infanticide.

Cases when an inquest must be held

The coroner must hold an inquest in the following cases:
  (a) when there is reasonable cause to suspect that a person has died either a violent or unnatural death, or has died a sudden death of which the cause is unknown;
  (b) where a person has died in prison;
  (c) when a person has died under such circumstances as to require an inquest in accordance with an Act of Parliament, eg an inmate of a mental home.

Inquests–place of holding and days on which not to be held

Inquests may be held anywhere, but should not be held in premises licensed for the sale of intoxicants if other premises are available. They should not be held on Christmas Day, Good Friday and bank holidays unless necessary on grounds of urgency, and shall not be held on Sundays.

Coroner's jury

The coroner decides whether the inquest shall be with or without a jury, except where the law requires him to have one, as follows:
- (a) where it appears that the deceased died as a result of murder, manslaughter or infanticide; or
- (b) where death occurred in prison, or in police custody, or was caused by a police officer in the execution of his duty; or
- (c) was caused by accident, poisoning or disease which must be notified to a government department or official under any Act, eg mining, factory or railway accidents, etc; or
- (d) occurred in circumstances, the continuance of which would be prejudicial to public health or safety, eg food poisoning, epidemics, etc; or
- (e) was caused by an accident arising out of the use of a vehicle in a street or public highway; or
- (f) in any other case, if it appears to the coroner there is a good reason for summoning a jury; or
- (g) regarding the finding of treasure trove.

(Treasure trove is where any gold or silver in coin, plate or bullion is found concealed in any building or in the earth. If the owner is unknown the treasure trove is the property of the Crown. Concealing the finding of treasure trove is a common law misdemeanour but is now dealt with as theft.)

Chapter 2
Evidence

EXPLANATION OF TERMS, ETC

Oath

All evidence must be given on oath or affirmation, except in the case of a child too young to know the nature of an oath.

The normal form of oath is taken on the New Testament as follows: 'I swear by Almighty God that the evidence I shall give shall be the truth, the whole truth and nothing but the truth'.

If this is contrary to any religious belief a witness may be sworn in the manner prescribed by his religion. In cases where a witness has no religious belief, or objects to taking any form of oath, he may affirm by saying 'I do solemnly and truly declare and affirm . . . '

In a juvenile court the prescribed oath is: 'I promise before Almighty God to tell the truth, the whole truth and nothing but the truth'.

Number of witnesses

Generally speaking, the uncorroborated evidence of one witness will suffice, but in certain instances evidence must be given by at least two witnesses, eg personation of voters at elections. In other cases the evidence of one witness must be corroborated by another witness or some other relevant fact.

Corroborative evidence

This is evidence tending to support the truthfulness and accuracy of evidence already given.

Corroboration is required by law in cases of:

(a) perjury;
(b) procuration;
(c) speeding, if it is based on opinion.
Corroboration is required in practice (but not by law) in cases of:
(a) evidence of an accomplice;
(b) sworn evidence of a child of tender years;
(c) evidence of the injured party in sexual cases (recent complaint).

Competency and compellability

As a general rule anyone is competent to give evidence. A court may decide, however, that children of tender years, mentally disordered and drunken persons are not competent. Special rules apply to husbands and wives.

In any proceedings the husband or wife of the accused (unless they are jointly charged with an offence) shall:
(a) be *competent* to give evidence for the prosecution, and on behalf of the accused or any person jointly charged with the accused;
(b) be *compellable* to give evidence on behalf of the accused;
(c) be *compellable* to give evidence for the prosecution or on behalf of any person jointly charged with the accused if the offence charged:
　　(i)   involves an assault on, or injury or a threat of injury to, the wife or husband of the accused, or a person under the age of 16; or
　　(ii) is a sexual offence on a person under the age of 16; or
　　(iii) consists of attempting, conspiring to commit, or aiding, abetting, counselling, procuring or inciting those offences.

Any person who is a competent witness can be compelled to attend court and give evidence. If a witness refuses to answer a summons or warrant to attend, or fails to give evidence, he may be committed to prison for contempt of court (Police and Criminal Evidence Act 1984, s80).

Cases out of court

On the application of either side, the court may order a witness out of court to prevent their testimony being influenced by that of other witnesses.

The nature of evidence

In law the term 'evidence' is used to indicate the means by which any fact or point in issue or question may be proved or disproved in a manner complying with the legal rules governing the subject.

Evidence may be presented in the following ways:
(a) Oral or parol–where a witness relates facts by word of mouth.
(b) Documentary–where a document is produced for inspection, or is read in court, eg medical certificate, plan or sketch, photograph.
(c) Real–actual articles used in or connected with the offence, eg a weapon.

The best evidence is primary evidence and generally speaking the court will only accept the best evidence, but in certain cases, on proof that the best evidence is not available, a court may accept secondary evidence. This is known as the 'best evidence rule'.

Primary evidence is evidence at first hand, eg production of actual witness, actual document or actual article.

Secondary evidence is only admitted where primary evidence is not available, eg production of a copy document when the original is not available.

Evidence may be direct or circumstantial:

Direct evidence is evidence of a fact actually in issue, eg where a witness says he saw the accused take the stolen property in a case of theft.

Circumstantial evidence is evidence not of the actual fact to be proved but of other facts from which that fact may be presumed with more or less certainty, eg where a witness says he sold the accused the weapon in a murder or wounding case.

Hearsay evidence

Hearsay evidence is evidence of a fact not actually perceived by a witness with his own senses, but proved by him to have been stated by another person.

Hearsay evidence is generally inadmissible because it was not on oath, the maker cannot be cross-examined on his statement, and the court has no opportunity of considering the maker's demeanour.

There are, however, several exceptions to the hearsay evidence rule. The following examples of 'hearsay' may be admissible, if the court so decides:
(a) statements made by the defendant;
(b) statement made in the presence *and* hearing of the defendant;
(c) public documents;
(d) dying declarations;
(e) statements by deceased persons in the course of duty or business;
(f) depositions;
(g) evidence by certificate or statutory declaration;
(h) *res gestae* (matters closely connected with the facts in issue);

   (i)   recent complaints in cases of rape, indecent assault and similar offences;

   (j)   statements made under the Criminal Justice Act 1967.

Presumptions

Presumptions are of two types:

   (a) Presumptions of Law, which may be sub-divided as follows:

      (i)   Irrebuttable Presumptions; these are conclusions which must, by law, be drawn by the court on proof of certain facts. They cannot be contradicted, eg a boy under 14 cannot commit rape, a child under 10 cannot commit a crime, everyone knows the law.

     (ii) Rebuttable Presumptions; these are inconclusive and can be disputed. They are taken as correct until rebutted by proof to the contrary; eg a person is innocent until proved guilty, a child between 10 and 14 cannot commit a crime, a person is deemed to be sane until the contrary is proved.

   (b) Presumptions of Fact

      Presumptions of fact are inferences which may logically be drawn from proved facts and are rebuttable by evidence of other facts. A 'presumption of fact' is usually raised by circumstantial evidence. An example is the presumption of continuance, ie that it may be inferred that an existing state of affairs will continue in the future.

Privilege

Certain witnesses may be able to claim privilege on specified matters in which case they cannot be compelled to answer questions:

   (a) incriminating statement, eg questions which would expose the witness to any criminal charge;

   (b) against public policy, eg names of informants or contents of confidential reports;

   (c) husband and wife, ie communication made during marriage;

   (d) adultery, ie evidence that marital intercourse did or did not take place;

   (e) lawyer and client, only the client can consent to disclosure.

No legal privilege is extended to doctors or priests.

Burden of proof

The task of proving an alleged offence rests with the prosecution, who have to satisfy the court beyond reasonable doubt of the guilt of the accused. However, when the necessary facts have been proved it is then up to the accused to prove his innocence or be convicted. Certain Acts of Parliament place the burden of proof on the accused, eg possessing drugs, living on the earnings of a prostitute.

Where the law makes a requirement, eg driving licences, the onus is on the driver to prove that he has one as it is a matter within his peculiar knowledge. This is known as a negative averment.

Judicial notice

The admitting without proof of certain facts of common knowledge, such as the calendar, the laws of the country, etc.

Evidence by certificate

Evidence can be given in the absence of the witness by means of certificates in certain cases, eg proof of previous convictions, evidence of blood alcohol content, etc.

Normally a copy of the certificate must be served on the accused at least seven days prior to the hearing. If he requires the attendance of the witness he must give three day's notice to the prosecution.

Opinion

Evidence of opinion is generally inadmissible, but it is allowed in certain cases, eg in matters of science, skill, character, identification etc.

Refreshing memory

A witness is allowed to refresh his memory by reference to any note made by him at the time or shortly after the occurrence.

Examination-in-chief

The questioning of a witness by the party calling him. In summary cases an experienced witness (eg a police officer) may be allowed to give his evidence direct.

Cross-examination

The questioning of a witness by the other side on evidence already given or to test credibility.

Re-examination

The party calling the witness may re-examine him upon any new facts elicited by or to explain doubts raised by cross-examination. New evidence cannot be introduced without leave of the court.

Recalling a witness

The court may at any time recall a witness and ask him questions.

Leading questions

Leading questions are questions which are framed so as to suggest a desired answer. They cannot be asked on material points by the side which produces the witness.

Exceptions are: introductory matters, for the purpose of identification, to contradict something to which another witness has sworn and in questioning a hostile witness (with the permission of the court).

Rebutting evidence

When new evidence is introduced by the defence, the court may allow the prosecution to call evidence in reply to rebut (or contradict) it.

Character

Evidence of good character may be given by the defence, but the prosecution cannot give evidence of bad character or of convictions, during the trial, except:

 (a) to rebut evidence of 'accident' or 'mistake';
 (b) when the defence puts 'character' in issue;
 (c) when character is a 'fact in issue', eg suspected person, reputed thief or common prostitute;
 (d) to prove guilty knowledge in cases of handling stolen goods.

After the conviction the accused's record of previous convictions may be given, the result of any police enquiry and any personal knowledge of the testifying officer.

Previous convictions

May be proved by documentary evidence from the convicting court and oral evidence of identity of the accused.

The general rule is that previous convictions should not be given to the court until after conviction except when it is necessary for the purpose of considering bail, or when they form part of the charge, eg common prostitute.

Where the accused is 21 years or over, previous convictions whilst under 14 years of age shall be disregarded.

Hostile witness

A hostile witness is a witness who shows himself to be adverse or opposed to the side which called him. This does not necessarily make him a hostile witness automatically, as this is a matter for the court to decide.

If the court permits, the side that called a hostile witness may:
(a) put leading questions to him;
(b) cross-examine him;
(c) contradict his evidence by other evidence;
(d) prove that he has previously made a statement inconsistent with his present testimony.

Unwilling witness

If a witness refuses to be sworn, give evidence, or produce any document or thing, without just excuse, the court may commit him to custody for up to seven days, or until he complies if this is sooner.

Handwriting

A person's handwriting may be proved by:
(a) the evidence of the writer;
(b) a person who saw him write it;
(c) a person with a knowledge of his writing;
(d) a person who has seen documents written by him in the ordinary course of business;
(e) comparison of the writing with other writing proved to be genuine, by persons acquainted with the handwriting or by handwriting experts.

DOCTRINE OF PRECEDENT

Cases decided by the House of Lords, the Court of Appeal or Crown Court are known as 'decided cases' or 'case decisions'. Appeals to the Queen's Bench Divisional Court by way of 'case stated' may be referred to as 'stated cases'.

The *ratio decidendi,* which is the rule of law on which the decision was made, is binding on lower courts. The *obiter dicta* (things said 'by the way' during the case) are not binding but may be persuasive.

INTERPRETATION OF STATUTES

Words used in statutes are generally to be interpreted according to their ordinary, or dictionary, meaning. Where, however, a word, expression or phrase is intended to have a special meaning for the purpose of a particular statute an interpretation section is included in the Act.

The Interpretation Act 1978 provides rules to assist interpretation as follows:

(a) Words importing a masculine gender usually include the feminine;

(b) Words in the singular usually include the plural, and vice versa;

(c) When general words follow particular ones, they must be construed as relating only to persons or places of the same kind or usage and not given their ordinary wide meaning. This is known as the *ejusdem generis* rule;

(d) An act required to be done, or a notice required to be given, within so many days 'at the least', means that number of 'clear days';

If the act is required to be done within so many days without the phrase 'at the least', the first day should be omitted and the last day included;

Where the statute says nothing about Sunday, the days mentioned mean consecutive days including Sundays.

Chapter 3
Procedure

SUMMONSES

A summons is a written order issued by a magistrate or magistrates' clerk directing the person named therein to appear at a given time, in the court named, with reference to the matter set out therein.

There are two types of summons:
- (a) Defendant summons; directing appearance to answer a charge.
- (b) Witness summons; directing appearance to give evidence and/or produce articles.

Service of summons

A defendant summons may be served:
- (a) personally by giving it to the defendant; or
- (b) by leaving it with a responsible adult at the defendant's last known or usual place of abode; or
- (c) by sending it by registered post or recorded delivery service, to the defendant's last or most usual place of abode, or to an address given by the defendant for the purpose.

A witness summons must not be served by post, but must be served personally with conduct money.

A summons for a corporation may be either left at or sent by post to its registered office.

Proof of service (if defendant does not appear in court)

Any summons served by one or other of the means described shall be deemed to have been effectively served and this can be proved by:

(a) the constable who served it giving evidence on oath; or
(b) production of the certificate of service; or
(c) production of the declaration of service.

In the case of a summons served otherwise than by personal service on the defendant and for an offence which is not purely summary, in addition to the above, an acknowledgment of receipt is required.

Subpoena

A subpoena is a writ directed to a person commanding him under a penalty to appear and give evidence, or requiring him not only to give evidence, but to bring with him such deeds or writings as the party who issued the subpoena may think material for his purpose.

WARRANTS

A warrant is a written authority issued by a justice directing the person or persons to whom it is addressed to do some act specified therein.

Warrants are issued by a magistrate, at his discretion, on an information disclosing sufficient grounds in law. A warrant of commitment and a warrant of distress can be signed by a justices' clerk on behalf of the issuing magistrate.

Types of warrant

(a) Warrants to arrest for an offence confer power on any police officer to arrest a named or described person. These warrants need not be in the possession of the arresting officer, but should be shown to the prisoner after arrest. They may be executed *at any time* and on any day.

(b) Warrants for arrest of defaulters direct that a person who has failed to pay a fine imposed at a magistrates' court within the time allowed, and no term of imprisonment having been fixed as an alternative, shall be arrested and brought before the court for an inquiry to be made into his means. The warrant is cancelled if the full amount is paid. Such a warrant must be in the possession of the arresting officer.

(c) Commitment warrants direct the conveyance of a person to prison or other lawful place of detention and may be of two kinds:

(i) For remand or sentence. When taking a person to prison or to a remand home, etc, the officer must take with him the warrant, the prisoner's property and the body receipt form. The signed body receipt must be handed in at the station on return and the warrant left at the place of detention.

(ii) For non-payment of fine, etc. The person named may either pay or go to prison.

(d) Detention warrants may be issued instead of commitment warrants for small sums. Unless the sum is paid, they authorise the arrest and detention of the person at the nearest police station until the next morning.

(e) Distress warrants authorise seizure, under stringent conditions, of chattels in lieu of outstanding money payments.

(f) Search warrants authorise the search of specified premises, the seizure of specified articles found therein, and sometimes arrest as well. A senior officer usually directs the search and he must be in possession of the warrant, which can be executed at any time. The information for a search warrant must be in writing and on oath.

(g) Ejectment warrants are civil procedure for retaking possession of premises. They are not normally executed by the police, whose duties are limited to preventing a breach of the peace and protecting those executing.

Note: In the case of warrants to search, or to eject, force may be used to enter premises, but only if necessary and after declaring office and purpose.

Restrictions on execution

Warrants usually remain in force until executed or withdrawn by the magistrate, but in some cases, eg certain search warrants, the period of validity is limited and they can be used on more than one occasion. All warrants must be in the possession of the officer executing except warrants to arrest for a criminal offence issued in England, Wales and Scotland.

After execution of a warrant it is endorsed on the back as to the date and method of execution.

In the case of warrants from Eire, the Isle of Man and the Channel Islands, special procedure must be followed before they are executed. Warrants for arrest and commitment from these places can be executed in England and Wales and vice-versa if backed (ie endorsed) by a magistrate in the place where executed, who can only do so if the warrant is accompanied by a declaration of handwriting, verifying the signature of the issuing justice (the declaration for Northern Ireland must be sworn).

A warrant of arrest for offence issued in Scotland or Northern Ireland may be executed in England and Wales without being in the possession of the arresting officer (Criminal Justice Act 1977, s38).

There is provision for the execution in Eire of warrants from outside, and warrants issued there may be executed in the British Isles if issued by a judicial authority and backed by a justice here (Backing of Warrants (Republic of Ireland) Act 1965, s1(1)).

THE MEANING OF CERTAIN TERMS

Information

An information is a verbal or written charge made before a magistrate or magistrates' clerk to the effect that some person has committed an offence or act for which he is liable to be punished: the preliminary to the issue of a summons.

Affidavit

An affidavit is a written statement on oath taken before any person duly authorised to administer the oath, such as a justice or a commissioner of oaths. Making a false statement in an affidavit is punishable under the Perjury Act 1911.

Complaint

A complaint is an application made to a magistrate or magistrates' clerk upon which the magistrate has authority to make an order for the payment of money or otherwise, eg a maintenance order, or dangerous dog to be kept under control, etc.

Indictment

A bill of indictment is the officially prepared document which sets out the charge or charges ('counts') on which a person is to be tried before the Crown Court. This is presented to the court, signed by the appropriate officer of the Crown Court and becomes an 'indictment'.

Bail

This is a recognisance or bond taken by a duly authorised person to ensure the appearance of an accused at an appointed place and time to answer to the charge made against him.

Where a magistrates' court refuses to remand or commit on bail any person who has attained the age of 17 years, the court shall, if he is not represented, inform him that he may apply to a Judge of the High Court to be admitted to bail. Reasons for refusal of bail must be given to the accused in writing, or if represented to his advocate on request. This requirement does not apply if the offence can only be dealt with at Crown Court.

Recognisance

A recognisance is an obligation or bond under which a person acknowledges that he owes the Crown a certain sum of money, if the condition(s) specified in the recognisance are not carried out. It can be with or without sureties.

A constable may arrest without warrant any person who has been admitted to bail if he has reasonable grounds for believing or suspecting that the person has been notified in writing by a surety that it is believed that the accused will not appear as required and the surety wishes to be relieved of his obligation.

Remand

A remand is an order for the defendant to appear on a later occasion at the same or another magistrates' court. This remand may be:

(a) in custody for not more than eight clear days, or in police custody for not more than three days; or

(b) on bail with or without sureties, for a longer period if he and the other party consent; or

(c) after conviction, for up to three weeks in custody, or four weeks on bail, for enquiries to be made to decide the best method of dealing with him.

METHODS OF DEALING WITH OFFENDERS

Acquittal and discharge

When a person has been tried on indictment and a verdict of not guilty is returned, the prisoner is acquitted and must be discharged at once. If, however, the discharge was the result of a defect in the proceedings he may be re-arrested and prosecuted again (this only applies where the prisoner has not been in danger of conviction).

If a person charged with an indictable offence is discharged by the examining justices, he may be taken before them again if fresh evidence is produced.

Dismissal

If a case is dismissed after having been tried on its merits the accused has been in danger and the dismissal is a bar to any future proceedings.

When a charge of common or aggravated assault is dismissed, the justices shall, on request, give the defendant a *certificate of dismissal* and this bars all subsequent proceedings whether civil or criminal.

Sentences of the court

Offenders may be dealt with in the following ways:
- (a) Binding over; which is a recognisance to keep the peace (common law), or to be of good behaviour (Justices of the Peace Act 1361).
- (b) Order of discharge; which may be absolute or conditional. In the case of a conditional discharge, which must be for a stated period not exceeding three years, the offender may be sentenced for the original offence if any further offence is committed during the period of the order (Powers of Criminal Courts Act 1973, s7).
- (c) Probation order; which can be applied to an offender aged 17 years or over, requiring him to be under the supervision of a probation officer for not less than one nor more than three years. Further requirements may be added, such as having to live in an approved hostel or to submit to medical treatment (Powers of Criminal Courts Act 1973, s2).
- (d) Imprisonment. Under s22 of the Powers of Criminal Courts Act 1973, a prison sentence not exceeding two years may be suspended for at least one year but for not more than two years. A sentence may also be deferred to enable the court to consider changed circumstances (Section 1).
- (e) Extended sentences. Section 28 of the Powers of Criminal Court Act 1973 provides for longer terms of imprisonment to be awarded in certain circumstances to protect the public from persistent offenders.
- (f) Detention in police cells. This may be for a period not exceeding four days, or until not later than 8.00 pm the same day. The detention may be either in the court precincts or at a police station. (Magistrates' Courts Act 1980, ss 134-136).

(g) Detention. Section 4 of the Criminal Justice Act 1982 provides that males aged between 14 and 21 may be given short periods of detention.

(h) Youth custody. Section 7 of the Criminal Justice Act 1982 provides for sentences of more than four months for male and female offenders aged between 15 and 21.

(i) Custody for life. For persons under 21 convicted of murder or other offences for which the statutory penalty is life imprisonment (Criminal Justice Act 1982, s8).

(j) Young offender institution. Where persons under 21 may be helped to prepare for their return to the outside community.

(k) Remand centre. This is a place for the detention of offenders between 14 and 21 years who are remanded for trial or sentence (Prison Act 1952, s48).

(l) Community service order. On conviction of offence punishable with imprisonment, the court can order an offender over 17 to perform unpaid work for not less than 40 nor more than 240 hours.

(m) Pecuniary penalties, ie fines, costs, compensation, restitution, or criminal bankruptcy.

Fines

Section 37 of Magistrates' Court Act 1980 provides a standard scale of maximum fines for summary offences. These are: level 1 - £200; level 2 - £500; level 3 - £1,000; level 4 - £2,500; level 5 - £5,000.

The statutory maximum fine on summary conviction of an offence triable either way is £5,000. Maximum fine for young person – £ 1,000; for a child - £250. (As amended by the Criminal Justice Act 1991).

MISCELLANEOUS INFORMATION

Certiorari

An order of the Queen's Bench Division directing that the proceedings are to be removed from an inferior court and taken to the Queen's Bench Division to be examined and quashed if necessary.

Mandamus

A peremptory command from the Queen's Bench Division to compel a person or lower court to do a certain duty.

Habeas corpus

A writ or order of the Queen's Bench Division to a person holding another in custody, directing him to produce the body of the prisoner and show the cause for his detention.

Judicial review

An application to consider whether a magistrates' court has failed to exercise its jurisdiction properly. Remedies are orders of certiorari or mandamus.

Contempt of court

Wilfully insulting justices, witnesses or officers of the court, interrupting proceedings, or otherwise misbehaving in court, or using a tape recorder without consent. An offender may be committed to custody for not exceeding a month, fined up to £1,000, or both.

Limitation of proceedings

There should be no delay in taking proceedings against an offender, and in many cases after a certain period has elapsed proceedings can no longer be taken.

At common law there is no limit of time for instituting proceedings for indictable offences, but time limits are imposed by various Acts of Parliament.

In the case of summary offences, proceedings may *not* be commenced (ie the information laid or complaint made) more than six months after the date of the offence, with certain exceptions.

Director of Public Prosecutions

It is the duty of the Director of Public Prosecutions, under the superintendence of the Attorney General, to institute, undertake or carry on criminal proceedings prescribed by regulations as subject to his consent, and to give advice and assistance to chief officers of police, magistrates' clerks, government departments and others concerned in criminal proceedings. He appears for the Crown in appeals to the Court of Criminal Appeal.

Attorney General

The Attorney General is the Crown's representative in the courts. Legal proceedings for the enforcement of public rights and on behalf of the interests of charity are conducted in his name. His consent is required for the institution of criminal proceedings for certain offences and he supervises the Director of Public Prosecutions.

Extradition

Extradition is the process by which a person who has committed a crime in the UK and has fled abroad, or vice versa, is arrested and taken for trial to the country in which he has committed the crime. The procedure is governed by the Extradition Acts and is only possible in the case of a person charged with a crime mentioned in the various treaties in force.

Crown Prosecution Service

The Crown Prosecution Service was introduced by the Prosecution of Offences Act 1985. The Director of Public Prosecutions is the head of the Service and Chief Crown Prosecutors are appointed for each area of England and Wales. Crown Prosecutors (solicitors or barristers) have the power of the Director to institute and conduct criminal proceedings and his other functions.

Chapter 4
Record of Evidence

ADMISSIONS AND CONFESSIONS

An admission is an agreement by the accused with some fact or facts which weigh against his innocence but does not amount to a complete confession.

A confession is a statement by the accused that he committed the offence, or from which an inference can be drawn that he committed the offence. It includes any statement wholly or partly adverse to the person who made it, whether made to a person in authority or not and whether made in words or otherwise.

Confessions made by an accused person may be given in evidence against him so far as they are relevant to the matter in issue and are not excluded by the court. If there is any suggestion that a confession was obtained by oppression, or in consequence of anything said or done which was likely to render it unreliable, the prosecution must prove beyond reasonable doubt that it was not so obtained.

DYING DECLARATIONS, DEPOSITIONS AND SWORN STATEMENTS

Dying declarations

A dying declaration is a statement by an injured and dying person as to the circumstances surrounding his injuries. It may in certain circumstances be given in evidence at the trial for murder or manslaughter of the person causing those injuries; as such it constitutes an exception to the rule against hearsay evidence.

It may only be put in evidence at such a trial if the maker of the dying declaration has, in fact, died as a result of the injuries, and at the time of making the declaration he was in settled, hopeless expectation of imminent death.

It differs from either kind of deposition in that it is not on oath; it need not be signed by the maker; no magistrate need be present; the accused need not be present; and it need not be in writing.

Depositions

A deposition is a statement made on oath before a magistrate, taken down in writing in the presence and hearing of the accused, and read over to and signed by the magistrate.

Depositions before examining justices

These depositions are the written record of the evidence given during committal proceedings before examining magistrates, by witnesses who will eventually be giving evidence at the trial at a higher court if the magistrates decide there is a case to answer. As such they provide a basis for the drawing up of the indictment and a check on the evidence ultimately given by the witness at the trial.

The evidence must be given on oath and before a magistrate. Although depositions are usually taken in court, this need not necessarily be so, eg a deposition may be taken in hospital from a witness not yet fit to travel to court. The accused *must* be present, and both the deponent and the magistrate must sign the deposition. (The magistrate must be one who has jurisdiction to commit the case for trial.)

A person making a deposition will have to attend and give evidence at the court of trial. However, the deposition could be read in his absence if it is proved that the maker:

(a) has since died;
(b) has become insane;
(c) is too ill to travel;
(d) has been kept away by the defence; or
(e) a conditional witness order has been made.

Sworn statements

These are in some ways similar to ordinary depositions, ie they are written records of the sworn testimony of the witness, taken before a magistrate. The following important differences should, however, be noted:

(a) The witness must, at the time of taking, be so seriously ill as to be unlikely to be able to give evidence at the trial, and must in fact be unable to attend the trial.

(b) The magistrate need not be one with jurisdiction to commit the case for trial, but may be any magistrate in the place where the witness is lying ill.

(c) There is no necessity for an accused person at whose trial they may be used to be present at the taking down of the statement, provided written notice of the intention to take it has been given to him if he is known.

RECORDABLE OFFENCES

A 'recordable offence' is any offence which may be recorded in national police records. There may be recorded convictions for offences punishable with imprisonment and offences under-

(a) s1 of the Street Offences Act 1959 (loitering or soliciting for purposes of prostitution);

(b) s43 of the Telecommunications Act 1984 (improper use of public telecommunications system);

(c) s29 of the Road Traffic Act 1988 (penalisation of tampering with motor vehicles); and

(d) s1 of the Malicious Communications Act 1988 (sending letters etc with intent to cause distress or anxiety).

(National Police Records (Recordable Offences) Regulations 1985.)

DATA PROTECTION

The Data Protection Act 1984 defines 'data' as information recorded in a form in which it can be processed by equipment operating automatically in response to instructions given for that purpose (ie recorded on a computer). Computer users must be registered with the Data Protection Registrar.

The data protection principles are:

1. The information to be contained in personal data must be obtained and processed fairly and lawfully.

2. Personal data must be held only for one or more specified and lawful purposes.

3. Personal data held for any purpose must not be used or disclosed in any manner incompatible with that purpose.

4. Personal data held for any purpose must be adequate, relevant and not excessive in relation to that purpose.

5. Personal data must be accurate and, where necessary, kept up to date.
6. Personal data held for any purpose must not be kept for longer than is necessary for that purpose.
7. An individual shall be entitled-
    (a) at reasonable intervals and without undue delay or expense - (i) to be informed by any data user whether he holds personal data of which that individual is the subject; and (ii) to access to any such data; and
    (b) where appropriate, to have such data corrected or erased.

Personal data held for the prevention or detection of crime, or the apprehension or prosecution of offenders, are exempt from the subject access provisions in any case in which this would be likely to prejudice any matters.

It is an offence to fail to comply with the provisions of the Act.

CODES OF PRACTICE

S66 of the Police and Criminal Evidence Act 1984 provides for the Secretary of State to issue codes of practice. The following codes have been issued:-
A - The exercise by police officers of statutory powers of stop and search.
B - The searching of premises by police officers and the seizure of property found by police officers on persons or premises.
C - The detention, treatment and questioning of persons by police officers.
D - The identification of persons by police officers.
E - Tape recording.

Revised versions of codes A, B, C and D came into force on 1 April 1991.

A police officer shall be liable to disciplinary proceedings for a failure to comply with any provision of a code. A failure on the part of a police officer to comply with the provisions of a code shall not of itself render him liable to any criminal or civil proceedings. Persons other than police officers who are charged with the duty of investigating offences or charging offenders shall in the discharge of that duty have regard to any relevant provision of such a code. (s67(8), (9) and (10).)

The codes of practice must be readily available at all police stations for consultation by police officers, detained persons and members of the public.

(Note that references to the codes of practice in this book have, of necessity, been abbreviated.)

Chapter 5
Powers and Mode of Arrest

DEFINITION OF 'ARREST'

'Arrest' means the taking or restraining of a person from his liberty in order that he shall be forthcoming to answer an alleged or suspected offence. A person is under arrest when a restraint which deprives him of his liberty is applied to him, usually by seizing or touching his body. Words alone can amount to an arrest, however, if they bring to a person's notice the fact that he is under compulsion and he submits to that compulsion.

POWERS OF ARREST

Arrest without warrant for arrestable offences (Police and Criminal Evidence Act 1984, s24)

Arrest without warrant for arrestable offences applies to offences:
    (a) for which the sentence is fixed by law;
    (b) for which a person of 21 years of age or over (not previously convicted) may be sentenced to imprisonment for a term of five years (or might be so sentenced but for the restrictions imposed by s33 of the Magistrates' Courts Act 1980) (ie offences of criminal damage below £2,000 in value); and
    (c) offences under the following statutes:
        (i)   Customs and Excise Acts (offences as defined in the Customs and Excise Management Act 1979, s1(1));
        (ii) Official Secrets Act 1920 (offences not arrestable by virtue of the term of imprisonment);
        (iii) Official Secrets Act 1989, except s8(1), (4) or (5);
        (iv) Sexual Offences Act 1956, s22 (causing prostitution of women) or s23 (procuration of girl under 21);

(v)   Theft Act 1968, s12(1) (taking motor vehicle or other conveyance without authority etc) or s25(1) (going equipped for stealing etc); and

(vi)   Football Offences Act 1991.

Without prejudice to s1 of the Criminal Attempts Act 1981, these powers also apply to the offences of conspiring to commit any of the offences under (c); attempting to commit any such offence other than taking a conveyance; and inciting, aiding, abetting, counselling or procuring the commission of any such offence.

Any person may arrest without a warrant anyone who is in the act of committing an arrestable offence, and anyone whom he has reasonable grounds for suspecting to be committing such an offence.

Where an arrestable offence has been committed, *any person* may arrest without a warrant anyone who is guilty of the offence, and anyone whom he has reasonable grounds for suspecting to be guilty of it.

Where a *constable* has reasonable grounds for suspecting that an arrestable offence has been committed, he may arrest without a warrant anyone whom he has reasonable grounds for suspecting to be guilty of the offence.

A *constable* may arrest without a warrant anyone who is about to commit an arrestable offence, and anyone whom he has reasonable grounds for suspecting to be about to commit an arrestable offence.

General arrest conditions (Police and Criminal Evidence Act 1984, s25)

Where a constable has reasonable grounds for suspecting that any offence which is not an arrestable offence has been committed or attempted, or is being committed or attempted, he may arrest any person whom he has reasonable grounds to suspect of having committed or having attempted to commit it, if it appears to him that the service of a summons is impracticable or inappropriate because any of the general arrest conditions are satisfied.

The general arrest conditions are that:

(a)   the name of the person is unknown to, and cannot be readily ascertained by, the constable;

(b)   the constable has reasonable grounds for doubting whether a name furnished by the person is his real name;

(c)   the person has failed to furnish a satisfactory address for service, or the constable has reasonable grounds for doubting whether an address furnished by the person is a satisfactory address for service;

(d) the constable has reasonable grounds for believing that arrest is necessary to prevent the person causing physical injury to himself or any other person, suffering physical injury, causing loss of or damage to property, committing an offence against public decency, or causing an unlawful obstruction of the highway;

(e) the constable has reasonable grounds for believing that arrest is necessary to protect a child or other vulnerable person from that person.

Preserved statutory powers of arrest (Police and Criminal Evidence Act 1984, s26 and Sch 2)

So much of any Act as enabled a *constable* to arrest a person without a warrant, ceased to have effect on the coming into force of this section. The following statutory powers of arrest are, however, preserved and may be used by a constable:

(a) Military Lands Act 1892, s17(2) (trespassing on military land);

(b) Protection of Animals Act 1911, s12(1) (any offence under the Act punishable with imprisonment);

(c) Emergency Powers Act 1920, s2 (offences relating to terrorism);

(d) Public Order Act 1936, s7(3) (wearing of political uniforms, quasi-military organisations and conduct conducive to breaches of the peace);

(e) Prison Act 1952, s49 (escaped prisoners);

(f) Visiting Forces Act 1952, s13; Army Act 1955, ss186 and 190B; Air Force Act 1955, ss186 and 190B; Naval Discipline Act 1957, ss104 and 105 (absentees and deserters from HM and visiting forces);

(g) Street Offences Act 1959, s1(3) (soliciting for prostitution);

(h) Children and Young Persons Act 1969, ss28(2) and 32 (absentees from remand homes etc);

(i) Immigration Act 1971, s24(3) (unlawful entrants etc);

(j) Bail Act 1976, s7 (failing to answer to bail);

(k) Criminal Law Act 1977, ss6(6), 7(11), 8(4), 9(7) and 10(5) (entering and remaining on property etc);

(l) Child Care Act 1980, s16 (child absentees from care);

(m) Reserve Forces Act 1950, Sch 5 (absentees and deserters from reserve forces);

(n) Animal Health Act 1981, ss60(5) and 61(1) (sick and rabid animals);

(o) Mental Health Act 1983, ss18, 35(10), 36(8), 136(1) and 138 (mentally ill persons);

(p) Representation of the People Act 1983, Sch 1 rule 36 (personation of elector);

(q) Repatriation of Prisoners Act 1984, s 5(5) (non-compliance).

(Note that only the statutory powers of arrest specifying constables in Acts prior to 1984 have been abolished. The Home Secretary is of the opinion that those Acts containing powers of arrest for 'any person' are unaffected, but that it may be prudent for constables to use such powers only where the general arrest conditions are also met.)

Powers of arrest at common law

Any person may arrest without warrant anyone committing a breach of the peace in his presence; or whom he reasonably believes will commit such a breach in the immediate future; or where a breach of the peace has been committed and it is reasonably believed that a renewal of it is threatened.

There is a breach of the peace whenever harm is done or is likely to be done to a person, or in his presence to his property, or a person is in fear of being so harmed through an assault, an affray, a riot, unlawful assembly or some other disturbance.

Arrest for fingerprinting (Police and Criminal Evidence Act 1984, s27)

If a person has been convicted of a recordable offence, has not at any time been in police detention for the offence, and has not had his fingerprints taken in the course of the investigation by the police or since the conviction, any constable may at any time not later than one month after the date of conviction, require him to attend a police station in order that his fingerprints may be taken.

Any constable may arrest without warrant a person who has failed to comply with such a requirement.

Use of force in effecting arrest

Where any provision of the 1984 Act confers a power on a constable, and does not provide that the power may only be exercised with the consent of some person, other than a police officer, the officer may use reasonable force, if necessary, in the exercise of the power (Police and Criminal Evidence Act 1984, s117).

A person may use such force as is reasonable in the circumstances in the prevention of crime, or in effecting or assisting in the lawful arrest of offenders or suspected offenders or of persons unlawfully at large (Criminal Law Act 1967, s3).

Serious arrestable offence

The term 'serious arrestable offence' has no relevance to powers of arrest but concerns certain procedural matter; examples are authorisation of road checks, continued detention, delay in allowing legal advice, etc.

Section 116 of the Police and Criminal Evidence Act 1984 provides that the term always includes: treason, murder, manslaughter, rape, kidnapping, incest with a girl under 13, buggery with a boy under 16 or a person who has not consented, indecent assault which constitutes gross indecency, causing explosion likely to endanger life, intercourse with a girl under 13, possession of firearms with intent to injure, use of firearms to resist arrest, carrying firearms with criminal intent, causing death by dangerous driving, hostage-taking, and hijacking.

Any other arrestable offence is serious only if its commission has led to, or is intended or likely to lead to: serious harm to the security of the State or to public order; serious interference with the administration of justice or the investigation of offences; the death of any person; serious injury to any person; substantial financial gain to any person; and serious financial loss to any person. An arrestable offence which consists of making a threat is serious if it would be likely to lead to any of these consequences. Offences under ss 1, 9 or 10 of the Prevention of Terrorism (Temporary Provisions) Act 1989 are also always serious arrestable offences for the purposes of the right to have someone informed when arrested and access to legal advice.

MODE OF ARREST

Points to be observed

An arrest should be made as quietly as possible and the person arrested treated with all possible consideration. However, since an arrest is an exercise of force, the arresting officer should normally intimate this by taking hold of the prisoner or in some way restraining his freedom of movement. Arresting officers in plain clothes should inform the prisoner that they are police officers and, if necessary, produce their warrant cards to confirm this.

It has already been mentioned that it is lawful in preventing crime or making an arrest to use such force as is reasonable in the circumstances. Handcuffing should not be resorted to unless there are reasonable grounds for believing that violence may be used or an attempt made to escape from custody. Truncheons are supplied to enable police officers to defend themselves if violently attacked, but if one has to be used the head should be avoided if possible. The fact that it has been necessary to use a truncheon should always be stated in evidence and no attempt made to hide the fact.

Information to be given on arrest

Where a person is arrested, otherwise than by being informed that he is under arrest, the arrest is not lawful unless he is informed that he is under arrest as soon as is practicable afterwards. No arrest is lawful unless the person arrested is informed of the ground for the arrest at the time of, or as soon as practicable after, the arrest. This applies to an arrest by a constable regardless of whether the fact of, or the ground for, the arrest is obvious.

The foregoing is not, however, to be taken to require a person to be informed that he is under arrest, or of the ground for the arrest, if it was not reasonably practicable for him to be so informed by reason of his having escaped from arrest before the information could be given (Police and Criminal Evidence Act 1984, s28).

A person must be cautioned upon arrest unless - (a) it is impracticable to do so by reason of his condition or behaviour at the time; or (b) he has already been cautioned immediately prior to arrest. The caution shall be as follows: '*You do not have to say anything unless you wish to do so, but what you say may be given in evidence*'. Minor deviations do not constitute a breach of this requirement provided that the sense of the caution is preserved (Code of Practice C).

Voluntary attendance at police station

Where for the purpose of assisting with an investigation a person attends voluntarily at a police station or at any other place where a constable is present, or accompanies a constable to a police station or any such other place, without having been arrested, he shall:
  (a) be entitled to leave at will unless he is placed under arrest; and
  (b) be informed at once that he is under arrest if a decision is taken by a constable to prevent him from leaving at will (Police and Criminal Evidence Act 1984, s29).

Arrest elsewhere than at a police station

Where a person is arrested by a constable for an offence, or is taken into custody by a constable after being arrested by some other person, at any place other than a police station, he shall be taken to a designated police station as soon as practicable after the arrest.

A constable to whom this applies may, however, take an arrested person to any police station, unless it appears that it may be necessary to keep the person in police detention for more than six hours. This applies to a constable who is working in a locality covered by a police station which is not a designated one; and a constable not belonging to a body maintained by a police authority. In addition, any constable may take an arrested person to any police station if he has arrested him, or taken him into custody, without the assistance of another constable; or if it appears that he will be unable to take the prisoner to a designated police station without the prisoner injuring himself or some other person.

A person arrested by a constable at a place other than a police station must be released if the constable is satisfied before the prisoner reaches a police station that there are no grounds for keeping him under arrest. This fact must be recorded as soon as practicable after the person has been released (Police and Criminal Evidence Act 1984, s30).

Arrest for further offence

Where a person has been arrested for an offence and is at a police station in consequence of that arrest, and it appears to a constable that, if he were released he would be liable to arrest for some other offence, he must be arrested for that other offence (Police and Criminal Evidence Act 1984, s31).

Search upon arrest

A constable may search an arrested person in any case where the person has been arrested at a place other than a police station, if he has reasonable grounds for believing that the person may present a danger to himself or others.

A constable shall also have power in such a case:

(a) to search the arrested person for anything which he might use to assist him to escape from lawful custody, or which might be evidence relating to an offence; and

(b) to enter and search any premises in which he was when arrested or immediately before he was arrested for evidence relating to the offence for which he has been arrested.

This power does not authorise a constable to require a person to remove any of his clothing in public other than an outer coat, jacket or gloves.

A constable searching a person in the exercise of this power may seize and retain anything he finds if he has reasonable grounds for believing:

(a) that the person might use it to cause physical injury to himself or any other person;
(b) that he might use it to assist him to escape from lawful custody; or
(c) that it is evidence of an offence or has been obtained in consequence of the commission of an offence.

(Police and Criminal Evidence Act 1984, s32.)

(See next chapter for further information on powers of search and entry.)

Chapter 6
Powers of Entry and Search, and Road Checks

ENTRY AND SEARCH WITHOUT WARRANT

Entry for purpose of arrest (Police and Criminal Evidence Act 1984, s17)

Without prejudice to any other enactment, a constable may enter and search premises for the purpose of:

(a) executing a warrant of arrest issued in connection with or arising out of criminal proceedings, or a warrant of commitment;

(b) arresting a person for an arrestable offence;

(c) arresting a person for an arrestable offence under s1 (prohibition of uniforms in connection with political objects) of the Public Order Act 1936; and enactment contained in ss 6, 7, 8 or 10 of the Criminal Law Act 1977 (offences relating to entering and remaining on property); or s4 of the Public Order Act 1986 (fear or provocation of violence);

(d) recapturing a person who is unlawfully at large and whom he is pursuing; or

(e) saving life or limb or preventing serious damage to property.

Except for the purposes of saving life or limb or preventing serious damage to property, these powers of entry and search are:

(a) only exercisable if the constable has reasonable grounds for believing that the person whom he is seeking is on the premises; and

(b) limited in relation to premises consisting of two or more separate dwellings, to powers to enter and search any parts of the premises which the occupiers use in common, and any such dwelling in which the constable has reasonable grounds for believing that the person whom he is seeking may be.

In the case of offences of entering and remaining on property, the powers are exercisable only by a constable in uniform.

An officer conducting a search must, unless it is impracticable to do so, provide the occupier with a Notice of Powers and Rights.

('Premises' includes any place and, in particular, includes any vehicle, vessel, aircraft or hovercraft; any offshore installation; and any tent or movable structure (s23)).

Entry and search after arrest (Police and Criminal Evidence Act 1984, s18)

A constable may enter and search any premises occupied or controlled by a person who is under arrest for an arrestable offence, if he has reasonable grounds for suspecting that there is on the premises evidence (other than items subject to legal privilege) that relates to that offence, or to some other arrestable offence which is connected with or similar to that offence.

A constable may seize and retain anything for which he may search under this power, which applies only to the extent that it is reasonably required for the purpose of discovering such evidence.

The power may not be exercised unless an officer of the rank of inspector or above has authorised the search in writing. A constable may, however, conduct such a search before taking the person to a police station without obtaining authorisation if the presence of the person at a place other than a police station is necessary for the effective investigation of the offence. If a search is conducted without prior authorisation an officer of the rank of inspector or above must be informed as soon as practicable.

('Items subject to legal privilege' means communications between a professional legal adviser and his client or any person representing his client, made in connection with the giving of legal advice or legal proceedings; and items enclosed with or referred to in such communications (s10)).

Statutory powers of entry and search

Numerous Acts of Parliament give power to enter premises. Some examples are:
   (a) The Fire Services Act 1947 empowers a constable to enter and, if necessary, break into any premises in which a fire has or is reasonably believed to have broken out.
   (b) The Licensing Act 1964 provides that a constable may enter licensed premises or premises in respect of which a special hours

certificate is in force, for the purpose of preventing or detecting the commission of any offence against the Act.

(c) The Road Traffic Act 1988 permits a constable to enter (by force if need be) any place to arrest a person for driving while unfit through drink or drugs, or to obtain a specimen of breath following a suspected injury accident.

Common law power of entry

Any person may enter premises without a warrant where a breach of the peace is being committed, or to prevent such a breach.

SEARCH WARRANTS

If on an application made by a constable a justice of the peace is satisfied that there are reasonable grounds for believing that:

(a) a serious arrestable offence has been committed; and

(b) there is material on premises specified in the application which is likely to be of substantial value (whether by itself or together with other material) to the investigation of the offence; and

(c) the material is likely to be relevant evidence; and

(d) it does not consist of or include items subject to legal privilege, excluded material or special procedure material; and

(e) any of the following conditions applies:

   (i) it is not practicable to communicate with any person entitled to grant entry to the premises;

   (ii) it is practicable to communicate with a person entitled to grant entry to the premises but it is not practicable to communicate with any person entitled to grant access to evidence;

   (iii) entry to the premises will not be granted unless a warrant is produced;

   (iv) the purpose of a search may be frustrated or seriously prejudiced unless a constable arriving at the premises can secure immediate entry to them;

he may issue a warrant authorising a constable to enter and search the premises.

A constable may seize and retain anything for which a search has been so authorised. The power to issue such a warrant is in addition to any such power otherwise conferred (Police and Criminal Evidence Act 1984, s8).

'Items subject to legal privilege' is defined on the previous page.

'Excluded material' means:

(a) personal records which a person has acquired or created in the course of any trade, business, profession or other occupation or for the purposes of any paid or unpaid office and which he holds in confidence;

(b) human tissue or tissue fluid which has been taken for the purposes of diagnosis or medical treatment and which a person holds in confidence;

(c) journalistic material which a person holds in confidence and which consists of documents or of records other than documents.

'Personal records' means documentary and other records concerning an individual (whether living or dead) who can be identified from them and relating to his physical or mental health, or to spiritual counselling or assistance given to him, etc.

'Journalistic material' means material acquired or created for the purposes of journalism (Police and Criminal Evidence Act 1984, ss10, 11, 12 and 13).

Execution of warrants

A warrant to enter and search premises may be executed by any constable, and may authorise other persons to accompany that constable.

Entry and search under a warrant must be within one month from the date of its issue, and must be at a reasonable hour unless it appears to the constable executing it that the purpose of a search may be frustrated on an entry at a reasonable hour.

Where the occupier of premises which are to be entered and searched is present at the time when a constable seeks to execute such a warrant, the constable shall identify himself and, if not in uniform, produce documentary evidence that he is a constable; and shall produce the warrant to him and supply him with a copy of it.

Where the occupier is not present but some other person who appears to be in charge of the premises is present, he shall be treated as if he were the occupier (Police and Criminal Evidence Act 1984, s16).

Search with consent

It should always be remembered that consent may be obtained from the occupier of premises in order to enter and search them.

Code B states that if it is proposed to search premises with the consent of a person entitled to grant entry to the premises the consent must if practicable be given in writing on the Notice of Powers and Rights. Before seeking consent the officer in charge of the search shall state the purpose of the proposed search and inform the person concerned that he is not obliged to consent and that anything seized may be produced in evidence. If at the time the person is not suspected of an offence, the officer shall tell him so when stating the purpose of the search.

It is unnecessary to seek consent where in the circumstances this would cause disproportionate inconvenience to the person concerned (eg where a person has been arrested in the night after a pursuit and it is necessary to check gardens to see whether stolen articles have been discarded).

POWERS TO STOP AND SEARCH (Police and Criminal Evidence Act 1984, s1)

A constable may:
    (a) search any person or vehicle and anything which is in or on a vehicle for stolen or prohibited articles; and
    (b) may detain a person or vehicle for the purpose of such a search;
in any place to which at the time the public or any section of the public has access, on payment or otherwise, as of right or by virtue of express or implied permission; or in any other place to which people have ready access at the time but which is not a dwelling.

This power only applies if a constable has reasonable grounds for suspecting that he will find stolen or prohibited articles or articles with blades or sharp points (Criminal Justice Act 1988, s139). An article is prohibited if it is an offensive weapon; or an article made or adapted for use in the course of or in connection with burglary, theft, taking a motor vehicle or other conveyance without authority, obtaining property by deception, or possessing a sharp pointed instrument; or intended by the person having it with him for such use by him or by some other person. 'Offensive weapon' means any article made or adapted for use for causing injury to persons, or intended by the person having it with him for such use by him or by some other person.

If a person is in a garden or yard occupied with and used for the purposes of a dwelling or on other land so occupied and used, he may not be searched under this power unless the constable has reasonable grounds for believing that he does not reside in the dwelling, and that he is not in that place with the express or implied permission of a person who resides there.

If a vehicle is in a garden or yard occupied with and used for the purposes of a dwelling or on other land so occupied and used, a constable may not search it or anything in or on it unless he has reasonable grounds for believing that the person in charge of the vehicle does not reside in the dwelling, and that it is not in that place with the express or implied permission of a person who resides there.

If in the course of such a search a constable discovers an article which he has reasonable grounds for suspecting to be a stolen or prohibited article, he may seize it. (Police and Criminal Evidence Act 1984, s1.)

Provisions and records relating to searches

A constable who detains a person or vehicle in the exercise of this power, or any other power to search a person or vehicle without making an arrest, need not conduct a search if it subsequently appears that no search is required or is impracticable. If a constable contemplates a search, other than of an unattended vehicle, he must take reasonable steps before he commences the search to bring to the attention of the appropriate person- (i) documentary evidence that he is a constable if he is not in uniform, and (ii) whether he is in uniform or not, his name and the name of the police station to which he is attached, the object of the proposed search, his grounds for proposing to make it, and that he may have a copy of the record of the search.

On completing a search of an unattended vehicle or anything in or on such a vehicle, a constable must leave a notice stating that he has done so, giving the name of his station, and that an application for compensation for any damage caused by the search may be made there. This notice must be left inside the vehicle unless it is not practicable to do so without damaging it. ('Vehicle' includes vessels, aircraft and hovercraft.)

This power does not authorise a constable to require a person to remove any of his clothing in public other than an outer coat, jacket or gloves; or a constable not in uniform to stop a vehicle.

The time for which a person or vehicle may be detained for the purposes of such a search is such time as is reasonably required to permit a search to be carried out either at the place where the person or vehicle was first detained or nearby.

Where a constable has carried out a search in the exercise of this power he shall make a record of it in writing unless it is not practicable to do so, in which case he must make it as soon as practicable after the completion of the search.

Every reasonable effort must be made to reduce to the minimum the embarrassment that a person being searched may experience. The co-operation of the person should be sought, even if he initially objects. A forcible search may be made only if the person is unwilling to co-operate or resists. Although force may only be used as a last resort, reasonable force may be used as necessary to conduct a search or to detain a person or vehicle for that purpose.

Searches in public must be restricted to superficial examination of outer clothing. Where it is considered necessary to conduct a more thorough search, this should be done out of public view (eg in a police van or nearby police station). Any search involving the removal of more than an outer coat, jacket, gloves, headgear or footwear may only be made by an officer of the same sex as the person searched. (Ss2 and 3 and Code A-3.)

Statutory powers to search

Code A governs the exercise by police officers of statutory powers to search a person without first arresting him. In addition to the power under s1 of the Police and Criminal Evidence Act 1984, examples are:

(a) The Firearms Act 1968 provides that a constable may search a person or vehicle on reasonable suspicion that a firearm is being carried in a public place, or that a person is trespassing with a firearm.

(b) The Misuse of Drugs Act 1971 authorises a constable to search any person reasonably suspected of being in possession of a controlled drug, and also any vehicle or vessel in which he suspects that a drug may be found.

(c) The Sporting Events (Control of Alcohol etc) Act 1985 empowers a constable to search a person reasonably suspected of having intoxicating liquor, bottle, can or other portable container in his possession during the period of any public service or railway passenger vehicle being used to carry persons to such events, on suspicion that alcohol is being carried.

(Note that the Code does not apply to s27 of the Aviation Security Act 1982 (search of airport employees etc); or s6(1) of the Police and Criminal Evidence Act 1984 (powers of constables employed by statutory undertakers)).

ROAD CHECKS

A road check consists of the exercise in a locality of the power conferred by s163 of the Road Traffic Act 1988 in such a way as to stop, during the period for which its exercise in that way in that locality continues, all vehicles or vehicles selected by any criterion. (Section 163 provides that 'a person driving a motor vehicle on a road and a person riding a cycle, not being a motor vehicle, on a road shall stop the same on being so required by a constable in uniform'. If such a driver fails to do so he is guilty of an offence.)

Road checks may be conducted by police officers for the purpose of ascertaining whether a vehicle is carrying:

(a) a person who has committed an offence other than a road traffic offence or a vehicles excise offence;

(b) a person who is a witness to such an offence;

(c) a person intending to commit such an offence; or

(d) a person who is unlawfully at large.

There may only be such a road check if a police officer of the rank of superintendent or above authorises it in writing. A check may only be authorised for the purpose of:

(a) ascertaining whether a vehicle is carrying a person who has committed an offence or intends to commit an offence and there must be reasonable grounds for believing that the offence is a serious arrestable offence, and for suspecting that the person is, or is about to be, in the locality of the proposed check;

(b) tracing a witness to an offence, in which case there must be reasonable grounds for believing that it is a serious arrestable offence; and

(c) finding a person who is unlawfully at large, with reasonable grounds for suspecting that the person is, or is about to be, in that locality.

If a road check is required as a matter of urgency, however, it may be authorised by an officer of any rank. In such circumstances the person giving authorisation must, as soon as it is practicable, make a written record of the time at which it was authorised and cause a superintendent or above to be informed. The senior officer will then decide if the road check should continue.

A road check may be for a continuous period or limited to specified times. When a vehicle is stopped in such a check the person in charge of the vehicle is entitled to obtain a written statement of its purpose if he makes application within 12 months (Police and Criminal Evidence Act 1984, s4).

(Note that there is also a common law power to stop and check vehicles in relation to apprehended breaches of the peace. It must honestly and reasonably be believed that there is a real risk of a breach of the peace.)

Chapter 7
Detention, Bail and Rehabilitation

THE CUSTODY OFFICER

In respect of persons in detention the custody officer is the most important person in a police station.

One or more custody officers must be appointed for each designated police station. No officer may be appointed a custody officer unless he is of at least the rank of sergeant. (Note the words 'at least' which suggest that normally a custody officer should be above the rank of sergeant.) An officer of any rank may, however, perform the functions of a custody officer if a custody officer is not readily available to perform them.

DETENTION

Condition and duration of police detention

A person arrested for an offence must not be kept in police detention except in accordance with the provisions of Part IV of the Police and Criminal Evidence Act 1984. A person is in police detention if:

(a) he has been taken to a police station after being arrested for an offence; or

(b) he is arrested at a police station after attending voluntarily at the station or accompanying a constable to it,

and is detained there or is detained elsewhere in the charge of a constable, except that a person who is at a court after being charged is not in police detention for those purposes.

If at any time a custody officer becomes aware that the grounds for the detention of a person have ceased to apply and he is not aware of any other grounds, it is his duty to order his immediate release. No person in police detention shall be released except on the authority of a custody officer.

Release shall be without bail unless it appears to the custody officer that there is need for further investigation, or that proceedings may be taken against the person (s34).

Where a person is arrested for an offence without warrant, under a warrant not endorsed for bail, or returns to a police station to answer to bail, the custody officer must determine whether he has sufficient evidence to charge that person and may detain him at the police station for such period as is necessary to enable him to do so (s37).

A person shall not be kept in police detention for more than 24 hours without being charged, unless an officer of the rank of superintendent or above has reasonable grounds for believing that detention without charge is necessary to secure or preserve evidence or to obtain such evidence, that the offence is a serious arrestable offence, and the investigation is being conducted diligently and expeditiously, when detention up to 36 hours may be authorised (ss 41 and 42).

Warrants may be obtained from magistrates' courts authorising further police detention (ss 43 and 44).

General matters (Code C)

If an officer has any suspicion, or is told in good faith, that a person of any age may be mentally disordered or mentally handicapped, or mentally incapable of understanding the significance of questions put to him or his replies, then he must be treated as such a person for the purposes of this code.

If anyone appears to be under the age of 17 he shall be treated as a juvenile in the absence of clear evidence to show that he is older.

A person who appears to be blind or seriously visually handicapped, deaf, unable to read or has difficulty orally because of a speech impediment, should be treated as such in the absence of clear evidence to the contrary.

Whenever this code requires a person to be given certain information, he does not have to be given it if he is incapable at the time of understanding what is said to him, or is violent or likely to become violent, or is in urgent need of medical attention, but he must be given it as soon as practicable.

Initial action (Code C)

When a person is taken to a police station under arrest or is arrested there after having attended voluntarily, the custody officer must inform him of his right to have someone informed of his arrest, to consult privately with a solicitor and that legal advice is free, and to consult the Codes of Practice.

The custody officer must then give the person a written notice setting out these three rights, the right to a copy of the custody record and the caution. The person must also be given an additional written notice setting out his entitlements while in custody. Receipt of these notices should be acknowledged on the custody record.

If the person does not understand English or appears to be deaf and the custody officer cannot communicate with him, the custody officer must as soon as practicable call an interpreter.

If the person is a juvenile, or is mentally disordered or mentally handicapped, the custody officer must as soon as practicable inform the appropriate adult and ask him to come to the police station.

'Appropriate adult' means:

(a)   in the case of a juvenile: his parent or guardian (or, if he is in care, the care authority, or voluntary organisation); a social worker; or failing either of the above, another responsible adult aged 18 or over who is not a police officer or employed by the police.

(b)   in the case of a person who is mentally disordered or mentally handicapped: a relative, guardian or other person responsible for his care or custody; someone who has experience of dealing with mentally disordered or mentally handicapped persons but is not a police officer or employed by the police (such as an approved social worker or a specialist social worker); or failing either of the above, some other responsible adult aged 18 or over who is not a police officer or employed by the police.

A solicitor may not act as the appropriate adult (Note 1F).

If the person is blind or seriously visually handicapped or is unable to read, the custody officer should ensure that his solicitor, relative, the appropriate adult or some other person likely to take an interest in him, is available to help in checking the documentation. Such a person may be asked to sign instead of the detained person.

Any person attending a police station voluntarily for the purpose of assisting with an investigation may leave at will unless placed under arrest. If it is decided that he should not be allowed to do so then he must be informed at once that he is under arrest and brought before the custody officer, who is responsible for ensuring that he is notified of his rights. If he is not placed under arrest but is cautioned, the officer who gives the caution must at the same time inform him that he is not under arrest and not obliged to remain at the police station but that if he remains he may obtain free legal advice if he wishes.

Reviews of detention (Police and Criminal Evidence Act 1984, s40)

Reviews of the detention of each person in police detention in connection with the investigation of an offence shall be carried out periodically-

(a) in the case of a person who has been arrested and charged, by the custody officer; and

(b) in the case of a person who has been arrested but not charged, by an officer of at least the rank of inspector who has not been directly involved in the investigation.

The officer to whom it falls to carry out a review is referred to as a 'review officer'. The first review must be not later than nine hours after the detention was first authorised; the second not later than nine hours after the first; and subsequent reviews must be at intervals of not more than nine hours.

(Note that review periods commence from the time that detention was first authorised and not the time of arrest.)

Condition of detention (Code C)

So far as practicable, not more than one person shall be detained in each cell.

Cells in use must be adequately heated, cleaned, ventilated and lit (subject to dimming compatible with safety and security to allow prisoners to sleep). No additional restraint should be used in locked cells unless absolutely necessary and then only suitable handcuffs.

Blankets, mattresses, pillows and other bedding supplied should be of a reasonable standard and in a clean and sanitary condition.

Access to toilet and washing facilities must be provided.

If it is necessary to remove a person's clothes for the purposes of investigation, hygiene, health, or cleaning, replacement clothing of a reasonable standard of comfort and cleanliness must be provided. A person may not be interviewed unless adequate clothing has been offered to him.

At least two light meals and one main meal must be offered in any period of 24 hours and drinks provided on reasonable request. Whenever necessary, advice shall be sought from the police surgeon on medical and dietary matters. As far as practicable, meals provided must offer a varied diet and meet any special dietary needs or religious beliefs that the person may have. Meals may also be supplied by family or friends at his own expense.

Brief outdoor exercise must be offered daily if practicable.

Juveniles must not be placed in police cells unless no other secure accommodation is available and the custody officer considers that it is not practicable to supervise them if they are not placed in cells, and then not in a cell with a detained adult.

Reasonable force may be used if necessary - (i) to secure compliance with reasonable instructions; or (ii) to prevent escape, injury, damage to property or the destruction of evidence.

Detained persons should be visited every hour, and those who are drunk every half hour.

A record must be kept of replacement clothing and meals offered, and if a juvenile is placed in a cell the reason must be recorded.

TREATMENT OF DETAINED PERSONS

Searching. The custody officer must ascertain and record everything that a prisoner has with him when brought to a police station after arrest or committal to custody. Clothes and personal effects may only be seized if it is believed - (a) that the prisoner may use them to cause physical injury to himself or any other person, damage property, interfere with evidence, or assist him to escape; or (b) that they may be evidence relating to an offence. The prisoner must be told the reason why anything is seized unless he is violent or likely to become violent, or is incapable of understanding what is said to him. Searches must only be carried out by constables of the same sex as the prisoner (s54).

Intimate searches. An intimate search is a search which consists of the physical examination of a person's body orifices, including the mouth, nose, ears, anus and vagina. An officer of at least the rank of superintendent may authorise such a search if he has reasonable grounds for believing that an arrested person in police detention may have concealed on him anything which he could use to cause physical injury and might so use while in police detention or the custody of the court; or that such a person may have a Class A drug concealed on him and was in possession of it with the appropriate criminal intent before his arrest. An intimate search must be made by a registered medical practitioner or a registered nurse, unless an officer of at least the rank of superintendent considers that this is not practicable (but must only be by such a qualified person if for a drug offence). Anything found may be seized as in any other search (s55 and Annex A of Code C).

Strip searches. A strip search (that is a search involving the removal of more than outer clothing) may take place only if the custody officer considers it to be necessary to remove an article which the detained person would not be allowed to keep. When carried out by a police officer, the officer must be of the same sex as the person searched. The custody officer must record the reasons for the search and its result. (Annex A)

Right to have someone informed. An arrested person held in police custody shall be entitled, if he so requests, to have one friend, relative or other person known to him or likely to take an interest in his welfare, told as soon as practicable that he has been arrested and is being detained there. Delay is only permitted in the case of a serious arrestable offence if authorised by an officer of at least the rank of superintendent (s57).

Children and young persons. Where a child or young person is in police detention all practicable steps must be taken to ascertain the identity of a person responsible for his welfare and inform that person that the juvenile has been arrested, the reason, and where he is detained. (Children and Young Persons Act 1933, s34(2)).

Access to legal advice. An arrested person in police custody shall be entitled, if he so requests, to consult a solicitor privately at any time. Delay in compliance with a request is only permitted in the case of a serious arrestable offence when authorised by an officer of at least the rank of superintendent (s58).

Fingerprinting. No person's fingerprints may be taken without his written consent, unless authorised by an officer of at least the rank of superintendent, or if the person has been charged with a recordable offence or informed that he will be reported for such an offence, and has not had his fingerprints taken in the course of the investigation of the offence. Any person's fingerprints may be taken without consent if he has been convicted of a recordable offence (s61).

Intimate samples. 'Intimate sample' means a sample of blood, semen or any other tissue fluid, urine, saliva or pubic hair, or a swab taken from a person's body orifice. Such a sample may be taken from a person in police detention only if authorised by an officer of at least the rank of superintendent and if the appropriate consent is given (ie the consent of a person who has attained the age of 17 years; the consent of a young person and that of his parent or guardian or in the case of a child, the consent of his parent or guardian). Such a sample, other than one of urine or saliva, may only be taken by a registered medical practitioner (s62).

Other samples. Non-intimate samples may not be taken from a person without the appropriate consent in writing, unless he is in police detention and it is authorised by an officer of at least the rank of superintendent. 'Non-intimate sample' means a sample of hair other than pubic hair, a sample taken from a nail or from under a nail, a swab taken from any part of a person's body other than a body orifice, a footprint or a similar impression of any part of a person's body other than a part of his hand (s63).

Medical treatment. The custody officer must immediately call the police surgeon (or in urgent cases send the person to hospital or call the nearest available medical practitioner) if a person brought to a police station or already detained there appears to be suffering from physical or mental illness; is injured; does not show signs of sensibility and awareness or fails to respond normally to questions or conversation (other than through drunkenness alone); or otherwise appears to need medical attention. If it appears that an arrested person may be suffering from an infectious disease of any significance, steps must be taken to isolate the person and his property until medical advice has been obtained. If a detained person requests a medical examination the police surgeon must be called as soon as practicable and he may, in addition, be examined by a doctor of his own choice at his own expense (Code C).

BAIL

Bail by police (Police and Criminal Evidence Act 1984)

Where a person arrested for an offence otherwise than under a warrant endorsed for bail is charged with an offence, the custody officer must order his release from police detention, either on bail or without bail, unless:

   (a) if he is not a juvenile:

      (i) his name or address cannot be ascertained or the custody officer has reasonable grounds for doubting whether a name or address furnished by him is his real name or address;

     (ii) the custody officer has reasonable grounds for believing that the detention of the person arrested is necessary for his own protection or to prevent him from causing physical injury to any other person, or from causing loss of or damage to property; or

    (iii) the custody officer has reasonable grounds for believing that the person arrested will fail to appear in court to answer to bail or that his detention is necessary to prevent him from interfering with the administration of justice or with the investigation of offences or of a particular offence;

   (b) if he is a juvenile:

      (i) any of the above requirements is satisfied; or

     (ii) the custody officer has reasonable grounds for believing that he ought to be detained in his own interests.

Where a custody officer authorises a person who has been charged to be kept in police detention, he must, as soon as practicable, make a written record of the grounds in the presence of the person charged. This does not apply, however, where the person charged is at the time incapable of understanding what is said to him, violent or likely to become violent, or in urgent need of medical attention. Arrangements must be made for arrested juveniles to be taken into the care of a local authority, unless the custody officer certifies that it is impracticable to do so (s 38).

A release on bail of a person under the 1984 Act shall be a release on bail granted in accordance with the Bail Act 1976. References to bail refer to bail subject to a duty to appear before a magistrates' court at such time and such place, or to attend at such police station at such time, as the custody officer may appoint. Nothing in the Bail Act 1976 shall prevent the re-arrest without warrant of a person released on bail subject to a duty to attend at a police station if new evidence justifying a further arrest comes to light (s47).

Bail Act 1976

Bail in criminal proceedings can only be granted in accordance with the provisions of this Act, eg no recognisance shall be required from the prisoner and, with certain exceptions, no surety or security for surrender need be found.

'Bail in criminal proceedings' means bail grantable in or in connection with proceedings for an offence to a person who is accused or convicted of the offence, or bail granted in connection with an offence to a person who is under arrest for the offence or for whose arrest a warrant (endorsed for bail) has issued.

If a person who has been released on bail in criminal proceedings fails without reasonable cause to surrender to custody he is guilty of an offence. Such an absconder may be arrested without warrant by a constable having reasonable grounds for believing that he is not likely to surrender to custody, or that he has broken, or is likely to break, any of the conditions of bail, or if a surety gives notice in writing that the person is unlikely to surrender.

This power of arrest applies only where a person is bailed under a duty to surrender into the custody of a court and not to a police station.

REHABILITATION OF OFFENDERS

The purpose of the Rehabilitation of Offenders Act 1974 is to enable an offender who avoids further convictions for a specified period (the rehabilitation period) to become a rehabilitated person. His conviction then becomes spent.

Spent convictions are inadmissible in evidence and in most judicial proceedings (exceptions are criminal proceedings and proceedings relating to the care or custody of children) a rehabilitated person is entitled to conceal spent convictions in most other circumstances.

The length of the rehabilitation period depends on the sentence for the original offence. It is the sentence imposed by the court that counts, even if it is a suspended sentence, not the time actually spent in prison. Anyone sentenced to more than 2½ years imprisonment keeps his conviction and it is never 'spent'.

There are some exceptions to the Act which are listed in the Rehabilitation of Offenders Act 1974 (Exceptions) Order 1975.

The main rehabilitation periods are as follows:

(a) For a sentence of imprisonment or youth custody between 6 months and 30 months ....10 years
(b) For a sentence of imprisonment or youth custody of 6 months or less ....7 years
(c) For a fine or any other sentence ....5 years
(d) For an absolute discharge ....6 months
       (All these periods, except the last one, are halved if the person convicted was under 17 at the time).
(e) Borstal training ....7 years
(f) Detention centre ....3 years

Offences of unauthorised disclosure of spent convictions

Section 9 creates the following offences:

(a) Being a person whose official duties involve custody of or access to official records and disclosing information about spent convictions otherwise than in the course of those duties.
(b) Obtaining specified information from an official record by fraud, dishonesty or bribe.

Application to police

No oral reference will be made to spent convictions in court. Previous convictions will not be given to any person, body or authority whose only interest can be in an employed context, unless permitted by Home Office circulars or the Chief Constable.

Chapter 8
Identification of Suspects

IDENTIFICATION BY WITNESSES

This subject is covered by the Code of Practice for the Identification of Persons by Police Officers (Code D).

Where the suspect is known

In a case which involves disputed identification evidence, and where the identity of the suspect is known to the police, the methods of identification by witnesses which may be used are: (i) a parade; (ii) a group identification; (iii) a video film; (iv) a confrontation.

The arrangements for, and conduct of, these types of identification are the responsibility of a uniformed officer not below the rank of inspector who is involved with the investigation (the 'identification officer'). No officer involved in the investigation may take any part.

A parade must be held if the suspect asks for one and it is practicable to hold one. A parade may also be held if the officer in charge of the investigation considers that it would be useful, and the suspect consents. A parade need not be held, however, if the identification officer considers that for any reason it would not be practicable to assemble sufficient people who resemble the suspect to make it fair.

If a suspect refuses or, having agreed, fails to attend an identification parade or it is impracticable to hold one, arrangements must if practicable be made to allow the witness an opportunity of seeing him in a group of people (a group identification). A group identification may also be arranged if the officer in charge of the identification considers that in the circumstances it would be more satisfactory than a parade. The suspect should be asked for his consent but, if this is refused, the identification officer has the discretion to proceed if it is practicable to do so. A group

identification should, as far as possible, follow the principles and procedures for a parade as in Annex A.

The identification officer may show a witness a video film of a suspect
if he considers that this would in the circumstances be the most satisfactory
course of action. The suspect should be asked for his consent but, if this is
refused, the identification officer has the discretion to proceed if it is
practicable to do so.

If neither a parade, a group identification nor a video identification is
arranged, the suspect may be confronted by a witness. Such a confrontation does not require the suspect's consent, but may not take place unless
none of the other procedures is practicable.

Notice to suspect

Before a parade takes place or a group or video identification is arranged,
the identification officer must explain to the suspect:
- (i)   the purposes of the parade or group or video identification;
- (ii) the fact that he is entitled to free legal advice;
- (iii) the procedures for holding it (including his right to have a solicitor
  or friend present);
- (iv) where appropriate the special arrangements for juveniles, mentally
  disordered and mentally handicapped persons;
- (v)   the fact that he does not have to take part in a parade or co-operate
  in a group identification or the making of a video film and, if it is
  proposed to hold a group or video identification, his entitlement to
  a parade if this can practicably be arranged;
- (vi) the fact that if he does not consent to take part in any of the
  procedures, his refusal may be given in evidence in any subsequent
  trial and the police may proceed covertly without his consent or
  make other arrangements to have him identified;
- (vii) whether the witness has been shown photographs, photofit, identikit
  or similar pictures by the police during the investigation before the
  identity of the suspect was known.

This information must be contained in a written notice and handed to
the suspect.

Where the identity of the suspect is not known

A police officer may take a witness to a particular neighbourhood or place
to see whether he can identify the person whom he said he saw on the
relevant occasion. Care should be taken not to direct the witness's attention
to any individual. A witness must not be shown pictures if a suspect is

available to stand on an identification parade, and if his identity is known the showing of pictures must be done in accordance with Annex D.

IDENTIFICATION PARADES (Annex A)

1. A suspect must be given a reasonable opportunity to have a solicitor or friend present, and the identification officer shall ask him to indicate on a second copy of the notice whether or not he so wishes.

2. A parade may take place either in a normal room or in one equipped with a screen permitting witnesses to see members of the parade without being seen. (A parade involving a screen may take place only when the suspect's solicitor, friend or appropriate adult is present, or the parade is recorded on video.)

3. If a prison inmate is required for identification and there are no security problems about his leaving the prison, he may be asked to participate in a parade or video identification. (A group identification must be arranged in the prison or a police station.)

4. A parade may be held in a Prison Department establishment, but must be conducted as far as practicable under normal parade rules. Members of the public must make up the parade unless there are serious security or control objections to their admission. In such cases, or if a group or video identification is arranged within the establishment, other inmates may participate. If an inmate is the suspect he should not be required to wear prison uniform unless all persons taking part do so.

5. Immediately before the parade, the identification officer must remind the suspect of the procedures governing its conduct and caution him.

6. All unauthorised persons must be excluded from the place where the parade is held.

7. Once the parade has been formed, everything afterwards in respect of it shall take place in the presence and hearing of the suspect and of any interpreter, solicitor, friend or appropriate adult who is present (unless a screen is used, in which case everything said to or by any witness must be in the hearing and presence of the persons mentioned, or be recorded on video.)

8. The parade shall consist of at least eight persons (in addition to the suspect) as far as possible, who resemble the suspect in age, height, general appearance and position in life. One suspect only shall be included unless there are two suspects of roughly similar appearance, in which case they may be paraded together with at least 12 other persons. In no circumstances shall more than two suspects be

included in one parade and where there are separate parades they must be made up of different persons.

9. Where all members of a similar group are possible suspects, separate parades must be held for each member of the group unless there are two suspects of similar appearance when they may appear on the same parade with at least 12 other members of the group who are not suspects.

Where police officers in uniform form an identification parade, any numerals or other identifying badges shall be concealed.

10. When the suspect is brought to the place where the parade is to be held, he shall be asked by the identification officer whether he has any objections to the arrangements or to any of the participants. The suspect may obtain advice from his solicitor or friend, if present, before the parade proceeds. Where practicable, steps shall be taken to remove grounds for objection, or the officer must explain why they cannot be met.

11. The suspect may select his own position in the line. Where there is more than one witness, the identification officer must tell the suspect, after each witness has left, that he can change his position in the line if he wishes.

Each position must be clearly numbered.

12. The identification officer is responsible for ensuring that, before they attend the parade, witnesses are not able to: (i) communicate with each other about the case or overhear a witness who has already seen the parade; (ii) see any member of the parade; (iii) on that occasion see or be reminded of any photograph or description of the suspect or be given any other indication of his identity; or (iv) see the suspect either before or after the parade.

13. The officer conducting a witness to a parade must not discuss the composition of the parade or disclose whether a previous witness has made any identification.

14. Witnesses must be brought in one at a time. Immediately before the witness inspects the parade, the identification officer must tell him that the person he saw may or may not be on the parade and if he cannot make a positive identification he should say so. The officer shall then ask him to walk along the parade at least twice, taking as much care and time as he wishes. When he has done so the officer shall ask him whether the person he saw is on the parade.

15. The witness should make an identification by indicating the number of the person concerned.

16. If the witness makes an identification after the parade has ended, the suspect and, if present, his solicitor, interpreter or friend, shall be informed. Where this occurs, consideration should be given to allowing the witness a second opportunity to identify the suspect.

17. If a witness wishes to hear any parade member speak, adopt any specified posture or see him move, the identification officer shall first ask whether he can identify any persons on the basis of appearance only. When the request is to hear members of the parade speak, the witness shall be reminded that the participants have been chosen on the basis of physical appearance only. Members of the parade may then be asked to comply with the witness's request.

18. When the last witness has left, the identification officer shall ask the suspect whether he wishes to make any comments on the conduct of the parade.

19. If a parade is held without a solicitor or friend of the suspect being present, a colour photograph or a video film of the parade shall be taken. A copy must be supplied on request to the suspect or his solicitor within a reasonable time.

20. Where a photograph or video film is taken, it shall be destroyed or wiped clean at the conclusion of the proceedings unless the person concerned is convicted or admits the offence and is cautioned for it.

21. If the identification officer asks any person to leave a parade because he is interfering with its conduct the circumstances must be recorded.

22. A record must be made of all those present at a parade or group identification whose names are known to the police.

23. If prison inmates make up a parade the circumstances must be recorded.

24. A record of the conduct of any parade must be made on the forms provided.

Video identification is covered in a similar manner in Annex B.

CONFRONTATION BY A WITNESS (Annex C)

The identification officer is responsible for the conduct of any confrontation of a suspect by a witness. Before it takes place he must tell the witness that the person he saw may or may not be the person he is to confront and that if he cannot make a positive identification he should say so.

The suspect must be confronted independently by each witness, who must be asked 'Is this the person?' Confrontation must take place in the presence of the suspect's solicitor, interpreter or friend, unless this would cause unreasonable delay.

The confrontation should normally take place in the police station, either in a normal room or in one equipped with a screen permitting the witness to see the suspect without being seen. A room with a screen may only be used when the suspect's solicitor, friend or appropriate adult is present, or the confrontation is recorded on video.

IDENTIFICATION BY FINGERPRINTS, BODY SAMPLES, SWABS AND IMPRESSIONS

A person's fingerprints may be taken only with his consent in writing at a police station, unless the powers under s61 of the Police and Criminal Evidence Act 1984 apply to take them without consent, ie with the authorisation of a superintendent or above, or where the person has been charged with a recordable offence. Any person's fingerprints may be taken without his consent if he has been convicted of a recordable offence. Reasonable force may be used if necessary.

S27 of the 1984 Act describes the circumstances in which a person convicted of a recordable offence may be required to attend at a police station in order that his fingerprints may be taken.

Dental impressions and intimate samples may be taken from a person in police detention only: (i) if a superintendent or above considers that the offence is a serious arrestable offence, and has reasonable grounds to believe that such an impression or sample will tend to confirm or disprove the suspect's involvements; and (ii) with the suspect's written consent.

Before a person is asked to provide an intimate sample he must be warned that a refusal may be treated, in any proceedings against him, as corroborating relevant prosecution evidence. He must also be reminded of his entitlement to free legal advice. Except for samples of urine or saliva, intimate samples may be taken only by a registered medical or dental practitioner.

In warning a person who refuses to provide an intimate sample the following words may be helpful:

'You do not have to provide this sample [allow this swab to be taken], but I must warn you that if you do not do so, a court may treat such a refusal as supporting any relevant evidence against you.'

'Intimate sample' means a sample of blood, semen or any other tissue fluid, saliva or pubic hair, or a swab taken from a person's body orifice.

A non-intimate sample may be taken from a detained suspect only with his written consent, unless a superintendent or above has reasonable grounds for suspecting that the offence is a serious arrestable offence and that the sample will tend to confirm or disprove the person's involvement in it. Reasonable force may be used if necessary to take non-intimate samples authorised to be taken without consent.

'Non-intimate sample' means: a sample of hair other than pubic hair, a sample taken from a nail or from under a nail, a swab from any part of a person's body other than a body orifice, or a footprint or similar impression of any part of a person's body other than a part of his hand.

IDENTIFICATION BY AND SHOWING OF PHOTOGRAPHS

The photograph of an arrested person may be taken at a police station only with his written consent. It may, however, be taken without consent if:

(a) he is arrested at the same time as other persons, or at a time when it is thought likely that other persons will be arrested, and when a photograph is necessary to establish who was arrested, at what time and at what place;

(b) he has been charged with or reported for a recordable offence and has not yet been released or brought before a court; or

(c) he is convicted of such an offence and his photograph is not already on record as a result of (a) or (b).

There is no power of arrest to take a photograph in pursuance of this provision.

Note that a 'recordable offence' is any offence which may be recorded in national police records, ie conviction for offences punishable with imprisonment and certain other specified offences (see Chapter 4).

The showing of photographs must be done in accordance with Annex D of Code D, as follows:

1. An officer of the rank of sergeant or above shall be responsible for supervising and directing their showing, but the actual showing may be done by a constable or a civilian police employee.

2. Only one witness shall be shown photographs at any one time. He shall be given as much privacy as practicable but not allowed to communicate with any other witness in the case.

3. The witness shall be shown not less than 12 photographs at a time, which must be either in an album or loose photographs mounted in a frame or a sequence of not fewer than 12 on optical disc, and all be of a similar type.

4. When the witness is shown the photographs, he shall be told that that of the person he saw may or may not be among them. He shall not be prompted or guided in any way but left to make any selection without help.

5. If a witness makes a positive identification from photographs then, unless the person identified is otherwise eliminated from enquiries, other witnesses shall not be shown photographs. Both they and the witness who has made the identification shall be asked to attend a parade or group identification if practicable unless there is no dispute about the identification of the suspect.

6. Where the use of a photofit, identikit or similar picture has led to there being a suspect available who can be asked to appear on a parade, or participate in a group or video identification, the picture shall not be shown to other potential witnesses.

7. Where a witness attending an identification parade has previously been shown photographs or photofit, identikit or similar pictures, the suspect and his solicitor must be informed of this fact before the identity parade takes place.

8. None of the photographs (or optical discs) used shall be destroyed, whether or not an identification is made, since they may be required for production in court. The photographs should be numbered and a separate photograph taken of the frame or part of the album from which the witness made an identification as an aid to reconstituting it.

9. Whether or not an identification is made, a record shall be kept of the showing of photographs and of any comment made by the witness.

Chapter 9
Interviews, Statements and Alibi

QUESTIONING OF WITNESSES AND TAKING STATEMENTS

A statement is the written record of the information a person can give concerning a matter under investigation.

Copies of statements should be used for routine purposes and the original kept for production at court. A person can be given a copy of his statement at his request.

A statement, generally, can be one of two kinds depending on the person from whom it is taken; ie a witness, or an alleged offender.

Statements from witnesses

Sit the witness down and put him at ease, then allow him to say all he knows. Questions may be necessary to bring out essential points, remove ambiguity, and arrange the order of the required statement. Only when this has been done should writing commence.

Privacy is important; never take a statement in the presence of another witness. Use only the official statement form. These may differ between forces but must all be in accordance with the requirements of the Criminal Justice Act 1967.

Always write in ink or type the statement. Commence with the name, age and personal details of the witness, as indicated on the statement form. Record events in proper sequence using the witness's own words (providing they make sense), and avoid 'official jargon'.

Start a fresh paragraph after each distinct feature or event, but do not leave any other spaces in the text of the statement. If corrections have to be made a line should be drawn through the incorrect word or words, leaving them still legible. Insert the correction above the deleted words and get the witness to sign, or initial, each correction or addition.

Before the witness signs the statement at the end it should be read over to him and he should also be allowed to read it. Any other correction, deletions or additions should then be invited.

The witness must also sign every page of the statement, but before he signs the final page the following declaration must be included:

'This statement, consisting of. . . pages, each signed by me, is true to the best of my knowledge and belief and I make it knowing that, if it is tendered in evidence, I shall be liable to prosecution if I have wilfully stated in it anything which I know to be false or do not believe to be true'.

If the witness is unable to read, the statement must finish with a declaration from the person reading it over to him that he did so.

An endorsement should now be added to the statement giving particulars of where, when and by whom it was taken, and this must be signed by the person who took the statement.

If has become common practice at this stage to add any observations considered necessary as to the person's suitability as a witness, including any apparent handicap, eg a speech impediment or deafness, etc.

Evidence by written statement (Criminal Justice Act 1967)

In both committal proceedings (s2) and other criminal proceedings (s9) a written statement by any person can be admissible in evidence to the same extent as oral evidence, providing the following conditions are observed:

(a) The statement must purport to be signed by the person who made it.

(b) The statement must include a declaration by the maker as to its truthfulness.

(c) Before being tendered in evidence, a copy of the statement must be given or served on each of the other parties to the proceedings.

(d) None of the other parties must object to the tendering of the statement in evidence.

Such a statement must contain a declaration by the person making it to the effect that it is true to the best of his knowledge and belief and that he made the statement knowing that, if it were tendered in evidence, he would be liable to prosecution if he wilfully stated in it anything which he knew to be false or did not believe true. The making of a false written statement is an offence.

Negative statements

When questioned, some persons may deny all knowledge of the facts under investigation, although a constable may have reason to believe that they do have such knowledge. It is then sometimes advisable for a constable to take a statement denying all knowledge from the person. This is known as a 'negative' statement. A negative statement can later be used to dispute the evidence which may be given for the defence by such a person.

THE CODE OF PRACTICE REGARDING THE QUESTIONING OF PERSONS BY POLICE OFFICERS (Code C)

General (Note 1B)

This code does not affect the principle that all citizens have a duty to help police officers to prevent crime and discover offenders. This is a civic rather than a legal duty; but when a police officer is trying to discover whether, or by whom, an offence has been committed he is entitled to question any person from whom he thinks useful information can be obtained, subject to the restrictions imposed by this code. A person's declaration that he is unwilling to reply does not alter this entitlement.

Meaning of interview (Note 11A)

An interview is the questioning of a person regarding his involvement or suspected involvement in a criminal offence or offences. Questioning a person only to obtain information or his explanation of the facts or in the ordinary course of the officer's duties does not constitute an interview for the purpose of this code. Neither does questioning which is confined to the proper and effective conduct of a search.

Right to legal advice

A person who asks for legal advice may not be interviewed until he has received it, unless:

   (a) Annex B applies, ie the person is in police detention in connection with a serious arrestable offence, has not yet been charged, and an officer of the rank of superintendent or above has reasonable grounds for believing that the exercise of this right will:

      (i) lead to interference with or harm to evidence connected with a serious arrestable offence or physical harm to other persons;

       (ii) lead to the alerting of other persons suspected of having committed such an offence but not yet arrested for it; or

      (iii) hinder the recovery of property obtained in consequence of the commission of such an offence.

(b) An officer of the rank of superintendent or above has reasonable grounds for believing that:

      (i) delay will involve an immediate risk of harm to persons or serious loss of, or damage to, property; or

      (ii) where a solicitor has been contacted and has agreed to attend, awaiting his arrival would cause unreasonable delay in the processes of investigation.

(c) The solicitor nominated by the person, or selected by him from a list:

      (i) cannot be contacted;

      (ii) has previously indicated that he does not wish to be contacted; or

      (iii) having been contacted, has declined to attend.

(d) The person has given his agreement in writing or on tape that the interview may be started at once.

Where a person has been permitted to consult a solicitor and the solicitor is available at the time the interview begins or is in progress, he must be allowed to have his solicitor present while he is being interviewed. The solicitor may only be required to leave the interview if his conduct is such that the investigating officer is unable properly to put questions to the suspect. If the investigating officer considers that a solicitor is acting in such a way, he will stop the interview and consult an officer not below the rank of superintendent if one is readily available, and otherwise an officer not below the rank of inspector who is not connected with the investigation.

Note that a person detained in police custody has a fundamental right to consult a solicitor. In order to deny a solicitor access to his client under Annex B there has to be a belief that he will go on to commit a serious crime. Confessions may be excluded by the court if obtained after denial of access to a solicitor.

If a suspect refuses to answer questions, his silence can fairly be taken as his acceptance of what a police officer has put to him. He has, however, a right to remain silent if he wishes.

The Law Society's Guidelines for Solicitors point out that the purpose of a solicitor's attendance at a police station is to advise the suspect of his rights and on the weight and admissibility of the prosecution evidence and, in appropriate cases, to advise of the substantial mitigation advantages of admitting guilt at the earliest opportunity, of assisting the recovery of stolen property, and of clearing up outstanding enquiries.

A solicitor can be an asset at an interview, especially if admissions are made, as his presence will dispel any claims of unfairness. Solicitors are as much on the side of law and order as police officers. They should always be treated as allies and seated with the interviewing officer opposite the suspect.

Cautions

A person whom there are grounds to suspect of an offence must be cautioned before any questions about it (or further questions if it is his answers to previous questions that provide grounds for suspicion) are put to him for the purpose of obtaining evidence which may be given to a court in a prosecution. He need not therefore be cautioned if questions are put for other purposes, eg to establish his identity, or his ownership of any vehicle, etc.

When a person who is under arrest is initially cautioned before or during an interview at a police station or other premises he must at the same time be told that he is not under arrest, is not obliged to remain with the officer and may obtain legal advice if he wishes.

A person must be cautioned upon arrest unless it is impracticable to do so by reason of his condition or behaviour at the time; or he has already been cautioned immediately prior to arrest.

The caution shall be in the following terms:

'You do not have to say anything unless you wish to do so, but what you say may be given in evidence.'

Minor deviations do not constitute a breach of this requirement provided that the sense of the caution is preserved.

When there is a break in questioning under caution the interviewing officer must ensure that the person being questioned is aware that he remains under caution. If there is any doubt the caution should always be given again in full when the interview resumes.

A record must be made when a caution is given under this section, either in the officer's pocket book or in the interview record as appropriate.

Interviews: general

No police officer may try to obtain answers to questions or elicit a statement by the use of oppression, or shall indicate, except in answer to a direct question, what action will be taken on the part of the police if the person being interviewed answers questions, makes a statement or refuses to do either. If the person asks the officer directly what action will be taken in the event of his answering questions, making a statement or refusing to do either, then the officer may inform the person what action the police propose to take in that event provided that that action is itself proper and warranted.

As soon as a police officer who is making enquiries of any person about an offence believes that a prosecution should be brought against him and that there is sufficient evidence for it to succeed, he shall without delay cease to question him.

An accurate record must be made of each interview with a person suspected of an offence, whether or not the interview takes place at a police station.

If the interview takes place in the police station or other premises:

(a) the record must state the place of the interview, the time it begins and ends, the time the record is made (if different), any breaks in the interview and the names of all those present; and must be made on the forms provided for this purpose or in the officer's pocket book or in accordance with the code of practice for the tape recording of police interviews with suspects;

(b) the record must be made during the course of the interview, unless in the investigating officer's view this would not be practicable and would interfere with the conduct of the interview, and must constitute either a verbatim record of what has been said or, failing this, an account of the interview which adequately and accurately summarises it.

If an interview record is not made during the course of the interview it must be made as soon as practicable after its completion. Written records must be timed and signed by the maker. If an interview record is not completed in the course of the interview the reason must be recorded in the officer's pocket book. Any refusal by a person to sign an interview record when asked to do so must itself be recorded.

Interviews in police stations

If a police officer wishes to interview, or conduct enquiries which require the presence of a detained person, the custody officer is responsible for deciding whether to deliver him into his custody.

In any period of 24 hours a detained person must be allowed a continuous period of at least 8 hours for rest, free from questioning, travel or any interruption arising out of the investigation concerned. This period should normally be at night.

The period of rest may not be interrupted or delayed unless there are reasonable grounds for believing that it would:

(a) involve a risk of harm to persons or serious loss of, or damage to, property;

(b) delay unnecessarily the person's release from custody; or

(c) otherwise prejudice the outcome of the investigation.

If a person is arrested at a police station after going there voluntarily, the period of 24 hours runs from the time of his arrest and not the time of arrival at the police station.

A detained person may not be supplied with intoxicating liquor except on medical directions. No person who is unfit through drink or drugs to the extent that he is unable to appreciate the significance of the questions put to him and his answers may be questioned about an alleged offence in that condition, unless an officer of the rank of superintendent or above considers that delay will involve an immediate risk of harm to persons or serious loss of or serious damage to property.

As far as practicable interviews shall take place in interview rooms which must be adequately heated, lit and ventilated. Persons being questioned or making statements shall not be required to stand.

Before the commencement of an interview each interviewing officer shall identify himself and any other officers present by name and rank to the person being interviewed.

Breaks from interviewing shall be made at recognised meal times. Short breaks for refreshment shall also be provided at intervals of approximately two hours, subject to the interviewing officer's discretion to delay a break if there are reasonable grounds for believing that it would:

(a) involve a risk of harm to persons or serious loss of, or damage to, property;

(b) delay unnecessarily the person's release from custody; or

(c) otherwise prejudice the outcome of the investigation.

If in the course of the interview a complaint is made by the person being questioned or on his behalf, concerning the provisions of this code, then the interviewing officer shall record it in the interview record, and inform the custody officer, who is then responsible for dealing with it.

A record must be made of the times at which a detained person is not in the custody of the custody officer, and why; and of the reason for any refusal to deliver him out of that custody. A record must be made of any intoxicating liquor supplied to a detained person on medical directions. Any decision to delay a break in an interview must be recorded, with grounds, in the interview record.

Where the person interviewed is in the police station at the time that a written record of the interview is made, he shall be given the opportunity to read it and to sign it as correct or to indicate the respects in which he considers it inaccurate, but no person shall be kept in custody for this sole purpose. If the interview is tape recorded the arrangements set out in the relevant code of practice apply.

All written statements made at police stations under caution shall be written on the forms provided for the purpose and taken in accordance with

Annex D to this code (see later).

Where the appropriate adult or another third party is present at an interview and is still in the police station at the time that a written record of the interview is made, he shall be asked to read it (or any written statement taken down by a police officer) and sign it as correct or to indicate the respects in which he considers it inaccurate. If the person refuses to read or sign the record as accurate or to indicate the respects in which he considers it inaccurate, the senior officer present shall record on the record itself, in the presence of the person concerned, what has happened. If the interview is tape recorded the arrangements set out in the relevant code of practice apply.

Persons at risk

A juvenile or a person who is mentally ill or mentally handicapped, whether suspected or not, must not be interviewed or asked to provide or sign a written statement in the absence of the appropriate adult, unless an officer of the rank of superintendent or above considers that delay will involve an immediate risk of harm to persons or serious loss of or serious damage to property. If he is cautioned in the absence of the appropriate adult, the caution must be repeated in the adult's presence (unless the interview has by then already finished).

If, having been informed of the right to legal advice, the appropriate adult considers that legal advice should be taken, the provisions of this code as to it apply.

Juveniles may only be interviewed at their places of education in exceptional circumstances and then only where the principal or his nominee agrees and is present.

Foreign languages

Except in the case of urgent interviews, a person must not be interviewed in the absence of a person capable of acting as interpreter if he has difficulty in understanding English, the interviewing officer cannot speak that language, and the person wishes an interpreter to be present. The interviewing officer must ensure that the interpreter makes a note of the interview at the time in the language of the person being interviewed, for use in the event of his being called to give evidence. In the case of a person making a statement in a language other than English the interpreter must take down the statement in the language in which it is made, the maker must be invited to sign it, and an official translation must be made in due course.

Deaf persons

If a person is deaf or there is doubt about his hearing ability, he must not be interviewed in the absence of an interpreter, unless he agrees in writing or in the case of urgent interviews.

WRITTEN STATEMENTS UNDER CAUTION (Annex D)

(a)   Written by a person under caution

A person shall always be invited to write down himself what he wants to say.

Where the person wishes to write it himself, he shall be asked to write out and sign before writing what he wants to say, the following:

'I make this statement of my own free will. I understand that I need not say anything unless I wish to do so and that what I say may be given in evidence.'

Any person writing his own statement shall be allowed to do so without any prompting except that a police officer may indicate to him which matters are material or question any ambiguity in the statement.

(b)   Written by a police officer

If a person says that he would like someone to write it for him, a police officer shall write the statement, but, before starting, he must ask him to sign, or make his mark, to the following:

'I, ... ,wish to make a statement. I want someone to write down what I say. I understand that I need not say anything unless I wish to do so and that what I say may be given in evidence.'

Where a police officer writes the statement, he must take down the exact words spoken by the person making it and he must not edit or paraphrase it. Any questions that are necessary (eg to make it more intelligible) and the answers given must be recorded contemporaneously on the statement form.

When the writing of a statement by a police officer is finished the person making it shall be asked to read it and to make any corrections, alterations or additions he wishes. When he has finished reading it he shall be asked to write and sign or make his mark on the following certificate at the end of the statement:

'I have read the above statement, and I have been able to correct, alter or add anything I wish. This statement is true. I have made it of my own free will.'

If the person making the statement cannot read, or refuses to read it, or to write the above-mentioned certificate at the end of it or to sign it, the senior police officer present shall read it over to him and ask him whether he would like to correct, alter or add anything and to put his signature or make his mark at the end. The police officer shall then certify on the statement itself what has occurred.

NOTICE OF ALIBI (Criminal Justice Act 1967, s11)

On a trial on indictment the defendant shall not without the leave of the court adduce evidence in support of an alibi unless, before the end of the prescribed period, he gives notice of particulars of the alibi.

Without prejudice to the foregoing the defendant shall not without the leave of the court call any other person to give such evidence unless:

(a) the notice includes the name and address of the witness or, if the name or address is not known to the defendant at the time he gives the notice, any information in his possession which might be of material assistance in finding the witness;

(b) if the name or the address is not included in that notice, the court is satisfied that the defendant, before giving the notice, took and thereafter continued to take all reasonable steps to secure that the name or address would be ascertained;

(c) if the name or the address is not included in that notice, but the defendant subsequently discovers the name or address or receives other information which might be of material assistance in finding the witness, he forthwith gives notice of the name, address or other information, as the case may be; and

(d) if the defendant is notified by or on behalf of the prosecutor that the witness has not been traced by the name or the address given, he forthwith gives notice of any such information which is then in his possession or, on subsequently receiving any such information, forthwith gives notice of it.

A notice shall either be given in court during, or at the end of, the proceedings before the examining justices or be given in writing to the solicitor for the prosecutor, and a notice under para (c) or (d) above shall be given in writing to the solicitor.

A notice required by this section to be given to the solicitor for the prosecutor may be given by delivering it to him or by leaving it at his office, or by sending it in a registered letter or by the recorded delivery service addressed to him at his office.

'Evidence in support of an alibi' means evidence tending to show that by reason of the presence of the defendant at a particular place or in a particular area at a particular time he was not, or was unlikely to have been, at the place where the offence is alleged to have been committed at the time of its alleged commission.

'The prescribed period' means the period of seven days from the end of the proceedings before the examining justices (not including Sunday, Christmas Day, Good Friday, bank holiday, or a day appointed for public thanksgiving or mourning).

TAPE RECORDING OF INTERVIEWS (Code of Practice E)

Tape recording must be used at police stations for any interview:
  (a) with a person who has been cautioned in respect of an indictable offence (including an offence triable either way);
  (b) which takes place as a result of an officer exceptionally putting further questions about such an offence after a suspect has been charged with it, or informed that he may be prosecuted; or
  (c) in which an officer wishes to bring to the notice of such a person any written statement or the content of an interview with another person.

Tape recording is not required in respect of interviews for terrorism or Official Secrets Act offences.

The police officer must tell the suspect formally about the tape recording. He must say that the interview is being recorded; give his name and rank and that of any other officer present; the date, time and place; and that a notice will be given about what will happen to the tapes. The suspect must then be cautioned.

OFFENCES TAKEN INTO CONSIDERATION

When deciding sentence a court may take into consideration other offences committed by a defendant with which he has not been charged. The express consent of the defendant is necessary to have these additional offences considered. The request should come from the defendant himself and no pressure should be brought to bear to encourage him to take this course of action. A written list should be prepared showing the date, place and nature of each offence, which the defendant should read and sign. In court the list should be put to the defendant either by reading out each offence, or by referring to a copy which he has been given, and asking whether he admits each offence and wishes it to be taken into consideration.

Code C limits the questioning of suspects about offences which may be taken into consideration and application may be made to a magistrates' court under s128 of the Magistrates' Courts Act 1980, as amended by s48 of the Police and Criminal Evidence Act 1984, to have a person charged with an offence committed to detention at a police station for up to three days for inquiries into other offences. Note that a person may only be kept in such detention 'for the purpose of enquiries into other offences' with which he has not been charged, so that it would appear that his review officer should be an inspector or above. An alternative would be to visit convicted offenders in prison to discuss other offences in accordance with Home Office guidelines.

Part 2
Traffic

Chapter 10
Classification of Motor Vehicles and Meaning of Terms

Introduction

In order to understand traffic law it is necessary to know what a motor vehicle is, the way motor vehicles are classified, and certain terms which are commonly used. Basic information is given in this chapter and other definitions are contained in chapters dealing with particular subjects.

MOTOR VEHICLE

Subject to s20 of the Chronically Sick and Disabled Persons Act 1970 (which makes special provision about invalid carriages), a mechanically propelled vehicle intended or adapted for use on roads.

The term mechanically propelled vehicle is not defined but covers all vehicles driven by petrol, oil, steam or electricity, whether intended for use on roads or not.

Pedestrian-controlled vehicles and electrically assisted pedal cycles are to be treated as not being motor vehicles.

Motor car

A mechanically propelled vehicle, not being a motor cycle or an invalid carriage, which is constructed itself to carry a load or passengers and the weight of which unladen:
  (a) if it is constructed solely for the carriage of passengers and their effects, is adapted to carry not more than seven passengers exclusive of the driver, and is fitted with tyres of such type as may be specified in regulations (ie pneumatic tyres), does not exceed 3050 kg;

(b)   if it is constructed or adapted for use for the conveyance of goods or burden of any description, does not exceed 3050 kg, or 3500 kg if the vehicle carries a container or containers for holding for the purpose of its propulsion any fuel which is wholly gaseous at 17.5° Celsius under a pressure of 1.013 bar, or plant and materials for producing such fuel;

(c)   does not exceed 2540 kg in any other case (ie a passenger vehicle adapted to carry more than seven passengers).

Heavy motor car

A mechanically propelled vehicle not being a motor car which is constructed itself to carry a load or passengers and the weight of which unladen exceeds 2540 kg.

Motor tractor

A mechanically propelled vehicle which is not constructed itself to carry a load other than water, fuel, accumulators and other equipment used for the purpose of propulsion, loose tools and loose equipment, and the weight of which unladen does not exceed 7370 kg.

Light locomotive

A mechanically propelled vehicle which is not constructed itself to carry any load other than water, fuel, accumulators and other equipment used for the purpose of propulsion, loose tools and loose equipment, and the weight of which unladen does not exceed 11,690 kg but does exceed 7370 kg.

Heavy locomotive

A mechanically propelled vehicle which is not constructed itself to carry a load other than water, fuel, accumulators and other equipment used for the purpose of propulsion, loose tools and loose equipment, and the weight of which unladen exceeds 11,690 kg.

Note that motor tractors and locomotives are all mechanically propelled vehicles which are not constructed to carry loads and only the weights differ.

Motor cycle

A mechanically propelled vehicle, not being an invalid carriage, with less than four wheels, the unladen weight of which does not exceed 410 kg.

Do not confuse the terms 'motor cycle' and 'motor bicycle' (a 'motor bicycle' is a two-wheeled motor cycle, whether having a sidecar attached or not).

A 'standard motor cycle' is a motor cycle which is not a moped.

Invalid carriage

A mechanically propelled vehicle the weight of which unladen does not exceed 254 kg, and which is specially designed and constructed, and not merely adapted, for the use of a person suffering from some physical defect or disability and is used solely by such a person.

Do not confuse invalid carriages with the blue fibre-glass bodied invalid tricycles, which are classified as either motor cycles or motor cars according to their unladen weight.

Three classes of invalid carriages are defined by the Use of Invalid Carriages on Highways Regulations 1989.

Electrically assisted pedal cycle

A bicycle or tricycle which has:
  (a) a kerbside weight not exceeding 40 kg, or 60 kg in the case of a tandem or tricycle;
  (b) pedals by means of which it is capable of being propelled;
  (c) an electric motor with an output not exceeding 0.2 kilowatts, or 0.25 kilowatts in the case of a tandem or tricycle, and which cannot propel the vehicle at more than 15 mph.

Carriage

A motor vehicle or trailer is to be deemed a carriage within the meaning of any Act of Parliament, and any rule, regulation or byelaw.

Hovercraft or hover vehicle

A hovercraft (or hover vehicle) is a motor vehicle, whether or not it is intended or adapted for use on roads.

Cycle

A bicycle, a tricycle, or a cycle having four or more wheels, not being in any case a motor vehicle.

Articulated vehicle

A heavy motor car or motor car with a trailer so attached to the drawing vehicle that part of the trailer is superimposed upon the drawing vehicle and when the trailer is uniformly loaded not less than 20% of the weight of the load is borne by the drawing vehicle (Road Traffic Regulation Act 1984 and Road Vehicles (Construction and Use) Regulations 1986).

A vehicle so constructed that it can be divided into two parts, both of which are vehicles and one of which is a motor vehicle, and shall (when not so divided) be treated as a motor vehicle with the other part attached as a trailer but this does not apply to a passenger vehicle so constructed which cannot be divided without the use of workshop facilities (Road Traffic Act 1988).

Trailer

A vehicle drawn by a motor vehicle.

Dual-purpose vehicle

A vehicle constructed or adapted for the carriage both of passengers and of goods or burden of any description, being a vehicle of which the unladen weight does not exceed 2040 kg, and which either:
  (i) is so constructed or adapted that the driving power of the engine is, or by the appropriate use of the controls of the vehicle can be, transmitted to all the wheels of the vehicle; or
  (ii) satisfies the following conditions as to construction, namely:
      (a) the vehicle must be permanently fitted with a rigid roof, with or without a sliding panel;
      (b) the area of the vehicle to the rear of the driver's seat must—
          (i) be permanently fitted with at least one row of transverse seats (fixed or folding) for two or more passengers and those seats must be properly sprung or cushioned and provided with upholstered back-rests, attached either to the seats or to a side or the floor of the vehicle; and

(ii) be lit on each side and at the rear by a window or windows of glass or other transparent material having an area or aggregate area of not less than 1850 sq cms on each side and not less than 770 sq cms at the rear.

(c) the distance between the rearmost part of the steering wheel and the back-rests of the row of transverse seats must, when the seats are ready for use, be not less than one-third of the distance between the rearmost part of the steering wheel and the rearmost part of the floor of the vehicle.

Goods vehicle

A motor vehicle constructed or adapted for use for the carriage of goods or a trailer so constructed or adapted.

'Carriage of goods' includes the haulage of goods.

'Goods' includes goods or burden of any description.

Works truck

A motor vehicle (other than a straddle carrier) designed for use in private premises and used on a road only in delivering goods from or to such premises to or from a vehicle on a road in the immediate neighbourhood, or in passing from one part of any such premises to another or to other private premises in the immediate neighbourhood or in connection with road works while at or in the immediate neighbourhood of the site of such works.

For registration and licensing purposes the terms 'mechanically pro-pelled vehicle' or 'goods vehicle' are substituted for 'motor vehicle'.

ROAD

(a) In relation to England and Wales, means any highway and any other road to which the public has access, and includes bridges over which a road passes, and

(b) in relation to Scotland, means any road within the meaning of the Roads (Scotland) Act 1984 and any other way to which the public has access, and includes bridges over which a road passes.

A highway is a way over which members of the public have a right to pass and re-pass. A footpath by the side of a road is part of the road.

Note that the Vehicles (Excise) Act 1971 refers to a 'public road', which is a road repairable at public expense.

BRIDLEWAY

A way over which the public have the following, but no other, rights of way: a right of way on foot and a right of way on horseback or leading a horse, with or without a right to drive animals of any description along the way.

DRIVER

Where a separate person acts as a steersman of a motor vehicle, includes (except for the purposes of s1 of the Road Traffic Act 1988) that person as well as any other person engaged in the driving of the vehicle, and 'drive' is to be interpreted accordingly.

Basically the test as to whether a person is or is not driving is whether he has control of the vehicle's steering and has something to do with the propulsion of the vehicle. It should be noted that propulsion includes the ability to stop the vehicle as well as to move it.

OWNER

In relation to a vehicle which is the subject of a hiring agreement or hire-purchase agreement, means the person in possession of the vehicle under the agreement.

Chapter 11
Offences connected with the Driving of Mechanically Propelled Vehicles, Motor Vehicles and Cycles

Unless otherwise stated, all matters in this chapter are contained in the Road Traffic Act 1988. as amended by the Road Traffic (Driver Licensing and Information Systems) Act 1989 and the Road Traffic Act 1991.

DRIVING AND CYCLING OFFENCES

Causing death by dangerous driving (s1)

A person who causes the death of another person by driving a mechanically propelled vehicle dangerously on a road or other public place is guilty of an offence.

The maximum penalty for this offence is 5 years' imprisonment, so it is an arrestable offence. It is charged where the circumstances do not amount to manslaughter, which requires a greater degree of criminal culpability. Notice of intended prosecution is not required.

Dangerous driving must be proved (ie an offence against s2), and that someone died as a result. The offence is triable only on indictment. If the court is not satisfied that the driving was the cause of death the accused may be convicted of dangerous driving, or careless and inconsiderate driving.

This offence may be committed by the dangerous driving of any mechanically propelled vehicle (which need not be a 'motor vehicle') on a road or other public place. However, a person shall not be guilty of the offence when driving in an authorised motoring event in a public place other than a road (s13A).

(Note the offence of causing death by careless driving when under influence of drink or drugs.)

Dangerous driving (s2)

A person who drives a mechanically propelled vehicle dangerously on a road or other public place is guilty of an offence.

Section 2A defines dangerous driving as follows:

For the purposes of ss 1 and 2 a person is to be regarded as driving dangerously if -

(a) the way he drives falls far below what would be expected of a competent and careful driver, and

(b) it would be obvious to a competent and careful driver that driving in that way would be dangerous.

A person is also to be regarded as driving dangerously for these purposes if it would be obvious to a competent and careful driver that driving the vehicle in its current state would be dangerous. In determining the state of a vehicle for this purpose, regard may be had to anything attached to or carried on or in it and to the manner in which it is attached or carried.

'Dangerous' refers to danger either of injury to any person or of serious damage to property; and in determining what would be expected of, or obvious to, a competent and careful driver in a particular case, regard should be had not only to the circumstances of which he could be expected to be aware but also to any circumstances shown to have been within the knowledge of the accused.

Notice of intended prosecution may be required. Alternative conviction - careless and inconsiderate driving.

Dangerous cycling (s28)

A person who rides a cycle on a road dangerously is guilty of an offence.

For this purpose a person is to be regarded as riding dangerously if (and only if) -

(a) the way he rides falls far below what would be expected of a competent and careful cyclist, and

(b) it would be obvious to a competent and careful cyclist that riding in that way would be dangerous.

'Dangerous' refers to danger either of injury to any person or of serious damage to property; and in determining what would be obvious to a competent and careful cyclist in a particular case, regard shall be had not only to the circumstances of which he could be expected to be aware but also to any circumstances shown to have been within the knowledge of the accused.

Notice of intended prosecution may be required. 'Cycle' means a bicycle, a tricycle, or a cycle having four or more wheels, not being in any case a motor vehicle.

Careless and inconsiderate driving (s3)

If a person drives a mechanically propelled vehicle on a road or other public place without due care and attention, or without reasonable consideration for other persons using the road or place, he is guilty of an offence.

This section creates two separate offences: careless driving and inconsiderate driving. A driver's inexperience is no excuse and an error of judgment may amount to an offence. Notice of intended prosecution may be required.

Careless and inconsiderate cycling (s29)

If a person rides a cycle on a road without due care and attention, or without reasonable consideration for other persons using the road, he is guilty of an offence.

Defences of automatism and mechanical defect

Automatism is where a person suffers a mishap for which he is in no way to blame and which renders him unconscious or otherwise prevents him from controlling the movement of his vehicle, eg a sudden unexpected epileptic fit, a blow on the head from a stone, or an attack by a swarm of bees.

Mechanical defect is where a person is suddenly deprived of all control over his vehicle by reason of some defect manifesting itself, eg a new tyre bursting, or an unexpected brake failure. This defence has no application where the defect is known or should have been discovered if the driver had exercised reasonable caution.

Either of these defences may be raised in charges of dangerous or careless driving.

OFFENCES SIMILAR TO DANGEROUS AND CARELESS DRIVING

Common law

Manslaughter may be charged where the risk of death caused by the manner of driving is very high. Such a charge may possibly also be applicable in hit-and-run accidents where an injured person is left to die.

Offences against the Person Act 1861, s35

Whosoever, having the charge of any carriage or vehicle, shall by wanton or furious driving or racing, or any other wilful misconduct, or by wilful neglect, do or cause to be done any bodily harm to any person.

Highway Act 1835, s78

While on any part of a highway driving any sort of carriage furiously so as to endanger the life or limb of any passenger, or riding any horse or beast in such a manner. 'Passenger' refers to any person on the highway.

Town Police Clauses Act 1847

In any street to the obstruction, annoyance or danger of the residents or passengers, rides or drives furiously any horse or carriage (s28). Driving a hackney carriage and by wanton and furious driving, or by any other misconduct, injures or endangers any person in his life, limbs or property (s61).

   (A motor vehicle or trailer is deemed to be a carriage (RTA 1988, s191), and a bicycle has been held to be a carriage.)

DRINK AND DRUGS

Causing death by careless driving when under influence of drink or drugs (s3A)

If a person causes the death of another person by driving a mechanically propelled vehicle on a road or other public place without due care and attention, or without reasonable consideration for other persons using the road or place, and -

   (a) he is, at the time when he is driving, unfit to drive through drink or drugs, or
   (b) he has consumed so much alcohol that the proportion of it in his breath, blood or urine at the time exceeds the prescribed limit, or
   (c) he is, within 18 hours after that time, required to provide a specimen in pursuance of section 7, but without reasonable excuse fails to provide it,

he is guilty of an offence.

   For the purposes of this section a person shall be taken to be unfit to drive at any time when his ability to drive properly is impaired. Paragraphs (b) and (c) do not apply to persons driving a mechanically propelled vehicle other than a motor vehicle.

An arrestable offence as the maximum penalty is 5 years' imprisonment. Other offences may be careless and inconsiderate driving; driving when unfit to drive through drink or drugs; driving with excess alcohol in breath, blood or urine; or failing to provide a specimen.

Driving or being in charge when under influence of drink or drugs (s4)

A person who, when driving or attempting to drive a mechanically propelled vehicle on a road or other public place, is unfit to drive through drink or drugs is guilty of an offence.

Without prejudice to the above, a person who, when in charge of a mechanically propelled vehicle which is on a road or other public place, is unfit to drive through drink or drugs is guilty of an offence.

A person shall be taken to be unfit to drive if his ability to drive properly is for the time being impaired.

A constable may arrest a person without warrant if he has reasonable cause to suspect that that person is or has been committing an offence under this section. For the purpose of arresting a person, a constable may enter (if need be by force) any place where that person is or where the constable, with reasonable cause, suspects him to be.

A person shall be deemed not to have been in charge of a mechanically propelled vehicle if he proves that at the material time the circumstances were such that there was no likelihood of his driving it so long as he remained unfit to drive through drink or drugs. The court may, in determining whether there was such a likelihood, disregard any injury to him and any damage to the vehicle.

A person found not guilty of driving or attempting to drive may be convicted of being in charge.

Cycling when under influence of drink or drugs (s30)

A person who, when riding a cycle on a road or other public place, is unfit to ride through drink or drugs (ie under the influence of drink or drugs to such an extent as to be incapable of having proper control of the cycle) is guilty of an offence.

Driving or being in charge of a motor vehicle with alcohol concentration above prescribed limit (s5)

If a person-
   (a) drives or attempts to drive a motor vehicle on a road or other public place, or
   (b) is in charge of a motor vehicle on a road or other public place,

after consuming so much alcohol that the proportion of it in his breath, blood or urine exceeds the prescribed limit he is guilty of an offence.

It is a defence for a person charged with being in charge to prove that at the time he is alleged to have committed the offence the circumstances were such that there was no likelihood of his driving the vehicle while the proportion of alcohol in his breath, blood or urine remained likely to exceed the prescribed limit. The court may, in determining whether there was such a likelihood, disregard any injury to him and any damage to the vehicle.

A person found not guilty of driving or attempting to drive may be convicted of being in charge.

Breath tests (s6)

Where a constable in uniform has reasonable cause to suspect that a person -

(a) driving or attempting to drive or in charge of a motor vehicle on a road or other public place has alcohol in his body or has committed a traffic offence while the vehicle was in motion, or

(b) has been driving or attempting to drive or been in charge of a motor vehicle on a road or other public place with alcohol in his body, or

(c) has been driving or attempting to drive or been in charge of a motor vehicle on a road or other public place and has committed a traffic offence whilst the vehicle was in motion,

he may, subject to s9, require him to provide a specimen of breath for a breath test either at or near the place where the requirement is made.

If an accident occurs owing to the presence of a motor vehicle on a road or other public place, a constable may, subject to s9, require any person whom he has reasonable cause to believe was driving or attempting to drive or in charge of the vehicle at the time of the accident to provide a specimen of breath for a breath test. This may be either at or near the place where the requirement is made or, if the constable making the requirement thinks fit, at a police station specified by the constable.

A person who, without reasonable excuse, fails to provide a specimen of breath when required to do so is guilty of an offence.

A constable may arrest a person without warrant, except when he is at a hospital as a patient, if -

(a) as a result of a breath test he has reasonable cause to suspect that the proportion of alcohol in that person's breath or blood exceeds the prescribed limit, or

(b) that person has failed to provide a specimen of breath for a breath test when required to do so and the constable has reasonable cause to suspect that he has alcohol in his body.

A constable may, for the purpose of requiring a person to provide a specimen of breath when an accident has occurred which he has reasonable cause to suspect involved injury to another person, or of arresting him in such a case following a positive or failed breath test, enter (if need be by force) any place where that person is or where the constable, with reasonable cause, suspects him to be.

Provision of specimens for analysis (s7)

In the course of an investigation into whether a person has committed an offence under ss3A, 4 or 5, a constable may require him to provide two specimens of breath for analysis by means of an approved device, or a specimen of blood or urine for a laboratory test.

A requirement for specimens of breath can only be made at a police station. A requirement for blood or urine can be made at a police station or a hospital, but cannot be made at a police station unless it is reasonably believed that there are medical reasons which prevent the provision of breath, or that an approved device is not available or not working properly, or that a doctor has advised that the person's condition may be due to a drug. Note that, while the choice of blood or urine is at the discretion of the constable making the requirement, a doctor may for medical reasons stipulate that the specimen should be of urine, and it has been held that the driver must be advised of the options.

A person who, without reasonable excuse, fails to provide a specimen when required to do so is guilty of an offence. A constable must, on requiring any person to provide a specimen, warn him that a failure to provide it may render him liable to prosecution.

Choice of specimens of breath (s8)

Of any two specimens provided by any person in pursuance of s7, that with the lower proportion of alcohol shall be used and the other disregarded. If the specimen with the lower proportion of alcohol contains no more than 50 microgrammes of alcohol in 100 millilitres of breath, the person who provided it may claim that it should be replaced by a specimen of blood or urine.

Protection for hospital patients (s9)

While a person is at a hospital as a patient he must not be required to provide a specimen of breath for a breath test or a specimen for a laboratory test unless the medical practitioner in immediate charge of the case is first notified and does not object on the grounds that its provision, or the requirement to provide it, would be prejudicial to the proper care or treatment of the patient.

Detention of persons affected by alcohol or a drug (s10)

A person required to provide a specimen of breath, blood or urine may afterwards be detained at a police station until it appears to the constable that, were that person then driving or attempting to drive a mechanically propelled vehicle on a road, he would not be committing an offence under ss4 or 5. A person shall not be detained, however, if it appears that there is no likelihood of his driving or attempting to drive a mechanically propelled vehicle while his ability to drive properly is impaired or while the proportion of alcohol in his breath, blood or urine exceeds the prescribed limit, and a doctor should be consulted in deciding this.

Interpretation of ss 3A to 10

'Traffic offence' means an offence under any provision of - (a) the Public Passenger Vehicles Act 1981, (b) the Road Traffic Regulation Act 1984, (c) the Road Traffic Offenders Act 1988 except Part III, or (d) the Road Traffic Act 1988 except Part V.

'Breath test' means a preliminary test for the purpose of obtaining by means of a device approved by the Secretary of State, an indication whether the proportion of alcohol in a person's breath or blood is likely to exceed the prescribed limit.

'Drug' includes any intoxicant other than alcohol, and has been held to mean any medicine taken to cure, alleviate or assist an ailing body.

'Drink' means alcoholic drink.

'Fail' includes refuse.

'Prescribed limit' means, as the case may require, 35 microgrammes of alcohol in 100 millilitres of breath; 80 milligrammes of alcohol in 100 millilitres of blood; or 107 milligrammes of alcohol in 100 millilitres of urine.

'Specimen of breath'. A person does not provide a specimen of breath for a breath test or for analysis unless the specimen is sufficient to enable the test or the analysis to be carried out, and is provided in such a way as to enable the objective of the test or analysis to be satisfactorily achieved.

'Specimen of blood'. A person provides a specimen of blood if and only if he consents to its being taken by a medical practitioner and it is so taken.

'Unfit to drive' means, for the purpose of ss 3A and 4, that a person's ability to drive properly is for the time being impaired.

Notes on driving while unfit or with excess alcohol

The purpose of s4 is to enable the prosecution of persons whose ability to drive is impaired through drink but whose blood alcohol concentration may be below the prescribed limit. It may also be used for impairment through drugs (remembering that these may have been taken for a medicinal purpose), and in cases where the breath-test procedure has not been properly carried out.

Note that s3A deals with persons driving while unfit who have caused the death of another person by driving carelessly.

When a person is found apparently under the influence of drink or drugs when driving, attempting to drive, or in charge of, a mechanically propelled vehicle on a road or other public place, the following points should be noted: his manner of driving or the way in which the vehicle was parked, the appearance of his eyes, smell of his breath, his speech, manner of walking, state of his clothing, general demeanour, and any complaint of illness.

While the foregoing offences relate to mechanically propelled vehicles s5 applies only to motor vehicles, ie mechanically propelled vehicles intended or adapted for use on roads. Ability to drive is of no concern, the only test being whether the driver has consumed so much alcohol that the proportion of it in his breath, blood or urine exceeds the prescribed limit. A breath test is required before action can be taken and, except after an accident, a constable must be in uniform. Where there is evidence of impairment it is often simpler to use the s4 procedure, and this must be used if the vehicle is not a 'motor vehicle' or the constable is not in uniform.

RACING ON PUBLIC WAYS

Motor racing on public ways (s12)

A person who promotes or takes part in a race or trial of speed between motor vehicles on a public way is guilty of an offence. In England and Wales 'public way' means a highway.

Regulation of motoring events on public ways (s13)

A person who promotes or takes part in a competition or trial (other than a race or trial of speed) involving the use of motor vehicles on a public way is guilty of an offence unless the competition or trial is authorised and is conducted in accordance with any condition imposed under the Motor Vehicles (Competitions and Trials) Regulations 1969. In England and Wales 'public way' means a highway.

Section 13A provides that a person shall not be guilty of an offence of causing death by dangerous driving, dangerous driving, or careless driving, by virtue of driving in a public place other than a road if he shows that he was driving in an authorised motoring event.

Regulation of cycle racing on public ways (s31)

A person who promotes or takes part in a race or trial of speed on a public way between cycles is guilty of an offence, unless the race or trial is authorised and is conducted in accordance with any conditions imposed under the Cycle Racing on Highways Regulations 1960. In England and Wales 'public way' means a highway but does not include a footpath.

'Cycle' means a bicycle, a tricycle, or a cycle having four or more wheels, not being in any case a motor vehicle.

Chapter 12
Offences connected with Traffic Generally

TRAFFIC SIGNS AND DIRECTIONS

Traffic signs

'Traffic sign' means any object or device and any line or mark on a road for conveying to traffic on roads, warnings, information, requirements, restrictions or prohibitions specified by regulations or authorised by the Secretary of State.

Highway authorities are authorised by the Road Traffic Regulation Act 1984 to erect such signs on or near roads in their area. Traffic signs must conform to the standards of size, colour and type as set out in the Traffic Signs Regulations and General Directions 1981. They are deemed to be of the prescribed size, colour and type, and to have been lawfully placed, unless the contrary is proved.

Types of signs

(a) Warnings, ie 'low bridge', 'roundabout', 'bend', etc (Red bordered triangular signs).
(b) Regulatory, ie 'stop', 'give way', 'keep left', etc (Circular signs with either a red ring or circle (prohibitory), or a blue circle (mandatory)).
(c) Directional informatory, eg 'station', 'Luton 5 miles', etc.
(d) Other informatory, eg 'dual carriageway ahead', 'bus lane', etc.

Significance of light signals (Traffic Signs Regulations and General Directions 1981, reg 34)

Red: vehicular traffic may not proceed beyond the stop line, or if the line is not visible, beyond the signals. On an occasion when a vehicle is being used for fire brigade, ambulance or police

purposes and observance of the red light would hinder such
use, it may be treated as if it were a 'Give Way' sign, ie it ma·
be passed so long as no danger is likely to be caused.

Amber: denotes an impending change to green, but does not alt·
with red   prohibition of the red signal.
Green: indicates that vehicular traffic may pass the signals
Amber: vehicular traffic may not proceed beyond the stop l·
            when a vehicle is so close that it cannot safely be ·

Offences

The Road Traffic Act 1988, s36 makes it an offence for drivers or
propellers of vehicles to fail to comply with the indication given by
lawfully placed signs which:

(a) indicate a statutory prohibition, restriction or requirement; or
(b) apply by statute (ie stop, give way, proceed in direction indicated
by arrow, keep left or right, red traffic light signal, double white
lines, no entry, and level crossing signs telling certain drivers to
request permission to cross).

(Note that local traffic regulation orders also create offences of failing to
comply with no waiting signs.)

Double white lines

Double white lines in the centre of a road are intended to control dangerous
overtaking and parking. They are traffic signs within the meaning of s36
of the Road Traffic Act 1988.

A solid line on the driver's side may be *crossed or straddled* only in the
following circumstances:

(a) to pass a stationary vehicle;
(b) to avoid an accident;
(c) in circumstances beyond the driver's control;
(d) to enter side roads or premises on the offside;
(e) to comply with directions given by a constable in uniform or a
traffic warden.

It is an offence to *stop* a vehicle in any length of road where there are
double white lines with the following exceptions:

(a) to pick up or set down passengers;
(b) to load or unload;
(c) in connection with building, demolition, removal of obstruction,

maintenance or reconstruction of road, or for any of the utility services;

(d) fire brigade, police or ambulance purposes;

(e) pedal bicycles with or without additional means of propulsion;

(f) with the permission of constable in uniform;

(g) to avoid an accident;

(h) circumstances beyond the driver's control;

(i) when required by law to stop.

Police signals

Any person driving a motor vehicle or riding a pedal cycle on a road shall stop on being required to do so by a police constable in uniform. Failure to do so is an offence (Road Traffic Act 1988, s163).

Where a police constable is for the time being engaged in the regulation of traffic on a road, any person driving or propelling any vehicle who neglects or refuses to stop the vehicle, or make it proceed in, or keep to, a particular line of traffic when directed to do so by a police constable in the execution of his duty, shall be guilty of an offence (Road Traffic Act 1988, s35(1)).

Section 35(2) applies to a direction given for the purpose of a traffic survey.

When a police constable in uniform is for the time being engaged in the regulation of traffic on a road, any person on foot who proceeds in contravention of a signal to stop by a police constable shall be guilty of an offence (Road Traffic Act 1988, s23).

Temporary obstructions

The Traffic Signs (Temporary Obstructions) Regulations 1985 permit traffic cones, traffic pyramids, traffic triangles and warning lamps to be used to convey warning of a temporary obstruction on any part of a road, other than road works.

LEAVING VEHICLES IN DANGEROUS POSITIONS

If a person in charge of a vehicle causes or permits the vehicle or a trailer drawn by it to remain at rest on a road in such a position or in such condition or in such circumstances as to involve a danger of injury to other persons using the road, he is guilty of an offence (Road Traffic Act 1988, s22).

CAUSING DANGER TO ROAD USERS

A person is guilty of an offence if he intentionally and without lawful authority or reasonable cause-

(a) causes anything to be on or over a road, or

(b) interferes with a motor vehicle, trailer or cycle, or

(c) interferes (directly or indirectly) with traffic equipment,

in such circumstances that it would be obvious to a reasonable person that to do so would be dangerous.

'Dangerous' refers to a danger either of injury to any person while on or near a road, or of serious damage to property on or near a road.

'Traffic equipment' means anything lawfully placed on or near a road by a highway authority; a traffic sign lawfully placed by any person; or any fence, barrier or light lawfully placed. Anything placed on or near a road shall be deemed to have been lawfully placed unless the contrary is proved.

'Road' does not include a footpath or bridleway in this section. (Road Traffic Act 1988, s22a)

RESTRICTION OF CARRIAGE OF PERSONS ON MOTOR CYCLES AND BICYCLES

Not more than one person in addition to the driver may be carried on a motor bicycle; and no person in addition to the driver may be carried otherwise than sitting astride the motor bicycle on a proper seat securely fixed behind the driver's seat (Road Traffic Act 1988, s23). (Reg 102 of the Road Vehicles (Construction and Use) Regulations 1986 requires foot-rests to be available for the passenger.) Offence committed by driver.

Not more than one person may be carried on a road on a bicycle not propelled by mechanical power unless it is constructed or adapted for the carriage of more than one person (Road Traffic Act 1988, s24). 'Road' includes bridleway. Each person so carried is guilty of an offence.

PROHIBITION OF DRIVING MOTOR VEHICLE ELSEWHERE THAN ON A ROAD

No person shall drive a motor vehicle without lawful authority on any common land, moorland, *or other land of whatever description*, not being land forming part of a road, or on any road, being a footpath or bridleway, except:

(a) within 15 yards of a road *for the purpose of parking*; or

(b) to save life, extinguish fire or meet a like emergency. (This section does not create a right of entry to land, or a right to park on land without permission.) (Road Traffic Act 1972, s36).

Section 36A and 36B prohibit the parking of vehicles on verges, central reservations and footways. Section 36A relates to heavy commercial vehicles which are goods vehicles over three tons unladen weight, whether mechanically propelled or not. Section 36B applies to all other vehicles, but was not in force at the time of writing.

SPEED LIMITS

General limits

Speed limits are dealt with by the Road Traffic Act 1984 in the following ways:

(a) Speed limits on restricted roads. Section 81 prescribes a general limit of 30 mph on such roads. A road is restricted if it is provided with a system of street lighting by means of lamps placed not more than 200 yards apart.

(b) Speed limit orders. Section 84 permits speed limit orders to be made by the Secretary of State in respect of trunk roads, and by local authorities on other roads. These must be indicated by signs.

(c) Speed limits for particular classes of vehicles. Section 86 provides limits in relation to vehicles of particular classes or descriptions prescribed by Sch 6 (see later).

(d) Temporary speed limits. Section 88 permits the making of temporary speed limit orders, eg the 70 mph, 60 mph and 50 mph, (Temporary Speed Limit) Order 1977.

(e) Motorway speed limits. Section 17 provides for the making of regulations in respect of motorways, eg the Motorways (Speed Limit) Regulations 1974 which imposes a general limit of 70 mph and lower limits on certain stretches.

Main speed limits applicable to particular classes of vehicles and roads (Road Traffic Regulation Act 1984, Sch 6, as amended)

(Maximum speeds are in miles per hour.)

	Motorways	*Dual Carriageway*	*Other roads*
(a) Passenger vehicles, motor caravans or dual-purpose vehicles over 3.05 tonnes unladen or adapted to carry			

more than 8 passengers and
not drawing a trailer:

	(i) not over 12 metres long	70	60	50
	(ii) over 12 metres long	60	60	50
(b)	Invalid carriages	n/a	20	20
(c)	Passenger vehicles, motor caravans, car-derived vans or dual-purpose vehicles:			
	(i) drawing one trailer	60	60	50
	(ii) drawing more than one trailer	40	20	20
(d)	Goods vehicles not over 7.5 tonnes maximum laden weight which are not articulated vehicles, drawing a trailer, or car-derived vans	70	60	50
(e)	Goods vehicles which are:			
	(i) articulated vehicles not over 7.5 tonnes maximum laden weight, or motor vehicles other than car-derived vans drawing one trailer with aggregate weight not over 7.5 tonnes	60	60	50
	(ii) articulated vehicles over 7.5 tonnes maximum laden weight, motor vehicles over 7.5 tonnes maximum laden weight not drawing a trailer, or drawing a trailer with aggregate weight over 7.5 tonnes	60	50	40
(f)	Motor vehicles other than car-derived vans drawing more than one trailer	40	20	20
(g)	Motor tractors (other than industrial tractors) and locomotives:			
	(i) if provisions regarding springs and wings are complied with and no trailer is drawn, or only one trailer is drawn which also complies	40	30	30

(ii) in any other case	20	20	20
(h) Works trucks	18	18	18
(i) Industrial tractors	n/a	18	18
(j) Agricultural motor vehicles	40	40	40

The foregoing list applies only to motor vehicles, not being track-laying vehicles, which are fitted with pneumatic tyres. Vehicles fitted with resilient tyres (ie soft or elastic) are restricted to 20 mph. Other vehicles which do not have either pneumatic or resilient tyres are restricted to 5 mph.

'Car-derived van' means a goods vehicle which is constructed or adapted as a derivative of a passenger vehicle and which has a maximum laden weight not exceeding two tonnes.

Offences

Under the Road Traffic Regulation Act 1984, s89, it is an offence to drive a motor vehicle on a road at a speed exceeding a limit imposed by any enactment. A person prosecuted for such an offence will not be liable to be convicted *solely* on the evidence of the opinion of one witness and corroboration is necessary. The reading of the speedometer of a following car or of a radar meter is evidence of fact and does not require corroboration.

It is also an offence under this section for a person who employs others to drive motor vehicles to issue a time-table for journeys which cannot be complied with without exceeding a speed limit.

Speeding offences on motorways, other than those under Sch 6, are dealt with under s17.

Exemption from speed limits (Road Traffic Regulation Act 1984, s87)

Any motor vehicle being used for fire brigade, ambulance or police purposes is exempted from speed limits if observance would be likely to hinder the use of the vehicle for the purpose for which it is being used on that occasion.

FOREIGN VEHICLES

The Road Traffic (Foreign Vehicles) Act 1972 provides legislation relating to the use of goods vehicles and public service vehicles temporarily visiting Great Britain. Department of Transport examiners are empowered to inspect vehicles coming into the country and may prohibit the driving on a road of any vehicles contravening construction and use and lighting regulations. It is an offence to drive a vehicle in contravention of such a prohibition.

REMOVAL OF VEHICLES (Removal and Disposal of Vehicles Regulations 1986)

A constable *may require the owner*, driver or person in charge of any vehicle, to remove it:

    (a) when broken down or permitted to remain at rest on a road and likely to cause danger or obstruction to other road users; or

    (b) when permitted to remain at rest on a road in contravention of any parking restriction or prohibition (reg 3).

A *constable may remove* or arrange to be removed any vehicle to which (a) and (b) above apply; or which appears to have been *abandoned* on a road or any land in the open air, whether broken down or not.

A charge is imposed for removal and storage.

The Refuse Disposal (Amenity) Act 1978 empowers a local authority to remove and dispose of vehicles and parts of vehicles which have been abandoned.

IMMOBILISATION OF VEHICLES ILLEGALLY PARKED (Road Traffic Regulation Act 1984, s104)

Where a constable finds on a road a vehicle which has been permitted to remain at rest there in contravention of any prohibition or restriction imposed by or under any enactment, he may:

    (a) fix an immobilisation device to the vehicle while it remains in that place; or

    (b) move it to another place and fix an immobilisation device to it there;

or authorise another person to take action under his direction.

'Immobilisation device' means any device or appliance designed or adapted to be fixed to a vehicle for the purpose of preventing it from being driven or otherwise put in motion, being a device or appliance of a type approved by the Secretary of State for use for that purpose in accordance with this section.

Note that this has no connection with the unofficial wheel-clamping of vehicles on private land.

OBSTRUCTION, NUISANCES AND DANGERS IN RELATION TO HIGHWAYS, STREETS, ROADS AND VEHICLES

Obstruction

A 'highway' is a strip of land over which all members of the public may lawfully pass. Any interference with that right amounts to obstruction of the highway.

Obstruction may be caused by persons, animals, vehicles and things. The following statutory offences are designed to prevent and control obstructions of various types:

Highway Act 1835, s78
By negligence or misbehaviour obstructing in any way the free passage of the highway.

Town Police Clauses Act 1847, s28
Wilful obstruction of the street by vehicle or animals to the obstruction, annoyance or danger of residents or passengers. Any person may arrest, but see general arrest powers in Chapter 5.

Highways Act 1980, s137
Without lawful authority or excuse *wilfully* obstructing the free passage along a highway.

Highways Act 1980, s162
No person shall place a rope, wire or other apparatus across a highway so as to be likely to cause danger to persons using the highway.

Road Vehicles (Construction and Use) Regulations 1986, reg 103
Causing unnecessary obstruction of the road by a motor vehicle or its trailer. This is an unreasonable use of the highway and may be committed either by physically obstructing traffic with a vehicle, or by simply leaving a vehicle in a particular place for an unreasonable length of time.

Nuisances and dangers

Highway Act 1835, s72
Wilfully riding on a footpath or driving or tethering cattle, or driving a carriage on a footpath.

Driving more than one cart (with exceptions).

Driving or riding a cart or horse and not being in a position to exercise control.

By negligence or misbehaviour causing hurt or damage to any person, cattle or goods in any carriage.

Negligently or wilfully being at such a distance from a carriage, or in such situation, as to have no control.

The driver of a carriage or beast of burden not keeping to nearside when meeting other traffic.

Riding or driving any horse or beast or any carriage furiously so as to endanger life or limb of any person on the highway.

Town Police Clauses Act 1847, s25

This Act creates similar offences to those in the Highway Act in respect of streets and public places, provided the offences are committed to the obstruction, annoyance or danger of residents or passengers. The Act has applied to *all* boroughs and urban districts since 1875, but may not apply to some rural districts. The following are some of the offences in s28:

Exhibiting in a caravan or otherwise any public entertainment or show.

Making or repairing any carriage, except for necessary repairs after an accident.

Making a bonfire or throwing or setting fire to a firework.

Flying a kite or making or using a slide on snow or ice.

Throwing any slate, brick, rubbish or other thing from a roof or any part of a building.

Leading or driving any horse or other animal, or drawing or driving any cart, carriage, sledge, truck or barrow on a footway of any street.

Highways Act 1980

This Act creates offences relating to:

Depositing things or pitching booths, etc, on the highway (s148).

Danger or annoyance, including lighting a fire, discharging a firearm or letting off a firework within 50 feet of the centre of the highway so that any user of the highway is injured, interrupted or endangered; playing football or any other game on the highway to the annoyance of a user thereof; allowing any offensive matter to run on to a highway from adjoining premises; and depositing anything on a highway so as to injure or endanger the user (s161).

Permitting certain animals to stray on or lie about a highway. The animals are: horses (including ponies, asses, mules), cattle, sheep, goats or swine (s155).

Where a hedge, tree or shrub overhangs a highway or any other road or footpath to which the public has access, or is dead, diseased, damaged, or has insecure roots, so as to endanger or obstruct vehicles or pedestrians or interfere with the view of the drivers of vehicles or the light from a public lamp, the highway authority may by notice require the owner or occupier of the land to lop or cut it so as to remove the danger, obstruction or interference (s154).

BUILDERS' SKIPS (Highways Act 1980, s139 and the Builders' Skips (Marking) Regulations 1984)

A builder's skip is a container designed to be carried on a road vehicle and to be placed on a highway or other land for the storage of builders' materials or for the removal and disposal of builders' rubble, waste, household and other rubbish or earth.

It is an offence to deposit on a highway a builder's skip without the permission of the highway authority, who may grant such permission either unconditionally or subject to such conditions as may be specified, eg siting of skip, dimensions, manner in which to be lighted or guarded.

Where a builder's skip has been deposited on a highway with the appropriate permission the owner of the skip shall ensure that:

(a)   The skip is properly lighted during the hours of darkness.

(b)   The skip is clearly and indelibly marked with the owner's name and with his telephone number or address.

(c)   The skip is removed as soon as practicable after it has been filled.

(d)   Each of the conditions subject to which permission was granted is complied with.

Failure to comply with any of the above is an offence.

PEDESTRIAN CROSSINGS

Uncontrolled crossings (zebra crossings) ('Zebra' Pedestrian Crossings Regulations 1971)

These are pedestrian crossings which are not controlled by light signals, a police constable in uniform, or a traffic warden. They are marked as follows:

(a)   Two lines of studs across the carriageway with alternate black and white strips between the lines of studs mark the limits of the crossing.

(b)   At each end of the crossing there is a beacon with a yellow globe emitting a flashing light (or steady light in exceptional cases).

(c)   A 'zebra controlled area' which is indicated by a pattern of white road markings consisting of a transverse 'give-way' line one metre from the crossing, longitudinal zig-zag lines and 'terminal lines'. The controlled areas will normally extend about 19 metres on each side of a crossing.

(d)   Where necessary a lamp not less than two metres from the ground may be provided to illuminate foot passengers during the hours of darkness.

Parts of a crossing on each side of a street refuge or central reservation are to be regarded as separate crossings, for the purpose of affording precedence only.

Offences

(a)   Drivers of all vehicles must give precedence to pedestrians on the crossing.

(b)   A driver shall not stop in the limits of a crossing unless to avoid an accident or owing to circumstances beyond his control.

(c)   A driver shall not stop in a 'zebra controlled area' except:
   (i)   to avoid an accident;
   (ii)   owing to circumstances beyond his control;
   (iii)   to enable a vehicle to be used for fire, ambulance or police purposes;
   (iv)   to enable a vehicle to be used for road repairs or public utility installations, where it is not possible to stop elsewhere;
   (v)   to make a left or right turn;
   (vi)   PSVs picking up or setting down passengers after having passed over the crossing;
   (vii) to accord precedence to pedestrians on the crossing.

Note that the above does not apply to pedal cycles without sidecars, whether mechanically propelled or not.

(d)   A driver shall not when approaching the crossing pass the foremost part of another moving motor vehicle which is proceeding in the same direction and is either wholly or partly within the 'controlled area'. (Note: if there is more than one vehicle in the controlled area, the restriction only applies to overtaking the vehicle nearest the crossing.)

(e)   A driver shall not pass the foremost part of a stationary vehicle on the same side of the crossing within a 'zebra controlled area' when the stationary vehicle has stopped for the purpose of affording precedence to someone on the crossing.

(f)   Foot passengers must not remain within the limits of a crossing longer than necessary for passing over the road with reasonable despatch.

Pelican crossings ('Pelican' Pedestrian Crossing Regulations and General Directions 1987)

This type of crossing allows a foot passenger to operate light signals by pushing a button in order to give himself precedence over traffic on the carriageway by bringing it to a stop at the crossing. They are marked as follows:

    (a) Two lines of studs across the carriageways.

    (b) A white stop line six feet from the crossing running from the nearside to the centre of the road.

    (c) An approach to each crossing, marked by a pattern of studs on the carriageway.

    (d) A broken white line along the centre of the road from the approach studs to the stop line.

    (e) Light signals; the crossings have lights controlling both pedestrians and motorists.

    (f) A 'pelican controlled area' indicated by zig-zag lines on the carriageway.

Offences

    (a) A driver shall not stop on a crossing unless to avoid an accident; or owing to circumstances beyond his control.

    (b) A driver shall not stop between a crossing and the studs marking the approach of it except;

        (i) to avoid an accident;

        (ii) owing to circumstances beyond his control;

        (iii) to enable a vehicle to be used for fire, ambulance or police purposes;

        (iv) to enable a vehicle to be used for road repairs or public utility installations;

        (v) when a vehicle is required to stop by indication given by vehicular traffic lights signals.

    (c) When the red light is showing, for any driver to proceed beyond the stop line or, if no stop line, the light signals.

    (d) Whilst the flashing amber light is showing, for any driver to fail to afford precedence to a pedestrian within the limits of the crossing before any part of the vehicle enters these limits.

LIGHTS

This subject is contained in the Road Vehicles Lighting Regulations 1989, made under s41 of the Road Traffic Act 1988. Offences are contrary to s42(1) - (a) contravening or failing to comply with regulations, or (b) using, causing or permitting a motor vehicle or trailer which does not comply to be used on a road.

Obligatory lamps, reflectors, rear markings and devices (reg 18 & Sch 1)

'Obligatory' means a lamp, reflector, rear marking or device with which a vehicle, its load or equipment is required by these Regulations to be fitted.

With certain exceptions, lamps, reflectors, rear markings and devices must be fitted to the various classes of vehicles as follows:

1.   *Motor vehicles having three or more wheels not falling into any other class*
Must have two white front position lamps (may be yellow if incorporated in yellow headlamps); two red rear position lamps (one on buses first used before 1 April 1955, or invalid carriages incapable of exceeding 4 mph); two rear retro reflectors; and one rear registration plate lamp.

Also, with exceptions: main-beam headlamps; dipped-beam headlamps; dim-dip lighting devices or running lamps; stop lamps operated by application of brakes; direction indicators; hazard warning signal devices; rear fog lamps with closed-circuit tell-tale; and on certain large vehicles, triangular amber side retro reflectors, end-outline marker lamps, and rear markings.

2.   *Solo motor bicycle and motor bicycle combination*
Must have one front position lamp unless fitted with a headlamp (two on combination); one rear position lamp (two on combination); one rear retro reflector; and rear registration plate lamp.

Also, with exceptions; a main-beam headlamp; dipped-beam headlamp; stop lamp; and direction indicators.

3.   *Pedal cycle*
Must have one front position lamp; one rear position lamp; and one rear retro reflector. Also, if manufactured on or after 1 October 1985, amber pedal retro reflectors.

4.   *Pedestrian-controlled vehicle, horse-drawn vehicle and track-laying vehicle*
Must have two front position lamps; two rear position lamps; and two rear retro reflectors.

5.   *Vehicle drawn or propelled by hand*
Must have one front position lamp (two if over 1250mm wide); and either a rear position lamp or a rear retro reflector.

6.   *Trailer drawn by a motor vehicle*
Must have two rear position lamps; two rear retro reflectors; and a rear registration plate lamp.

Also, with exceptions: two front position lamps and front retro reflectors on wide trailers; stop lamps; direction indicators; rear fog lamp; side marker lamps and side retro reflectors on long trailers; and rear markings if over 3500kg maximum gross weight.

7.   *Trailer drawn by a pedal cycle*
Must have one rear position lamp and one rear retro reflector.

Exceptions and exemptions (regs 4 - 9)

Exceptions relate to dates of manufacture and first use, types of vehicle, maximum speeds, etc: eg stop lamps are not required on vehicles having a maximum speed not exceeding 25 mph, agricultural vehicles or works trucks first used before 1 April 1986, and vehicles first used before 1 January 1936.

No lamps or reflectors need be fitted between sunrise and sunset to vehicles not fitted with position lamps, incomplete vehicles going to works for completion, pedal cycles, pedestrian-controlled and horse-drawn vehicles, or vehicles propelled by hand. Lamps painted over or masked, or without wiring, are not treated as being lamps. Other exemptions relate to vehicles temporarily imported or going to ports for export, vehicles with rear lights obscured by trailers, broken-down vehicles being towed in daylight, combat vehicles, invalid carriages incapable of exceeding 4 mph, and handcarts not over 800mm wide during the day or close to the nearside at night.

Optional lamps, reflectors, rear markings and devices (reg 20 & Sch 2-21)

'Optional' means a lamp, reflector, rear marking or device with which a vehicle, its load or equipment is not required by the Regulations to be fitted.

Every optional front position lamp, dipped-beam handlamp, main-beam headlamp, direction indicator, hazard warning signal device, rear position lamp, rear fog lamp, stop lamp, end-outline marker lamp, reversing lamp, warning beacon, side retro reflector, rear marking, pedal retro reflector and front retro reflector, fitted to a vehicle must comply with Part II of the relevant Schedule: eg-

(a) main-beam headlamps - any number may be fitted, must be white or yellow, be capable of being dipped or extinguished when other lamps are dipped and if the vehicle was first used on or after 1 April 1991 they must bear approval marks;

(b) optional stop lamps - any number may be fitted, must be red and operated by application of the brakes, and on vehicles first used on or after 1 April 1991 must be fitted either centrally or so as to project light through rear window with an intensity of 20 to 60 candelas.

Colour of light shown by lamps and reflectors (reg 11)

1. No vehicle shall be fitted with a lamp capable of showing a red light to the front, except:

(a) a red and white chequered domed lamp or segmented mast-mounted beacon fitted to a fire service control vehicle;

(b) a side marker lamp or side retro reflector;

(c) retro reflective material or retro reflector on a wheel or tyre of a pedal cycle, motor bicycle or invalid carriage;

(d) a traffic sign.

2. No vehicle shall be fitted with a lamp capable of showing other than a red light to the rear, except:

(a) amber light from a direction indicator or side marker lamp; or from a warning beacon fitted to a vehicle used for road clearance, refuse collection, breakdowns, road maintenance or cleaning etc, inspection or maintenance etc of apparatus on or under roads, carrying or escorting abnormal loads, testing of fuels by Customs and Excise, surveying, removal or immobilisation of vehicles, or vehicles with a maximum speed not over 25 mph or with an over-all width over 2.9 metres;

(b) white light from a reversing lamp, work lamp, or red and white chequered domed lamp or segmented mast-mounted warning beacon fitted to a fire service control vehicle;

(c) light to illuminate the interior of a vehicle, a rear registration plate, a taxi meter, or route indicator on a bus;

(d) blue and white light from a chequered domed lamp fitted to a police control vehicle;

(e) green and white light from a chequered domed lamp fitted to an ambulance control vehicle;

(f) blue light from warning beacon or rear special warning lamp fitted to an emergency vehicle, or from any device fitted to a vehicle for police purposes;

(g) green light from a warning beacon fitted to vehicle used by a registered medical practitioner;

(h) yellow light from a warning beacon fitted to a vehicle for use at airports;

(i) light of any colour from a traffic sign attached to a vehicle;

(j) reflected light from pedal retro reflectors, retro reflective material or retro reflectors on wheels or tyres of a pedal cycle, motor bicycle or invalid carriage; retro reflective material on a road clearance vehicle; retro reflective registration plates; reflective material incorporated in a rear marking on certain large vehicles; and retro reflective material on dangerous substance signs.

Moving and steady lights

With certain exceptions, no person shall use, or cause or permit to be used, on a road any vehicle to which is fitted a lamp, reflector or marking which is capable of being moved by swivelling, deflecting or otherwise while the vehicle is in motion (reg 12).

With certain exceptions, no vehicle shall be fitted with a lamp which automatically emits a flashing light (reg 13).

Restrictions on fitting blue warning beacons, special warning lamps and similar devices (reg 16)

No vehicle, other than an emergency vehicle, shall be fitted with a blue warning beacon or special warning lamp, or a device which resembles one of these, whether it is in working order or not.

A 'warning beacon' is a lamp that is capable of emitting a flashing or rotating beam of light throughout 360 degrees in the horizontal plane.

A 'special warning lamp' is a lamp, fitted to the front or rear of a vehicle, capable of emitting a blue flashing light and not any other kind of light.

An 'emergency vehicle' is a motor vehicle of any of the following descriptions:

   (a) a vehicle used for fire brigade, ambulance or police purposes;

   (b) an ambulance constructed or adapted for conveying sick, injured or disabled persons and used for such purposes;

   (c) a vehicle owned and used for fire salvage purposes;

   (d) a vehicle owned by the Forestry Commission or a local authority and used from time to time for fighting fires;

   (e) a vehicle owned by the Secretary of State for Defence and used for the disposal of bombs or explosives, by the Naval Emergency Monitoring Organisation for nuclear accidents or incidents involving radioactivity, by the RAF Mountain Rescue Service for rescue operations or other emergencies, or by the RAF Armament Support Unit;

   (f) a vehicle primarily used for the Blood Transfusion Service;

   (g) a vehicle used by HM Coastguard or Coastguard Auxiliary Service for giving aid to persons in danger or vessels in distress;

   (h) a vehicle owned by the British Coal Corporation used for rescue operations at mines;

   (i) a vehicle owned by the RNLI used for launching lifeboats; and

   (j) a vehicle primarily used for conveying human tissue for transplants, etc.

Obligatory warning beacons (reg 17)

With exceptions, no person shall use, or cause or permit to be used, on an unrestricted dual-carriageway any motor vehicle with four or more wheels having a maximum speed not exceeding 25 mph, unless it is fitted with at least one warning beacon showing an amber light.

Maintenance of lamps, reflectors, rear markings and devices (reg 23)

No person shall use, or cause or permit to be used, on a road a vehicle unless every front position lamp, rear position lamp, headlamp, rear registration plate lamp, side marker lamp, end-outline marker lamp, rear fog lamp, retro reflector, and rear marking, which is required to be fitted and every stop lamp, direction indicator, running lamp, dim-dip device, and hazard warning signal device, which is fitted, is in good working order and, in the case of a lamp, clean.

This does not apply to rear fog lamps not required to be fitted on a vehicle which is part of a combination, or on a motor vehicle drawing a trailer; defective lamps, dim-dip devices or headlamp levelling devices between sunrise and sunset, which became defective during the journey or if arrangements have been made to remedy the defect with all reasonable expedition; or lamps on combat vehicles between sunrise and sunset.

Use of front and rear position lamps, rear registration plate lamps, side marker lamps and end-outline marker lamps (reg 24(1), (2), (3), (4) & (9))

No person shall-
   (a)   use, or cause or permit to be used, on a road any vehicle which is in motion between sunset and sunrise, or in seriously reduced visibility between sunrise and sunset; or
   (b)   allow to remain at rest, or cause or permit to be allowed to remain at rest, on a road any vehicle between sunset and sunrise,
unless every front position lamp, rear position lamp, rear registration plate lamp, side marker lamp and end-outline marker lamp with which the vehicle is required to be fitted is kept lit and unobscured.

A solo motor bicycle not fitted with a front position lamp must keep a headlamp lit and unobscured (except when parked). On a motor bicycle combination fitted only with a front position lamp on the sidecar, or an unattached trailer which is not required to be fitted with front position lamps, a pair of such lamps must be fitted and kept lit and unobscured when the vehicle is parked between sunset and sunrise.

The above provisions do not apply to solo motor bicycles or pedal cycles being pushed along the left-hand edge of a carriageway; to pedal cycles waiting to proceed provided they are kept to the near side edge of a carriageway; or to vehicles parked on a part of a highway where roadworks are being carried out which is bounded by amber lamps and traffic signs to prevent the vehicle being a danger to persons using the road.

Exemptions permitting parking without lights (reg 24(5), (6), (7) & (8))

The following classes of vehicle are permitted to park without lights in certain places, provided they do not have a trailer attached or have an

overhanging or projecting load required to be fitted with marker lamps:
- (a)   goods vehicles not exceeding 1525kg unladen;
- (b)   passenger vehicles other than buses;
- (c)   invalid carriages; and
- (d)   motor cycles or pedal cycles with or without a sidecar.

The vehicle must be on a road on which a speed limit of 30 mph or less is in force and be parked:
- (a)   in an authorised parking place in a manner which does not contravene any enactment relating to the place;
- (b)   in a lay-by, the limits of which are indicated by a traffic sign or the colour or texture of the road surface; or
- (c)   elsewhere than in such a parking place or lay-by so that its left or near side is as close as may be to the edge of the carriageway (or close to either side in a one-way street), and no part of the vehicle is less than 10 metres from a junction on either side (measured from where the road straightens out after the bend).

Requirements about the use of headlamps, fog lamps, warning beacons, etc (reg 25, 26 and 27)

- (a)   Obligatory dipped-beam headlamps must be kept lit during the hours of darkness (half an hour after sunset to half an hour before sunrise) except on restricted roads when street lamps are lit, and in seriously reduced visibility (not defined). This does not apply if main beam headlamps or front fog lamps are lit, to a vehicle drawn by another vehicle, a snow plough, or a parked vehicle. (Note that a headlamp is not regarded as lit if its intensity is reduced by a dim-dip device.)
- (b)   Headlamps must not be used so as to cause undue dazzle or discomfort to other persons using the road, or when a vehicle is parked.
- (c)   Front fog lamps must not be used so as to cause undue dazzle or discomfort to other persons using the road, or be lit at any time other than in conditions of seriously reduced visibility, or when a vehicle is parked.
- (d)   Rear fog lamps must not be used so as to cause undue dazzle or discomfort to drivers of following vehicles, or be lit at any time other than in conditions of seriously reduced visibility, or when a vehicle (other than an emergency vehicle) is parked.
- (e)   Reversing lamps must not be lit except for the purpose of reversing a vehicle.
- (f)   Hazard warning signal devices must not be used other than for the purposes of: (i) warning persons using the road of a temporary

obstruction when the vehicle is at rest; (ii) on a motorway or unrestricted dual-carriageway to warn following drivers of a temporary obstruction ahead; or (iii) in the case of a bus to summon assistance for the driver or any person acting as a conductor or inspector on the vehicle.

(g) Warning beacons emitting blue light and special warning lamps must not be lit except: (i) at the scene of an emergency; or (ii) when it is necessary or desirable either to indicate to persons using the road the urgency of the purpose for which the vehicle is being used, or to warn persons of the presence of the vehicle or a hazard on the road.

(h) Warning beacons emitting amber light must not be lit except: (i) at the scene of an emergency; (ii) when it is necessary or desirable to warn persons of the presence of the vehicle; and (iii) in the case of a breakdown vehicle, while it is being used in connection with, and in the immediate vicinity of, an accident or breakdown, or while it is being used to draw a broken-down vehicle.

(i) Warning beacons emitting green light must not be lit except on vehicles occupied by a registered medical practitioner and used for the purposes of an emergency.

(j) Warning beacons emitting yellow light must not be lit on a road.

(k) Warning beacons required to be fitted to slow-moving vehicles on unrestricted dual-carriageways must be kept lit.

(l) Work lamps must not be used so as to cause undue dazzle or discomfort to the driver of a vehicle, or be lit except for the purpose of illuminating a working area, accident, breakdown or works in the vicinity of the vehicle.

(m) No other lamp may be used so as to cause undue dazzle or discomfort to other persons using the road.

WEARING OF SEAT BELTS

Offences (Road Traffic Act 1988)

(a) Driving or riding in a motor vehicle in contravention of the regulations (person actually committing only is guilty) (s14(3)).

(b) Without reasonable excuse driving a motor vehicle on a road with a child under 14 years in the front not wearing a seat belt (s15(1)&(2)).

(c) Without reasonable excuse driving a motor vehicle on a road with a child under 14 years in the rear not wearing a seat belt if one is fitted (s15(3)&(4)).

Regulations

The Motor Vehicles (Wearing of Seat Belts) Regulations 1982 provide that a person driving a motor vehicle required to be fitted with seat belts, or a person riding in the specified passenger seat, must wear a seat belt. A 'specified passenger seat' is a forward facing front passenger seat or, if there is more than one, that furthest from the driver's seat.

This does not apply to a person who is:

(a)   using a vehicle constructed or adapted for the delivery or collection of goods or mail, while engaged in making local deliveries or collections;

(b)   driving while performing a manoeuvre which includes reversing;

(c)   supervising a learner driver while performing a manoeuvre which includes reversing;

(d)   the holder of a valid medical certificate to the effect that it is inadvisable for him to wear a seat belt;

(e)   a constable protecting or escorting another person;

(f)   a person with powers similar to a constable protecting or escorting another person;

(g)   a fire fighter donning operational clothing or equipment;

(h)   a taxi driver seeking, answering a call for, or carrying a passenger for hire; or a private hire vehicle driver carrying a passenger for hire;

(i)   a person conducting a driving test if wearing a seat belt would endanger himself or another person;

(j)   occupying a seat for which the belt either does not comply with the regulations, or has an inertia reel mechanism which is locked as a result of the vehicle being on a steep incline;

(k)   riding in a vehicle being used under a trade licence for the purpose of investigating or remedying a mechanical fault.

The Motor Vehicles (Wearing of Seat Belts by Children) Regulations 1982 deal with the seat belts which may be provided for persons under the age of 14 years.

The Motor Vehicles (Wearing of Seat Belts by Children in Rear Seats) Regulations 1989 state that a child is regarded as wearing a seat belt in the rear seats of a vehicle if wearing a child restraint, ie an approved child seat with either its own anchorage or held in place by an adult belt. A child aged one year or older may use an adult seat belt, but if under four years must also have a booster cushion.

Lastly come the Motor Vehicles (Wearing of Seat Belts in Rear Seats by Adults) Regulations 1991. These apply to motor cars (not motor vehicles) which are constructed or adapted to carry not more than 8 passengers in addition to the driver. With exceptions, persons aged 14 years or over must wear adult seat belts when riding in the rear of such motor cars.

Note that the fitting of seat belts and anchorage points and their maintenance is dealt with in Chapter 14.

Chapter 14
Construction and Use of Vehicles

USING VEHICLE IN DANGEROUS CONDITION ETC (Road Traffic Act 1988, s40A)

A person is guilty of an offence if he uses, or causes or permits another to use, a motor vehicle or trailer on a road when:
  (a) the condition of the motor vehicle or trailer, or of its accessories or equipment, or
  (b) the purpose for which it is used, or
  (c) the number of passengers carried by it, or the manner in which they are carried, or
  (d) the weight, position or distribution of its load, or the manner in which it is secured,
is such that the use of the motor vehicle or trailer involves a danger of injury to any person.

THE ROAD VEHICLES (CONSTRUCTION AND USE) REGULATIONS 1986

These Regulations are made under s41(1) of the Road Traffic Act 1988. They are divided into two main parts: Part II - construction, weight and equipment; and Part III - use on roads. Many of the 'construction' provisions have been replaced by 'type approval', but this is of little concern to police officers who are usually involved with 'use' offences.

OFFENCES

Construction and use offences are committed contrary to the particular regulation and the following sections of the Road Traffic Act 1988:

S41A - Breach of requirement as to brakes, steering-gear or tyres.

A person who:

    (a) contravenes or fails to comply with a construction and use requirement as to brakes, steering-gear or tyres, or

    (b) uses on a road a motor vehicle or trailer which does not comply with such a requirement, or causes or permits a motor vehicle or trailer to be so used,

is guilty of an offence.

S41B - Breach of requirement as to weight: goods and passenger vehicles.

A person who:

    (a) contravenes or fails to comply with a construction and use requirement as to any description of weight applicable to a goods vehicle, or a motor vehicle or trailer adapted to carry more than 8 passengers, or

    (b) uses on a road a vehicle which does not comply with such a requirement, or causes or permits a vehicle to be so used,

is guilty of an offence.

S42 - Breach of other construction and use requirements.

A person who -

    (a) contravenes or fails to comply with any construction or use requirement other than one within s41A(a) or 41B(a) of this Act, or

    (b) uses on a road a motor vehicle or trailer which does not comply with such a requirement, or causes or permits a motor vehicle to be so used,

is guilty of an offence.

USING, CAUSING AND PERMITTING

Offences under the Road Vehicles (Construction and Use) Regulations 1986 may be committed by persons using, causing or permitting the use of a motor vehicle.

'Using'. The driver of a vehicle is using it and, if the driver is an employee going about his employer's business, the owner is also using. Using involves vicarious liability, ie the absolute responsibility of owners of vehicles for the acts of their employed drivers. No evidence of mens rea is required.

'Permitting'. This implies some control over the use of the vehicle; therefore, permitting is a matter of allowing someone else to use a vehicle.

'Causing' requires a direct instruction or order to a person using a vehicle.

In permitting and causing some evidence of mens rea is necessary, but this is not so in a charge of using. It is, therefore, customary to charge both drivers and owners with 'using'.

Audible warning instruments (regs 37 and 99)

Every motor vehicle with maximum speed of more than 20 mph must be fitted with a horn, not being a reversing alarm or a two-tone horn. This does not apply to an agricultural motor vehicle, however, unless it is being driven at more than 20 mph. The sound emitted by any horn, other than a reversing alarm or two-tone horn, fitted to a wheeled vehicle first used on or after 1st August 1973, must be continuous and uniform and not strident. A reversing alarm must not be strident.

With certain exceptions, no motor vehicle shall be fitted with a bell, gong, siren or two-tone horn. It is not unlawful, however, for a motor vehicle to be fitted with an instrument or apparatus, other than a two-tone horn, for the purpose of informing members of the public that goods are on the vehicle for sale. In addition, it is not unlawful for a vehicle to be fitted with a bell, gong or siren if its purpose is to prevent theft of the vehicle or its contents, or to summon help for a bus driver, conductor or inspector.

Every bell, gong, siren or anti-theft device fitted to a motor vehicle first used on or after 1st October 1982, must be fitted with a device designed to stop it emitting noise for a continuous period of more than five minutes.

'Horn' means an instrument, not being a bell, gong or siren, capable of giving audible and sufficient warning of the approach or position of the vehicle to which it is fitted. 'Reversing alarm' means a device fitted to a motor vehicle and designed to warn persons that the vehicle is reversing or is about to reverse.

No person shall sound any horn, gong, bell or siren when stationary on a road, other than at times of danger due to another moving vehicle; or when in motion on a restricted road between 23.30 hours and 07.00 hours. This does not apply to instruments on emergency vehicles, or those used as theft alarms or, in the case of buses, to summon assistance.

Brakes (regs 15 to 19 and Sch 4)

Briefly, motor vehicles (with certain exceptions) must be equipped with parking brakes; and all motor vehicles, and trailers exceeding 102 kg unladen, must have brakes which are maintained in good and efficient working order and properly adjusted.

Closets (reg 62)

No wheeled vehicle first used after 15 January 1931 shall be equipped with any closet or urinal which can discharge directly on to a road. Tanks into which closets or urinals empty and those which do not empty into a tank, must contain chemicals which are non-inflammable and non-irritant and provide an efficient germicide.

Dangerous use of vehicles (reg 100)

Motor vehicles and trailers and all their parts and accessories must at all times be in such condition that no danger is caused or likely to be caused to any person in the vehicle or on a road, by reason of their condition, the number of passengers or manner in which they are carried, or the weight, distribution, packing and adjustment of the load. Loads carried must at all times be so secured and be in such a position that neither danger nor nuisance is likely to be caused to any person or property. No motor vehicle or trailer must be used for any purpose for which it is so unsuitable as to cause or be likely to cause danger or nuisance to any person.

Driver's control (reg 104)

No person shall drive or cause or permit any other person to drive a motor vehicle on a road if he is in such a position that he cannot have proper control of the vehicle or a full view of the road and traffic ahead.

Emission of smoke, etc (reg 61)

Motor vehicles must not emit any smoke, grit, sparks or oily substance which causes, or is likely to cause, damage to property or injury or danger to persons who might reasonably be expected to be on a road.

Excessive noise (reg 97)

No motor vehicle shall be used on a road in such manner as to cause any excessive noise which could have been avoided by the exercise of reasonable care on the part of the driver.

Glass (regs 31 and 32)

Wheeled motor vehicles first used on or after 1 January 1959 which are:
- (a) passenger vehicles or dual-purpose vehicles - must have windscreens and all outside windows of safety glass;
- (b) goods vehicles (other than dual-purpose vehicles), locomotives or motor tractors - must have windscreens and all windows in front of and on either side of the driver's seat of safety glass;
- (c) other than those mentioned in (a) and (b) - must have windscreens and windows facing to the front on the outside of safety glass, with the exception of glass fitted to the upper decks of double-decked vehicles.

With certain exceptions, wheeled motor vehicles first used on or after 1 June 1978 must have windscreens and windows on either side of the driver's seat constructed of specified safety glass, and all other windows of either specified safety glass or safety glazing.

Windows in the upper deck of a double-decked bus and windows in the roof of vehicles must be constructed of either specified safety glass or safety glazing.

Leaving motor vehicles unattended (reg 107)

No person shall leave or cause or permit to be left on a road, a motor vehicle which is not attended by a person licensed to drive it, unless the engine is stopped and any parking brake with which the vehicle is required to be equipped is effectively set. The requirement as to the stopping of the engine does not apply to vehicles being used for ambulance, fire brigade or police purposes; or in such a position or condition as not to be likely to endanger any person or property and engaged in any operation which requires the engine to be used to drive machinery on the vehicle.

Mascots (reg 53)

No mascot, emblem or other ornamental object shall be carried by a motor vehicle first used on or after 1 October 1937, in any position where it is likely to strike any person with whom the vehicle may collide, unless the mascot is not liable to cause injury to such person.

Mirrors (reg 33)

'Mirror' means a mirror to assist the driver of a vehicle to become aware of traffic - (i) if it is an internal mirror, to the rear of the vehicle; and (ii) if it is an external mirror fitted to one side of the vehicle, rearwards on that side of the vehicle.

Motor vehicles (not being road rollers) must be fitted with mirrors as follows:

(a)   Wheeled locomotives or wheeled motor tractors first used on or after 1 June 1978, agricultural motor vehicles not exceeding 7370 kg unladen, wheeled agricultural motor vehicles first used after 1 June 1986 and driven at more than 20 mph, and works trucks - at least one mirror fitted externally on the offside.

(b)   Buses or goods vehicles exceeding 3500 kg maximum gross weight first used on or after 1 April 1983 - mirrors complying with Community Directive 85/205.

(c)   Goods vehicles exceeding 12,000 kg maximum gross weight first used on or after 1 October 1988 - mirrors complying with Community Directive 85/205.

(d)   Other wheeled motor vehicles first used on or after 1 June 1978, and Ford Transits first used on or after 10 July 1978 - at least one mirror fitted externally on the offside, at least one mirror fitted internally unless this would give no view to the rear, and at least one mirror fitted externally on the nearside unless an internal mirror is fitted which gives an adequate view to the rear.

(e)   Buses, dual-purpose vehicles, or goods vehicles first used before 1 June 1978 (or 10 July 1978 in the case of a Ford Transit) - at least one mirror fitted externally on the offside and at least one mirror fitted either internally or externally on the nearside.

(f)   Any vehicles not included above - at least one mirror fitted either internally or externally.

(Note that mirrors are not required to be fitted to two-wheeled motor cycles with or without sidecars, works trucks, pedestrian-controlled vehicles, chassis being driven from the place of manufacture, and motor vehicles drawing trailers if a person carried on the trailer has an uninterrupted view to the rear and an efficient means of communicating with the driver.)

The edges of internal mirrors of vehicles first used on or after 1 April 1969 must be surrounded by material to render it unlikely that severe cuts will be caused if it were struck by any occupant of the vehicle.

Obstruction (reg 103)

No person in charge of a motor vehicle or trailer shall cause or permit the vehicle to stand on a road so as to cause any unnecessary obstruction of the road.

Opening of doors (reg 105)

No person shall open, or cause or permit to be opened, any door of a vehicle on a road so as to injure or endanger any person.

Parking in darkness (reg 101)

No person shall, except with the permission of a police officer in uniform, cause or permit any motor vehicle to stand on a road at any time between half an hour after sunset and half an hour before sunrise unless the nearside of the vehicle is as close as may be to the edge of the carriageway. (Exceptions provided for emergency and construction vehicles, etc.)

Petrol tanks (reg 39)

Every tank containing petroleum spirit fitted to a wheeled vehicle first used on or after 1 July 1973 must be made only of metal, be fixed and maintained so as to be reasonably secure from damage, and be constructed and maintained so that leakage of any liquid or vapour is adequately prevented.

Reversing (reg 106)

No person shall drive, or cause or permit to be driven, a motor vehicle backwards on a road further than may be requisite for the safety or reasonable convenience of the occupants of the vehicle or other traffic, unless it is a road roller or is engaged in the construction, maintenance or repair of the road.

Seat belts and anchorage points (regs 46, 47 and 28)

With certain exceptions, every wheeled motor car first used on or after 1 January 1965, and every three-wheeled motor cycle exceeding 255 kg unladen first used on or after 1 September 1970, must be fitted with anchorage points and seat belts for the driver's seat and specified passenger seat (if any).

A vehicle which is first used on or after 1 April 1982: in the case of a bus, motor ambulance or motor caravan, for the driver's seat and specified passenger seat (if any); and in any other case for every forward-facing seat.

'Specified passenger's seat' means the forward-facing front seat alongside the driver's seat, or in the case of a vehicle with more than one such seat the one furthest from the driver's seat.

In the case of vehicles first used on or after 1 October 1988, seat belts and anchorage points must be fitted to certain seats on coaches; the front seats of minibuses constructed or adapted to carry more than 12 passengers; the centre front seat of minibuses, motor ambulances and motor caravans; and anchorages capable of taking lap belts must be fitted to heavy goods vehicles.

(See Chapter 19 regarding the wearing of seat belts.)

Silencers (reg 54)

Every vehicle propelled by an internal combustion engine must be fitted with an exhaust system including a silencer and the exhaust gases from the engine must not escape into the atmosphere without first passing through the silencer. The exhaust system and silencer must be maintained in good and efficient working order and not be altered so as to increase the noise made by the escape of exhaust gases.

Speedometers (regs 35 and 36)

With certain exceptions, all motor vehicles must be fitted with a speedometer which, if the vehicle is first used on or after 1 April 1984, must be capable of indicating speed in both miles per hour and kilometres per hour, either simultaneously or, by the operation of a switch, separately. This does not apply to vehicles incapable of exceeding 25 mph, motor cycles under 100 cc first used before 1 April 1984, invalid carriages and works trucks first used before 1 April 1984, and vehicles equipped with tachographs.

Speedometers must be kept free from obstruction and be maintained in good working order at all material times, ie at all times except when a defect occurs during a journey, or when steps have been taken to have a defect repaired with all reasonable expedition.

Speed limiters (regs 36A and 70A)

Every coach first used on or after 1 April 1974 which is capable of exceeding 70 mph, must not be used on a road unless fitted with a speed limiter restricting its speed to not more than 70 mph.

All such vehicles must be equipped with a plate in a conspicuous position reading 'SPEED LIMITER FITTED', and showing the set speed and the supplier's name.

Steering gear (reg 29)

All steering gear fitted to a motor vehicle shall at all times while the vehicle is used on a road be maintained in good and efficient working order and be properly adjusted.

Stopping engine when stationary (reg 98)

The driver of a vehicle shall, when it is stationary, stop the action of any machinery attached to or forming part of the vehicle so far as may be necessary for the prevention of noise. This does not apply when the vehicle is stationary owing to the necessities of traffic, to prevent the examination of the working of the machinery in the event of any failure or derangement, or in respect of a vehicle propelled by gas produced on the vehicle.

Television sets (reg 109)

No person shall drive, or cause or permit to be driven, a motor vehicle on a road, if the driver is in such a position as to be able to see (whether directly or by reflection) a television receiving apparatus or other cinematographic apparatus used to display anything other than information about the state or location of the vehicle, or to assist the driver to see the adjacent road and to reach his destination.

'Television receiving apparatus' means any cathode ray tube carried on a vehicle and on which there can be displayed an image derived from a television broadcast, a recording or a camera or computer.

Trailers (regs 83 to 90)

A bus, not being an articulated bus or a minibus, may draw a broken down bus if no person other than the driver is carried in either vehicle, or one trailer not exceeding 5 metres long provided the overall length of the combination does not exceed 15 metres.

A locomotive may draw three trailers.

A motor tractor may draw one laden trailer or two unladen trailers.

A heavy motor car or a motor car may draw two trailers if one is a towing implement and part of the other is secured to the implement, or one trailer in any other case.

An agricultural motor vehicle may draw two unladen agricultural trailers, or one agricultural trailer and one agricultural trailed appliance, or two agricultural trailed appliances. (Other trailers only as permitted above.)

A motor cycle may draw one trailer not exceeding 254 kg unladen and not carrying a passenger, except in the case of a broken down motor cycle.

A two-wheeled motor cycle under 125 cc, without a sidecar, may not draw any trailer except one less than 1 metre in width and not exceeding 150 kg laden or two-thirds of the kerbside weight of the motor cycle, whichever is the less. Such motor cycle and trailer must be marked with kerbside and unladen weight respectively, and the distance between the rear axle of the motor cycle and the rearmost part of the trailer must not exceed 2.5 metres. (This does not apply in the case of a broken down motor cycle.)

Where a trailer is attached solely by means of a rope or chain, the distance between it and the towing vehicle must not exceed 4.5 metres, and must not exceed 1.5 metres unless the rope or chain is made clearly visible to any other person using the road.

Unbraked trailers may not be used if their laden weight exceeds the maximum gross weight, or they are drawn by vehicles whose kerbside weight is less than twice the weight of the trailer and its load. (Does not apply to agricultural trailers.)

Trailers must not be permitted to stand on roads when detached from drawing vehicles unless at least one wheel is prevented from revolving by means of a brake, chain, chock or other efficient device.

No trailer may be used for the carriage of passengers for hire or reward, except a trailer carrying a broken down motor vehicle which does not exceed 30 mph, and a trailer is a broken down bus attached by a rigid draw bar. No person may be carried in a living van which has less than four wheels and two close-coupled wheels on each side.

Tyres (regs 24 to 27)

With the exception of locomotives, motor tractors and agricultural motor vehicles not exceeding 20 mph (which may have resilient tyres), all motor vehicles must be fitted with pneumatic tyres. Re-cut tyres may not be fitted to motor cycles, or to motor cars except goods vehicles which are electrically propelled or which exceed 2540 kg unladen and have a wheel rim diameter of at least 405 mm.

Pneumatic tyres of different types of structure may not be fitted to the same axle of a motor vehicle; and vehicles with only two axles may not be fitted with:

(a) a diagonal-ply or bias-belted tyre at the rear if a radial-ply tyre is fitted at the front, or

(b) a diagonal-ply tyre at the rear if a bias-belted tyre is fitted at the front.

Special provision is made for tyres designed to run when deflated, such as the 'Denovo'.

No wheel of a wheeled motor vehicle or trailer may be fitted with a pneumatic tyre which:

(a) is unsuitable for the use to which it is put;

(b) is incorrectly inflated;

(c) has a cut in excess of 25 mm or 10% of its width, deep enough to reach the ply or cord;
(d) has any lump, bulge or tear caused by separation or failure of its structure;
(e) has any portion of the ply or cord exposed;
(f) the base of any groove of the original tread pattern is not clearly visible;
(g) the grooves of the tread pattern are not at least 1 mm deep throughout at least three-quarters of the breadth and round the entire circumference;
(h) is not maintained in such condition as to be fit for the use to which the vehicle or trailer is put or has a defect which might cause damage to the road surface or any person.

The provisions at (f) and (g) above do not apply to passenger vehicles constructed for not more than 8 passengers in addition to the driver, goods vehicles of maximum gross weight not exceeding 3500kg, or light trailers. With effect from 1st January 1992, such vehicles must have tread pattern grooves at least 1.6 mm deep throughout a continuous band in the centre three-quarters of the breadth and round the entire circumference.

View to the front (reg 30)

Every motor vehicle shall be so designed and constructed that the driver can at all times have a full view of the road and traffic ahead.

All glass or other transparent material shall be maintained in such condition that it does not obscure the vision of the driver while a vehicle is being driven on a road.

Windscreen wipers and washers (reg 34)

Every vehicle fitted with a windscreen shall, unless the driver can obtain an adequate view to the front without looking through the windscreen, be fitted with one or more efficient automatic windscreen wipers capable of clearing the windscreen so that the driver has an adequate view of the road in front of both sides of the vehicle and to the front of the vehicle.

Every wheeled vehicle required to be fitted with a wiper or wipers must also be fitted with a windscreen washer capable of cleaning, in conjunction with the wiper, the area of windscreen swept by the wiper of mud or similar deposit. This does not apply to agricultural motor vehicles not exceeding 20 mph, track-laying vehicles, vehicles with a maximum speed not exceeding 20 mph, and buses providing a local service.

Every wiper and washer must at all times while a vehicle is being used on a road be maintained in efficient working order and be properly adjusted.

Wings (reg 63)

Invalid carriages; heavy motor cars, motor cars and motor cycles, not being agricultural motor vehicles or pedestrian-controlled vehicles; agricultural motor vehicles driven at more than 20 mph; and trailers, must be equipped with wings or other similar fittings to catch, so far as practicable, mud or water thrown up by the rotation of its wheels or tracks. Certain vehicles are excepted, such as works trucks, living vans, water carts, broken down vehicles, and trailers used for the carriage of round timber.

TESTING OF THE CONDITION OF VEHICLES

Testing on roads (Road Traffic Act 1988, s67 & Sch 2)

An authorised examiner (which includes a constable authorised so to act by or on behalf of a chief officer of police) may test a motor vehicle on a road for the purpose of:
(a) ascertaining whether the construction and use requirements, and the requirement that the condition of the vehicle is not such that its use on a road would involve a danger of injury to any person, are complied with;
(b) bringing to the notice of the driver any failure to comply with those requirements.

For the purpose of testing a vehicle the examiner may require the driver to comply with his reasonable instructions and may drive the vehicle.

A vehicle shall not be required to stop for a test except by a constable in uniform. An authorised constable or a person appointed by the police authority to act under the direction of a chief officer does not have to produce his authority.

A driver may elect to have the test deferred to another time and place. The owner will be given the opportunity to specify a period of seven days within the next 30 days during which the test may be carried out and he may name a suitable place. At least two days' notice in writing must be given to the owner (or if no period has been specified, at least seven days' notice).

Where it appears to a constable that by reason of a road accident a test should be carried out forthwith or where the vehicle is so defective that in his opinion it would be dangerous for it to proceed, he may then arrange for a test to be carried out by an authorised examiner before the vehicle is moved.

Inspection of public passenger vehicles and goods vehicles (Road Traffic Act 1988, ss68 & 69)

A vehicle examiner may at any time inspect any goods vehicles, public service vehicles, or motor vehicles which are not PSVs but are adapted to carry more than 8 passengers (except vehicles used by education and other bodies, etc) (s68).

If on any inspection of a vehicle it appears to a vehicle examiner that owing to defects the vehicle is, or is likely to become, unfit for service, he may prohibit the driving of the vehicle on a road either absolutely or for specified purposes (s69). It is an offence to fail to comply with such a prohibition (s71).

Testing on premises (Road Vehicles (Construction and Use) Regulations 1986, reg 74)

Any constable in uniform or authorised examiner is empowered to test and inspect brakes, steering gear, silencer and tyres of any vehicle or trailer on premises, provided: the owner of the premises consents, and either
  (i)   the owner of the vehicle consents, or
  (ii) notice of inspection has been given to the owner of the vehicle personally or left at his address not less than 48 hours before the proposed test and inspection or shall be sent to him not less than 72 hours before that time by recorded delivery post at his address.

The consent of the vehicle owner is not required where the test is carried out on private premises within 48 hours of the vehicle being involved in an accident to which s170 of the Road Traffic Act 1988 applies.

Sale of unroadworthy vehicles (Road Traffic Act 1988, s77)

Authorised examiners (including police officers specially appointed in writing by the chief officer of police) may test and inspect used motor vehicles and trailers in sale rooms, auctions, etc, in order to ensure that these vehicles are not sold in any unroadworthy condition. It is an offence under s75 to sell, offer to sell or supply, or expose for sale, a motor vehicle or trailer.

Test certificates

Section 47 of the Road Traffic Act 1988 and the Motor Vehicles (Tests) Regulations 1976 state that certain motor vehicles shall not be used on a road unless they have been tested, during the previous 12 months, at an approved vehicle testing station. On satisfactorily passing the test, a test certificate is issued.

This section applies to motor vehicles either:
  (a) After three years from the date of their first registration under the Vehicles (Excise) Act 1971; or
  (b) After three years from the date of manufacture, if used on any roads anywhere, in Great Britain or otherwise, before registration under the Vehicles (Excise) Act 1971. (Note: 'Date of manufacture' is the last day of the year in which the motor vehicle is finally assembled.)

The motor vehicle must be tested by an authorised examiner. Such an examiner must ascertain that the requirements of construction and condition are complied with in relation to a vehicle's brakes, steering, lights and reflectors, stop lamps, tyres, seat belts and anchorage points, windscreen wipers and washers, exhaust, audible warning instruments, bodywork and suspension.

Exemptions

Section 47 does not apply to: heavy locomotives; light locomotives; motor tractors; track-laying vehicles; goods vehicles exceeding 1525 kg unladen; articulated vehicles other than articulated buses; vehicles exempt from excise duty; works trucks; pedestrian-controlled vehicles; invalid vehicles not over 306 kg unladen, or not over 510 kg if supplied by DSS; vehicles temporarily in Great Britain; vehicles proceeding to a port for export; visiting forces' vehicles; police vehicles maintained in approved workshops; imported vehicles used for naval, military or air force purposes; vehicles with Northern Ireland test certificates; electrically propelled goods vehicles not over 1525 kg unladen; certain hackney carriages; certain private hire cars; agricultural motor vehicles.

Special provisions

The following uses on a road are exempt from the requirement to have a test certificate:
  (a) taking a vehicle to or from a pre-arranged test;

(b) by examiner, or person acting on his behalf when carrying out a test;

(c) where a test certificate has been refused; when taking the vehicle to or from a pre-arranged place for the required repairs, or towing it to a place for breaking up.

Production of test certificate

A test certificate, where applicable, must be produced to a police constable on demand, by any person driving, using, etc a motor vehicle under circumstances similar to those when a certificate of insurance could be demanded.

PLATING AND TESTING OF GOODS VEHICLES

Testing of goods vehicles

The Goods Vehicles (Plating and Testing) Regulations 1988 apply to the following goods vehicles:

(a) heavy motor cars and motor cars forming part of articulated vehicles;

(b) other heavy motor cars and motors cars over 1525 kg unladen;

(c) semi-trailers;

(d) converter dollies manufactured on or after 1st January 1979; and

(e) other trailers over 1020 kg unladen.

These goods vehicles undergo two different examinations:

(a) For 'plating' purposes; and

(b) Testing to see that they comply with the prescribed construction and use requirements.

Certificates

If the vehicle or trailer complies then the following are issued in respect of it:

(a) Plating certificate;

(b) Goods Vehicle Test Certificate;

(c) 'Ministry' plate.

Plating Certificates, Goods Vehicle Test Certificates and any certificate issued under s54 of the Road Traffic Act 1988, must be produced to a police constable on demand in the same manner as a Test Certificate issued under s47 of the Road Traffic Act 1988.

Plating of goods vehicles

Plating is carried out by ascertaining the maximum weight applicable to a goods vehicle and marking it on the vehicle by means of a 'plate' (which is a paper certificate).

In accordance with reg 66 of the Road Vehicles (Construction and Use) Regulations 1986, the following goods vehicles must have a plate securely fixed to them, in a conspicuous position, showing the 'prescribed particulars':

(a) heavy motor cars and motor cars first used on or after 1st January, not being dual-purpose vehicles, agricultural motor vehicles, works trucks, pedestrian-controlled vehicles, or passenger vehicles;

(b) large passenger-carrying vehicles manufactured on or after 1st October 1981 and first used on or after 1 April 1982;

(c) locomotives and motor tractors first used on or after 1 April 1973, not being agricultural motor vehicles, industrial tractors, works trucks, engineering plant, pedestrian-controlled vehicles, or vehicles manufactured before 1 October 1972;

(d) trailers manufactured on or after 1 January 1968 over 1020 kg unladen, other than trailers permanently carrying plant or special apparatus and not over 2290 kg total weight, living vans with pneumatic tyres not over 2040 kg unladen, works trailers, trailers mentioned in reg 75(4), and trailers manufactured and first used outside Great Britain;

(e) converter dollies manufactured on or after 1 January 1979.

New *types* of vehicle are issued with a Manufacturer's Plate and do not need to be tested until 12 months after first registration.

The prescribed particulars which must be shown on the plate affixed to goods vehicles are: manufacturer's name; vehicle type (motor vehicles only); engine type (motor vehicles only); chassis or serial number; number of axles; maximum axle weight for each axle; maximum gross weight; maximum load imposed on drawing vehicle (articulated vehicles); and maximum train weight (combined weight of motor vehicle and any trailer drawn thereby).

BRAKES ON PEDAL CYCLES (Pedal Cycles (Construction and Use) Regulations 1983)

These Regulations are made under s81 of the Road Traffic Act 1988 and any offences are under s91 of the Road Traffic Offenders Act 1988.

No person shall ride or cause or permit any pedal cycle manufactured on or after 1 August 1984 which has a saddle height exceeding 635 mm, or manufactured before that date and having any wheel exceeding 460 mm in diameter, unless it has:

(a) if fitted with a fixed wheel, a braking system acting on the front wheel; or

(b) if fitted with a free wheel, two independent braking systems acting on front and rear wheels.

Every other pedal cycle must have at least one braking system.

All brakes must be maintained in efficient working order.

A constable in uniform may test and inspect the brakes of any pedal cycle either on a road, or on premises within 48 hours of an accident with the consent of the owner of the premises.

Chapter 15
Driving Licences, etc

PURPOSE OF DRIVING LICENCES

The purpose of driving licences is to ensure that only competent persons
are allowed to drive motor vehicles on roads. Their issue is controlled by
Part III of the Road Traffic Act 1988, as amended by the Road Traffic
(Driver Licensing and Information Systems) Act 1989 and the Road
Traffic Act 1991, and the Motor Vehicles (Driving Licences) Regulations
1987.

Under s87 of the 1988 Act it is an offence for a person to drive on a road
a motor vehicle of any class otherwise than in accordance with a licence
authorising him to drive a motor vehicle of that class.

It is also an offence for a person to cause or permit another person to
drive on a road a motor vehicle of any class otherwise than in accordance
with a licence authorising that other person to drive a motor vehicle of that
class.

**MINIMUM AGES FOR DRIVING MOTOR VEHICLES (s101, as
amended by reg 4)**

16 years
   (a) Invalid carriages (up to 510 kg unladen).
   (b) Mopeds.
   (c) Motor cycles which are mowing machines.
   (d) Motor cycles which are vehicles controlled by pedestrians.
   (e) Small passenger and small goods vehicles driven by persons in
       receipt of a mobility allowance.
   (f) Agricultural tractors, provided:
       (i) they are wheeled vehicles not exceeding 2.45 metres in width;
       (ii) they are licensed as agricultural machines, or not chargeable
            with duty by virtue of s7, Vehicles (Excise) Act 1971;

(iii) any trailer drawn has either two wheels or four close-coupled wheels, and does not exceed 2.45 metres in width.

(In the case of persons who have not passed a test, only while taking, proceeding to, or returning from a test.)

17 years
- (a)   Small passenger vehicles or small goods vehicles.
- (b)   Agricultural tractors (other than those under age 16 above).
- (c)   Motor cycles.
- (d)   Road rollers, not steam propelled, not exceeding 11690 kg unladen or carrying any load other than propulsion equipment, and not fitted with pneumatic, soft or elastic tyres.
- (e)   Medium-sized goods vehicles and other vehicles (eg LGVs), in the case of members of the armed forces using them in the course of urgent work of national importance.
- (f)   Large goods vehicles, in the case of members of the armed forces receiving driving instruction or when taking, proceeding to, or returning from a test.

18 years
- (a)   Medium-sized goods vehicles.
- (b)   Vehicles driven by persons employed by a health authority for the purpose of an ambulance service.
- (c)   Any other vehicle in the case of a person who is a registered employee of a registered employer in the HGV training scheme, and the vehicle is of a class to which his training agreement applies and is owned by his employer or a registered HGV training establishment.
- (d)   Large passenger vehicles, where passengers are not carried and the driver either holds a PSV licence, is taking a PSV driving test, or is acting under the supervision of a PSV licence holder; or the driver holds a PSV licence and is carrying passengers on a regular route not over 50 kilometres, or is using a vehicle constructed to carry not more than 17 persons including the driver, and in either case the operator holds a PSV operator's licence.

21 years
Other motor vehicles (ie any classes not already listed).

(Note that electrically assisted pedal cycles are deemed not to be motor vehicles. They may be ridden by persons aged 14 years or over. (Road Traffic Act 1988, s 32, and the Electrically Assisted Pedal Cycles Regulations 1983.))

DEFINITIONS OF CLASSES OF VEHICLES FOR DRIVING LICENCE PURPOSES

'Large goods vehicle' means any of the following vehicles:
- (a)   an articulated goods vehicle;
- (b)   a motor vehicle (not being an articulated goods vehicle) which is constructed or adapted to carry or to haul goods and the permissible maximum weight of which exceeds 7.5 tonnes. (Formerly 'heavy goods vehicles'.)

'Large passenger vehicle' means a motor vehicle which is constructed solely to carry passengers and is adapted to carry more than 9 persons inclusive of the driver and the permissible maximum weight of which exceeds 3.5 tonnes but not 7.5 tonnes.

'Moped' means -
- (i)   in the case of motor cycles first used on or after 1 August 1977, a motor cycle which has a maximum design speed which does not exceed 30 mph, a kerbside weight which does not exceed 250 kg and, if propelled by an internal combustion engine, an engine the cylinder capacity of which does not exceed 50 cc; or
- (ii)   in the case of motor cycles which are first used before 1 August 1977, a motor cycle which has an engine with a cylinder capacity not exceeding 50 cc and is equipped with pedals by means of which the cycle is capable of being propelled.

'Passenger-carrying vehicle' means:
- (a)   a large passenger-carrying vehicle, that is to say, a vehicle used for carrying passengers which is constructed or adapted to carry more than 16 passengers, or
- (b)   a small passenger-carrying vehicle, that is to say, a vehicle used for carrying passengers for hire or reward which is constructed or adapted to carry more than 8 but not more than 16 passengers.

'Small goods vehicle' means a motor vehicle (other than a motor cycle or invalid carriage) which is constructed or adapted to carry or to haul goods and is not adapted to carry more than 9 persons inclusive of the driver and the permissible maximum weight of which does not exceed 3.5 tonnes.

'Small passenger vehicle' means a motor vehicle (other than a motor cycle or invalid carriage) which is constructed solely to carry passengers and their effects and is adapted to carry not more than 9 persons inclusive of the driver.

'Vehicle propelled by electrical power' means a vehicle of which the motive power is solely derived from any electrical storage battery carried on the vehicle and not connected to any source of power when the vehicle is in motion.

'Vehicle with automatic transmission' means a vehicle in which the driver is not provided with any means whereby he may, independently of the use of the accelerator or the brakes, vary gradually the proportion of power being produced by the engine which is transmitted to the road wheels of the vehicle.

TYPES OF DRIVING LICENCES

(a) Full driving licence - a licence other than a provisional licence for use by a qualified driver.

(b) Provisional driving licence - a licence issued for the purpose of enabling a person to drive a motor vehicle with a view to passing a test of competence to drive.

(c) Community licence - a document issued in respect of a member state other than the UK by an authority of that or another member state (including the UK) authorising the holder to drive a motor vehicle.

(d) Exchangeable licence - a Community licence or a document which would be a Community licence if Gibraltar were or formed part of a member state other than the UK.

(e) Convention driving permit - a permit to drive issued under the authority of a country outside the UK in a form prescribed by the Motor Vehicles (International Circulation) Order 1975.

(f) Domestic driving permit -a licence issued under the law of a foreign country authorising driving in that country.

(g) British Forces (Germany) driving licence - a licence issued to members of British forces in Germany (including civilian components) or their dependants.

(Note that licences issued under Part III of the Road Traffic Act 1988 are valid until age 70 or for 3 years, whichever is the longer. Licences authorising the driving of prescribed goods or passenger-carrying vehicles will expire at age 45 or after 5 years, whichever is the longer; or if issued after the age of 45, at the age of 66 or after 5 years, whichever is the shorter.)

CATEGORIES OF MOTOR VEHICLES FOR DRIVING TEST PURPOSES (Motor Vehicles (Driving Licences) Regulations 1987, Schedule 3)

Category	Class of vehicle included in the category	Additional categories
A	Motor bicycle (with or without side-car) excluding vehicles in category K or P	B1 & P
B	Motor vehicle with maximum authorised mass not exceeding 3.5 tonnes and not more than 8 seats in addition to driver's seat, not included in any other category, including such a vehicle drawing trailer with maximum authorised mass not exceeding 750 kg.	B plus E, B1, C1, C1 plus E, D1, D1 plus E, F, K, L, N & P
B1	Motor tricycle with unladen mass not exceeding 500 kg and with maximum design speed exceeding 50 kph, excluding any vehicle in category K, L or P	
C1	Motor vehicle used for the carriage of goods with maximum authorised mass exceeding 3.5 tonnes but not exceeding 7.5 tonnes, including such a vehicle drawing trailer with maximum authorised mass not exceeding 750 kg.	B, B plus E, B1, C1 plus E, D1, D1 plus E, F, K, L, N & P
D1	Motor vehicle used for the carriage of passengers (not for hire or reward) with more than 8 seats in addition to the driver's seat, including such vehicle-drawing trailer with maximum authorised mass not exceeding 750 kg.	B, B plus E, B1, C1, C1 plus E, D1 plus E, F, K, L, N & P
B plus E	Combination of motor vehicle in category B and trailer with maximum authorised mass exceeding 750 kg.	
C1 plus E	Combination of motor vehicle in category C1 and trailer with maximum authorised mass exceeding 750 kg.	

D1 plus E	Combination of motor vehicle in category D1 and trailer with maximum authorised mass exceeding 750 kg.	
F	Agricultural tractor, excluding any vehicle in category H	K
G	Road roller	
H	Track-laying vehicle steered by its tracks	
K	Mowing machine or pedestrian-controlled vehicle	
L	Vehicle propelled by electrical power, excluding any vehicle in category A,K or P	K
N	Vehicle exempted from duty under s7(1), Vehicles (Excise) Act 1971	
P	Moped	

PRODUCTION OF DRIVING LICENCE (s164)

A constable or vehicle examiner may require the production of a driving licence and its counterpart, to enable him to ascertain the name and address of the holder, the date of issue, and in prescribed circumstances the holder's date of birth, from any person:

(a) driving a motor vehicle on a road,
(b) reasonably believed to have been the driver of a motor vehicle at a time when an accident occurred owing to its presence on a road,
(c) reasonably believed to have committed an offence in relation to the use of a motor vehicle on a road, or
(d) supervising the holder of a provisional licence while the holder is driving a motor vehicle on a road, or reasonably believed to have been supervising when an accident occurred or at a time when an offence is suspected of having been committed.

Production of a licence may also be required from any person -

(a) reasonably believed to have knowingly made a false statement to obtain its grant,
(b) where it has been revoked and the holder has failed to deliver it up (may be seized), or
(c) where its production has been required by a court and the holder has failed to do so (may be seized).

Failure to produce a driving licence in any of the foregoing circumstances constitutes an offence at the time of the requirement. It is a defence, however, for a person to show that he produced a licence in person at a police station specified by him - within 7 days of the requirement, or as soon as was reasonably practicable, or that it was not reasonably practicable to produce it before the day on which the proceedings commenced.

DATE OF BIRTH (s164 (2) and reg 26)

A person shall be required to state his date of birth to a constable:
  (a) if he fails to produce his licence forthwith for examination,
  (b) where the constable has reason to suspect that the licence produced was not granted to that person, was granted in error, or contains an alteration in the particulars made with intent to deceive,
  (c) the driver number of the licence produced has been altered, removed or defaced.

DRIVING LICENCE OFFENCES

  (a) Driving on a road a motor vehicle of any class otherwise than in accordance with a licence authorising the driving of a motor vehicle of that class (s87(1)).
  (b) Causing or permitting another person to drive on a road a motor vehicle of any class otherwise than in accordance with a licence authorising that other person to drive a motor vehicle of that class (s87(2)).
  (c) Failing, without reasonable excuse, to deliver a revoked licence forthwith to the Secretary of State (s92(7C) and s93(3)).
  (d) Failing, without reasonable excuse, to notify the Secretary of State forthwith of a relevant or prospective disability, or of one which has become more acute (s94(3)).
  (e) Driving a motor vehicle on a road after having failed to notify a relevant or prospective disability (s94(3A)).
  (f) Driving a motor vehicle on a road in accordance with a licence which has previously been refused or revoked (s94A(1)).
  (g) Driving with uncorrected defective eyesight, or refusing to submit to a test (s96(1) &(3)).
  (h) Failing, without reasonable excuse, to surrender a licence forthwith where the name or address of the holder ceases to be correct (s99(5)).
  (i) Obtaining a licence or driving a motor vehicle on a road while disqualified from holding or obtaining a licence (s103(1)). A constable in uniform may arrest on reasonable suspicion.
  (j) Failing to comply with the conditions of a large goods vehicle or passenger-carrying vehicle licence issued as a provisional licence

or to a person under 21; or causing or permitting a person under 21 to drive such a vehicle in contravention of the conditions (s114(1) & (2)).

(k) Failing to surrender a revoked or suspended large goods vehicle or passenger-carrying vehicle licence forthwith (s118(3)).

(l) Contravening or failing to comply with regulations relating to large goods vehicles or passenger-carrying vehicles (s120(5)).

(m) Failing to produce a licence or state date of birth in prescribed circumstances (s164(6)).

(n) Failing to comply with a notice requiring evidence of date of birth or name (s164(9)).

(o) Forging, altering, using, lending or allowing another person to use a licence (s173(1)).

(p) Knowingly making a false statement to obtain or prevent the grant of a licence (s174(1)).

(q) Failing to produce a licence to a court when prosecuted for certain offences (s45, Road Traffic Offenders Act 1988).

(r) Failing to sign a licence forthwith in ink (reg 12 and s91 of Road Traffic Offenders Act 1988).

PROVISIONAL DRIVING LICENCES (regs 8 and 9)

Provisional licences are granted to enable learner drivers to pass a test. Full licences have a provisional entitlement for certain other classes of vehicles. In the case of motor cycles of category A provisional licence normally last for two years.

The holder of a provisional licence must not drive or ride a motor vehicle of a class authorised:

(a) otherwise than under the supervision of a qualified driver who is present with him in or on the vehicle;

(b) unless a distinguishing mark (an 'L' plate) is displayed on the vehicle in such manner as to be clearly visible to other persons using the road from a reasonable distance from the front and back of the vehicle;

(c) while it is being used to draw a trailer (not agricultural tractor or articulated vehicle);

(d) in the case of a motor bicycle not having a sidecar attached, while carrying on it another person.

Where the holder of a provisional licence has passed a test the foregoing conditions cease to apply in relation to vehicles of that class.

The plate to be displayed by a provisional licence holder must be a red letter 'L' 102 mm high, 89 mm wide, and 38 mm thick, on a white background 178 mm square.

If a person drives a vehicle of a class not covered by his provisional licence or after his provisional licence has expired, the conditions attached to the licence do not apply and an offence of driving without a licence is committed.

In the case of motor bicycles, provisional licence holders may only ride 'learner motor cycles' (either propelled by electric power or having engines not exceeding 125 cc and a specified power output and power to weight ratio) or motor cycles under 125 cc first used before 1 January 1982. Part 1 of the test must have been passed before riding on a road.

Qualified drivers and supervision (reg 9)

'Qualified driver' means a person who holds: (i) a full (British) licence authorising the driving of a vehicle of the same class as the provisional licence holder; or (ii) in the case of a driver whose licence is limited to vehicles of a particular construction or design by reason of a leg disability, a full licence authorising the driving of vehicles of a class falling within the same category; and who in either such case, except in the case of a member of the armed forces of the Crown acting in the course of his duties, is at least 21 years of age and has held the licence referred to for at least 3 years.

The holder of a provisional licence does not have to be under the supervision of a qualified driver when:

(a) undergoing a test;
(b) driving a vehicle (not a motor car) constructed to carry only one person and not adapted to carry more than one;
(c) driving an electrically propelled goods vehicle not exceeding 815 kg unladen, constructed or adapted to carry only one person;
(d) driving a road roller not exceeding 3050 kg unladen, constructed or adapted to carry a load or burden;
(e) riding a motor bicycle, with or without a sidecar attached;
(f) driving on a road in an exempted island.

'Exempted island' briefly means any island outside the mainland of Great Britain to which motor vehicles cannot conveniently be driven by reason of the absence of any bridge, tunnel, ford or other suitable way, but does not include the Isle of Wight, St Mary's and certain Scottish islands. (Note that this is the only exemption mentioning a road.)

TESTS OF COMPETENCE TO DRIVE (regs 14 and 150)

A full driving licence shall not be granted unless the applicant has:

(a) passed a test of competence to drive; or
(b) held a full licence within the preceding 10 years; or

(c)   held a full licence issued in Northern Ireland, the Isle of Man, or the Channel Islands, and is not disqualified.

Tests may be conducted by:

(a)   examiners appointed by the licensing authority;

(b)   the Secretary of State for Defence in the case of persons in the service of the Crown;

(c)   the chief officer of a fire brigade in the case of members and persons employed as drivers;

(d)   the chief officer of police in the case of members and persons employed as drivers;

(e)   the Commissioner of Police of the Metropolis in the case of cab drivers;

(f)   any person who employs more than 250 persons and is appointed for the purpose by the licensing authority; and

(g)   any body of persons appointed by the licensing authority to conduct Part 1 motor bicycle tests.

FOREIGN DRIVERS (regs 9 and 25)

A person who becomes a resident in Great Britain may be treated as the holder of a licence for one year if he holds a valid domestic permit. If during that year he acquires a provisional licence he is exempt for the remainder of the year from the conditions applying to provisional licence holders (displaying 'L' plates, etc).

PHYSICAL FITNESS OF DRIVERS (ss92 - 94 and reg 24)

An applicant for a driving licence must make a declaration stating whether he is suffering or has at any time suffered from a relevant disability likely to cause his driving to be a source of danger to the public. 'Disability' includes disease.

The following disabilities are prescribed:

(a)   epilepsy;

(b)   severe mental handicap;

(c)   liability to sudden attacks of disabling giddiness;

(d)   liability to sudden attacks of disabling giddiness or fainting which are caused by any heart disorder or defect as a result of which the applicant has a device implanted in his body to correct it (a 'pacemaker');

(e)   inability to read in good daylight (with the aid of glasses or contact lenses if worn) a registration mark containing letters and figures

79.4 mm high at a distance of 20.5 metres, or 12.3 metres in the case of group K vehicles.

The Secretary of State shall refuse to grant a licence if satisfied that a person is suffering from a relevant disability, but not if:

(a) the disability is one of absence, deformity or loss of one or more limbs, the applicant has passed a test and the disability has not arisen or become more acute since that time;

(b) (i) the disability is epilepsy and the applicant has been free from any attack for two years, or three years in the case of attacks while asleep, and his driving is not likely to be a source of danger; or (ii) the applicant has a 'pacemaker' implanted, his driving is not likely to be a source of danger and he is regularly supervised by a cardiologist;

(c) the disability is one of absence, deformity or loss of use of one or more limbs and the application is for a provisional licence.

If at any time a licence holder becomes aware that he is suffering from a relevant or prospective disability which he has not previously disclosed, or which has not become more acute since his licence was granted, he must forthwith notify the Secretary of State unless it is one not previously suffered and he has reasonable grounds for believing that it will not last longer than three months.

Driving with uncorrected defective eyesight (s96 and reg 24)

It is an offence for a person to drive a motor vehicle on a road while his eyesight is such that he cannot comply with the prescribed eyesight test (as described in reg 24 above). A constable may, on reasonable suspicion, require a driver to submit to a test (in good daylight) and it is an offence to refuse.

DISQUALIFICATION AND ENDORSEMENT

A person may be disqualified from holding or obtaining a driving licence by order of a court (s34, Road Traffic Offenders Act 1988) or by reason of age (s101, Road Traffic Act 1988).

Where a person is convicted of an offence for which disqualification is obligatory, the court *shall* order him to be disqualified for not less than 12 months, unless for special reasons it thinks fit to disqualify him for a shorter period or not at all. These offences are causing death by dangerous driving, a second conviction of dangerous driving within three years, driving while unfit through drink or drugs, driving with excess alcohol in breath, blood or urine, failing to provide a specimen for analysis, and motor racing on highways. In the case of a drink/driving conviction within three years of a previous conviction for such an offence, the court must disqualify for not less than three years, unless there are special reasons for not doing so.

Where a person is convicted of an offence for which disqualification is discretionary, the court *may* order him to be disqualified for such period as it thinks fit. Such offences include careless and inconsiderate driving, being in charge while unfit or with excess alcohol, failing to provide a breath test, and carrying an unauthorised passenger on a motor cycle.

Under s35 of the Road Traffic Offenders Act 1988, where a person is convicted of an offence involving obligatory or discretionary disqualification and the court does not order disqualification, it may order particulars of the conviction and the number of penalty points in respect of it to be endorsed on his licence. Examples are 3-11 points for dangerous driving, 5-10 for failing to stop after an accident, 3-9 for careless driving, 3-6 for exceeding a speed limit, and 3 for failing to submit to an eyesight test.

When 12 points are accumulated within a period of three years by a person, he must be disqualified for at least six months, unless the court thinks fit to disqualify for a shorter period or not at all. This is usually known as the 'totting-up' procedure.

If the court does not disqualify a person or does so for a shorter period for special reasons, the reasons must be stated in open court and entered in the court register. A 'special reason' is one which is special to the facts of the case and *not* to the offender.

Appeal against disqualification

A person disqualified may appeal against the order in the same manner as against a conviction. The disqualification may be suspended pending the appeal.

Both the prosecutor and the defendant can appeal on the issue of 'special reasons' as a matter of law.

Removal of disqualification and endorsement

A person disqualified by order of a court may apply to such court to remove the disqualification after a certain period.

An application shall not be made for:
(a) two years, if disqualification is for less than four years;
(b) half the period of disqualification if it is for less than ten years, but not less than four years.
(c) five years in any other case.

A licence free from endorsement may be obtained after four years from the last conviction, or 11 years in the case of drink/driving offences.

Criminal disqualification and forfeiture

Section 44 of the Powers of Criminal Courts Act 1973, as amended by the Road Traffic Act 1991, empowers a crown court to disqualify a person convicted of an indictable offence involving a motor vehicle. This also applies to a person convicted by any court of common assault or of any other offence involving an assault (including aiding, abetting, counselling or procuring, or inciting an offence), if satisfied that the assault was committed by driving a motor vehicle.

Section 43 provides courts with a power to order forfeiture of a vehicle used for crime. This includes conviction for manslaughter, wanton and furious driving, and any offence under the Road Traffic Act 1988 which is punishable with imprisonment.

LARGE GOODS VEHICLE AND PASSENGER-CARRYING VEHICLE LICENCE

On 1st April 1991, by virtue of the Road Traffic (Driver Licensing and Information Systems) Act 1989, Part IV of the Road Traffic Act 1988 and s22 of the Public Passenger Vehicles Act 1981 (which required special driving licences to be held for driving heavy goods vehicles and public service vehicles) ceased to have effect. While HGV and PSV licences have ceased to be issued, existing licences are still valid until their expiry date.

A new Part IV was substituted in the 1988 Act. Section 110 provides that licences under Part III to drive motor vehicles of classes which include LGVs or PCVs shall be granted in accordance with Part IV.

'Large goods vehicle driver's licence' means a licence under Part III in so far as it authorises a person to drive large goods vehicles of any class. 'Passenger-carrying vehicle driver's licence' means a licence under Part III in so far as it authorises a person to drive passenger-carrying vehicles of any class. Provision is made for the issue of provisional LGV and PCV licences, subject to conditions if the holder is under the age of 21.

'Large goods vehicle' means - (a) an articulated goods vehicle, or (b) a motor vehicle (not being an articulated goods vehicle) which is constructed or adapted to carry or to haul goods and the permissible maximum weight of which exceeds 7.5 tonnes.

'Passenger-carrying vehicle' means - (a) a large passenger-carrying vehicle, that is to say, a vehicle used for carrying passengers which is constructed or adapted to carry more than 16 passengers, or (b) a small passenger-carrying vehicle, that is to say, a vehicle used for carrying passengers for hire or reward which is constructed or adapted to carry more than 8 but not more than 16 passengers.

Chapter 16
Public Service Vehicles

Legislation and definition

The law relating to public service vehicles is contained in the Public Passenger Vehicles Act 1981, as amended, and the Transport Act 1985.

A public service vehicle is a motor vehicle (other than a tramcar) which:

(a) being a vehicle adapted to carry more than eight passengers, is used for carrying passengers for hire or reward; or

(b) being a vehicle not so adapted, is used for carrying passengers for hire or reward at separate fares in the course of a business of carrying passengers.

(Note that a public service vehicle is not a type of vehicle but may be many kinds of motor vehicle adapted or used as in the above definition.)

Local services

Special provision is made in the 1985 Act for local services.

'Local service' means a service, using one or more public service vehicles, for the carriage of passengers by road at separate fares, other than one:

(a) which is excluded because the conditions regarding trips organised privately by persons acting independently of vehicle operators in Sch 1 to the 1981 Act are met; or every vehicle used in providing the service is operated under a permit granted under s 19 of the 1985 Act; or

(b) in relation to which (except in an emergency) the place where passengers are set down is 15 miles or more, measured in a straight line, from the place where they were taken up, or some point on the route between those places is 15 miles or more from either of those places.

The reference to s19 of the 1985 Act relates to the use of buses by educational and other bodies.

The reference to Sch 1 of the 1981 Act concerns the condition in Part III. Arrangements for the bringing together of all the passengers must have been made otherwise than by the holder of the PSV operator's licence, if such a licence is in force, or the driver or owner of the vehicle if not, and otherwise than by any person who receives any remuneration; the journey must be made without previous advertisement to the public; all passengers must be carried to the destination, or in the case of a tour for the greater part of the journey; and there must be no differentiation of fares on the basis of distance or time.

Licensing and certification

Before a vehicle can be used on a road as a public service vehicle it must have a certificate of initial fitness and a public service vehicle operator's licence. Details are as follows:

(a) A certificate of initial fitness indicates that a public service vehicle has been examined by a certifying officer and found fit for such use. It does not, however, take the place of a test certificate and public service vehicles must be tested in the normal way.

(b) Public service vehicle operators' licences are issued to an operator and permit him to operate a specified number of vehicles. Each of the licensed vehicles must display an operator's disc alongside its vehicle excise licence.

PSV operators' licences are of two types: standard licences, which authorise the use of any type of public service vehicle and may permit use on both national and international operations, or national operations only; and restricted licences, which authorise the use on national or international operations of public service vehicles not adapted to carry more than 8 passengers, or not more than 16 passengers when used otherwise than in the course of a business of carrying passengers, or by a person for whom this is not his main occupation.

The foregoing relates to the documentation required by vehicles and operators. In addition, before a person may act as the driver of a public service vehicle he must have a licence under Part IV of the Road Traffic Act 1988 covering him to drive a passenger-carrying vehicle of that class.

PSV drivers are issued with numbered badges, which must be worn in a conspicuous position so that the number is easily legible.

CONDUCT OF DRIVERS, INSPECTORS, CONDUCTORS AND PASSENGERS

Legislation and offence

The Public Service Vehicles (Conduct of Drivers, Inspectors, Conductors and Passengers) Regulations 1990 are made under the Public Passenger Vehicles Act 1981.

Regulation 8 provides that any passenger on a vehicle who is reasonably suspected by the driver, inspector or conductor of contravening the Regulations must give his name and address on demand, and may be removed from the vehicle by them, or on their request by a police constable.

Contravention of the Regulations by a driver, inspector or conductor of a public service vehicle is an offence under s24(1) of the 1981 Act.

Drivers, inspectors and conductors (regs 4 and 5)

(a) A driver must not, when a vehicle is in motion hold a microphone or any attachment thereto, unless it is necessary in an emergency or on grounds of safety, to speak into the microphone.

(b) A driver must not, when a vehicle is in motion, speak to any person either directly or by means of a microphone. This does not prevent the driver from : (i) speaking when he is obliged to do so by reason of an emergency or on grounds of safety; (ii) speaking to an employee of the company in relation to the operation of the vehicle if he can do so without being distracted from his driving; or (iii) if driving on an excursion or sightseeing tour, from making short statements from time to time to indicate the location of the vehicle if he can do so without being distracted from his driving.

(c) A driver and a conductor must take all reasonable precautions to ensure the safety of passengers who are on, or are entering or leaving the vehicle.

(d) A driver, inspector and conductor must take all reasonable steps to ensure that the regulations relating to the conduct of passengers are complied with.

(e) A driver, inspector or conductor: (i) must, if requested by a constable or other person having reasonable cause, give his name, his employer, and in the case of a driver particulars of his licence; and (ii) must not smoke in or on a vehicle, except when it is not available for the carriage of passengers and smoking is not prohibited in that part, or the vehicle is hired as a whole and he has the permission of the operator and the hirer.

(f)   A driver must, when picking up or setting down passengers, stop the vehicle as close as is reasonably practicable to the left or near side of the road.

(g)   A conductor must not, while the vehicle is in motion and without reasonable cause, distract the driver's attention or obstruct his vision.

Passengers (regs 6 and 7)

No passenger on a vehicle shall :

(a)   where the vehicle has a door for a particular purpose, use it for any other purpose, unless directed or authorised by a driver, inspector or conductor;

(b)   put at risk or unreasonably impede or cause discomfort to any person travelling on or entering or leaving the vehicle, a driver, inspector, conductor or employee doing his work;

(c)   throw or trail any article from the vehicle;

(d)   smoke or carry lighted tobacco or light a match or cigarette lighter in or on any part of the vehicle where smoking is prohibited, unless the vehicle is hired as a whole and both the operator and the hirer have given permission to the contrary;

(e)   distribute any paper or other article for the purpose of giving or seeking information about or comment upon any matter, except with the permission of the operator;

(f)   sell or offer for sale any article, except with the permission of the operator;

(g)   speak to the driver unless in an emergency or on grounds of safety, or give directions as to the stopping of the vehicle;

(h)   without reasonable cause distract the driver's attention, obstruct his vision or give any signal which might reasonably be interpreted as a signal to stop in an emergency or to start the vehicle;

(i)   travel on any part of the vehicle not provided for the carriage of passengers;

(j)   remain on the vehicle when directed to leave by the driver, inspector or conductor on the grounds that the number of passengers exceeds the maximum capacity, that he has been causing a nuisance, or that his condition is such as would be likely to cause offence to a reasonable passenger, or the condition of his clothing would be reasonably expected to soil the fittings of the vehicles or passengers' clothing;

(k)   play or operate any musical instrument or sound reproducing equipment to the annoyance of any person or in a manner which is likely to cause annoyance to any person on the vehicle;

(l)   intentionally interfere with any equipment with which the vehicle is fitted;

(m) fail to put any bulky or cumbersome article, any article which causes or would be reasonably expected to cause annoyance, risk of injury or of damage, or any animal, in a particular place on the vehicle as directed by the driver, inspector or conductor. (The reference to an animal does not apply to the bearer of a card issued by the Guide Dogs for the Blind Association who has with him a guide dog unless there are already two dogs on board, or one dog if the vehicle is less than 8.5 metres long.)

No passenger on a vehicle being used for the carriage of passengers at separate fares shall:

(a)   use any ticket which has been altered or defaced, issued for use by another person and is not transferable, or expired;

(b)   fail to declare the journey to be taken on request;

(c)   fail to pay the fare;

(d)   fail to accept and retain a ticket;

(e)   fail to produce a ticket for inspection on being requested by the driver, inspector or conductor;

(f)   fail to leave the vehicle on completion of a journey or pay a fare for a further journey;

(g)   fail to surrender a ticket he is not entitled to retain by reason of its having been altered or defaced, etc.

Found property

Under the PSV (Lost Property) Regulations 1978, as amended, all property found in a PSV must be handed to the conductor immediately. The conductor must search his vehicle at the end of each journey for left property and hand it to the operator within 24 hours.

Objectionable property may be disposed of at any time and perishable property may be destroyed or disposed of after 48 hours.

MODIFICATION OF PSV REQUIREMENTS IN RELATION TO VEHICLES USED FOR CERTAIN PURPOSES

Exemption from PSV requirements

Section 18 of the Transport Act 1985 states that the provisions of the Public Passenger Vehicles Act 1981 relating to the licensing of operators and drivers in relation to the use of public service vehicles for the carriage of passengers, shall not apply:

(a) to the use of any vehicle under a permit granted in relation to the use of buses by educational and other bodies, if and so long as the requirements are met;

(b) to the use of any vehicle under a permit granted for a community bus service; or

(c) in relation to the driving of any vehicle at a time when it is being used as mentioned in (a) or (b).

Use of buses by educational and other bodies (s19)

Permits may be granted for the exemption under section 18 above if the bus is:

(a) being used by a qualifying body;

(b) not being used for the carriage of members of the general public nor with a view to profit nor incidental to an activity which is itself carried on with a view to profit;

(c) being used in every respect in accordance with any conditions attached to the permit; and

(d) not being used in contravention of any provision of any regulation made under this Act.

'Bus' means a vehicle which is adapted to carry more than 8 passengers.

'Large bus' means a vehicle which is adapted to carry more than 16 passengers.

'Small bus' means a vehicle which is adapted to carry more than 8 but not more than 16 passengers.

A permit in relation to the use of a small bus may be granted by a body designated by an order made by the Secretary of State, either to itself or to any other body to whom, in accordance with the order, it is entitled to grant a permit. A permit in relation to the use of a small bus may also be granted by a traffic commissioner to any body concerned with education, religion, social welfare, recreation or other activities of benefit to the community, appearing to be carrying on in his area an activity which makes it so eligible.

A permit in relation to the use of a large bus may be granted by a traffic commissioner to any body which assists and co-ordinates the activities of bodies within his area, which appears to him to be concerned with education, religion, social welfare, or other activities of benefit to the community. He shall not, however, grant such a permit unless satisfied that there will be adequate facilities or arrangements for maintaining any bus used under the permit in a fit and serviceable condition.

A body may hold more than one permit but may not use more than one bus at any one time under the same permit.

This enables certain voluntary bodies using what used to be called 'minibuses' to charge passengers in order to recoup their running costs, without the need to obtain PSV operators' licences. Such vehicles must carry a driver's notice and display a disc readable from the outside, and comply with conditions of fitness as specified in regulations.

Such vehicles are known as 'section 19 permit buses'. The Minibus and Other Section 19 Permit Buses Regulations 1987 make conditions for the use of such vehicles. The driver of a vehicle used under a permit must, if not the holder of a PSV driver's licence, be the holder of a current full licence authorising him to drive vehicles adapted to carry more than 8 passengers, and be 21 years of age or over. A disc must be displayed; that for a large bus being red, and that for a small bus, purple.

The Section 19 Minibus (Designated Bodies) Order 1987 designates the bodies which may grant permits in relation to the use of small buses.

Community buses

Sections 22 and 23 of the 1985 Act and the Community Bus Regulations 1986 provide that community bus permits may be granted in relation to the use of public service vehicles:

(a) in providing a community bus service; or

(b) in providing a community bus service and (other than in the course of a local service) carrying passengers for hire or reward where the carriage of those passengers will directly assist the provision of such a service by providing financial support for it.

'Community bus service' means a local service provided:

(a) by a body concerned for the social and welfare needs of one or more communities;

(b) without a view to profit, either on the part of that body or of anyone else; and

(c) by means of a vehicle adapted to carry more than 8 but not more than 16 passengers.

A community bus permit may be granted by the traffic commissioner for the area in which the operating centre for any vehicle used will be. He shall not grant a permit, however, unless he is satisfied that there will be adequate facilities or arrangements for maintaining any vehicle used in a fit and serviceable condition.

Drivers of community buses must not receive any payment except reimbursement of any reasonable expenses incurred and any amount representing any earnings lost. They must either hold a PSV driver's licence or fulfil any conditions prescribed in relation to persons driving vehicles being used under community bus permits. Any vehicle used must fulfil any prescribed conditions of fitness for such use.

SCHOOL BUSES

A 'school bus', in relation to a local education authority, is a motor vehicle
which is used by that authority to provide free school transport.

Section 46 of the 1981 Act provides that:

(a) a local education authority may use a school bus when it is being
    used to provide free transport, to carry, as fare-paying passengers,
    persons other than those for whom the free transport is provided;

(b) it may also use a school bus belonging to the authority, when it is
    not being used to provide free school transport, to provide a local
    service.

Chapter 17
Regulation of Carriage of Goods by Road

OPERATORS' LICENCES

Subject to certain exceptions, no person shall use a goods vehicle on a road for the carriage of goods; for hire or reward; or for, or in connection with, any trade or business carried on by him except under an operator's licence. (Section 60, Transport Act 1968).

There are two types of operators' licences:

(a) Standard operators' licence; which authorises the use of goods vehicles for hire or reward and in connection with any trade or business carried on by the holder. (May be either for both international and national transport operations, or national operations only.)

(b) Restricted operators' licence; which authorises the use of goods vehicles for or in connection with a trade or business carried on by the holder only, not being the trade or business of carrying goods for hire or reward.

Exemptions

Small goods vehicles (defined later) are not required to have operators' licences.

Schedule 5 to the Goods Vehicles (Operators' Licences and Fees) Regulations 1984 exempts the following vehicles: tractors, ploughing machines and other agricultural engines used for agricultural and similar purposes; dual-purpose vehicles and trailers drawn thereby; vehicles used between neighbouring premises, not over six miles in a week; public service vehicles; motor vehicles constructed solely for carriage of not more than 16 passengers when drawing a trailer; hackney carriages; vehicles used for funerals; vehicles used for police, fire brigade or ambulance purposes; vehicles used for mine rescue operations; vehicles without permanent bodies and on test, etc; vehicles used under a trade licence; vehicles used for armed or visiting forces; trailers used for road works; road rollers and their trailer; vehicles used for lifeboat purposes; vehicles fitted with machines, appliances or apparatus; vehicles used by a local authority for road cleansing, watering, snow clearing, disposal of refuse, weights and measures or sale of food and drugs purposes, or distributing grit, salt, etc on roads; vehicles used for civil defence purposes; vehicles used by highway authorities for weighing vehicles; tower wagons and their trailers; steam propelled vehicles; vehicles carrying goods within an aerodrome; electrically propelled vehicles; showman's vehicles and trailers; vehicles first used before 1 January 1977 which have an unladen weight below 1525 kg, and a maximum gross weight exceeding 3.5 tonnes but not exceeding $3^1/_2$ tons; vehicles used for weighing by highway authorities, or held for emergencies by water, electricity, gas or telephone undertakers.

Identity discs

Each operator's licence will specify the motor vehicles which may be used under that licence. An identity disc will be issued in respect of each individual motor vehicle. The identity disc must be affixed to the appropriate motor vehicle, in a waterproof container, in a place on the vehicle adjacent to the vehicle excise licence.

Application for operators' licences

A person may apply for an operator's licence to the Licensing Authority for each area in which he will have an 'operating centre' or 'operating centres'. A person may hold separate operators' licences in respect of different areas, but cannot hold more that one licence in respect of the same area.

The Licensing Authority must publish applications for new operators' licences. Objection to the grant of such a licence may be lodged by a trade union or association whose members include persons holding operators' licences, or employees of such persons; a chief officer of police; or a local authority.

Vehicles temporarily in Great Britain

The Goods Vehicles (Operators' Licences) (Temporary Use in Great Britain) Regulations 1980 authorise foreign and Northern Ireland goods vehicles to carry goods in certain circumstances without having an operator's licence in force. Such vehicles must not remain in Great Britain for more than three months.

Definitions

A 'goods vehicle' is a motor vehicle constructed or adapted for use for the carriage of goods or a trailer so constructed or adapted.

'Goods' includes goods or burden of any description. Carriage of goods includes haulage of goods.

A 'small goods vehicle' is, briefly, a goods vehicle, including an articulated vehicle or a combination of vehicles (exclusive of a small trailer), which has a relevant plated weight not exceeding 3.5 tonnes; or, not having a relevant plated weight, has an unladen weight not exceeding 1525 kg.

A 'small trailer' is a trailer having an unladen weight not exceeding 1020 kg.

A 'large goods vehicle' is a goods vehicle which has a plated weight exceeding 16,260 kg, or an unladen weight exceeding 5080 kg; or forms part of a combination of vehicles exceeding those weights.

(Do not confuse with the definitions of small and large goods vehicles for driving licence purposes.)

LIMITATION OF DRIVERS' HOURS OF WORK

EEC rules

The limitation of hours of work for drivers of goods vehicles operating in all member countries of the European Economic Community is largely governed by Regulation (EEC) No 543/69. This Regulation applies to:

(a) all goods vehicles exceeding 3.5 tonnes permissible maximum weight; and

(b) all passenger vehicles which are constructed and suitable for the carriage of more than nine persons including the driver.

Article 4 states that this Regulation shall not apply to carriage of goods by:

(a) Passenger vehicles constructed to carry not more than nine passengers including the driver;

(b) Goods vehicles the permissible maximum weight of which, including any trailer, does not exceed 3.5 tonnes;

(c) Passenger vehicles on regular services where the route covered does not exceed 50 km;

(d) Vehicles used by the police; gendarmerie; armed forces; fire brigades; civil defence; drainage or flood prevention authorities; water, gas or electricity services; highway authorities; telegraph or telephone services; by postal authorities for the carriage of mail; or by radio or television services;

(e) Vehicles used for the carriage of sick or injured persons and for carrying rescue material;

(f) Tractors with a maximum authorised speed of 30 kph;

(g) Tractors and other machines used exclusively for local agricultural and forestry work;

(h) Vehicles used to transport circus or fun fair equipment;

(i) Specialised breakdown vehicles;

(j) Vehicles undergoing road tests for the purpose of repair or maintenance;

(k) Transport of live animals from farms to local markets;

(l) Transport of animal carcasses;

(m) Transport of organic waste not intended for human consumption;

(n) Specialised vehicles used at local markets; for door-to-door selling; for mobile banking, exchange or savings transactions; for worship; for the lending of books, records or cassettes; or for cultural events or mobile exhibitions;

(o) Transport of milk between farm and dairy or distribution centre.

Definitions

'Carriage by road' means any journey by road of a vehicle, whether laden or not, used for the carriage of passengers or goods.

'Crew member' means the driver, driver's mate and conductor, defined as follows:

'driver': any person who drives the vehicle even for a short period, or who is carried in the vehicle in order to be available for driving if necessary;

'driver's mate': any person accompanying the driver of a vehicle in order to assist him in certain manoeuvres and habitually taking an effective part in the transport operations but not being a driver as defined above;

'conductor': any person who accompanies the driver of a vehicle used for the carriage of passengers and has the particular duty of issuing and checking tickets.

'Week' means any period of seven consecutive days.

'Daily rest period' means any uninterrupted period of at least eight hours during which the crew members may freely dispose of their time and are entirely free to move about as they please.

'Permissible maximum weight' means the maximum authorised operating weight of the vehicle fully laden.

'Working week' means a week beginning at midnight between Sunday and Monday.

'Working day' in relation to a driver means:

(a) any period during which he is on duty and which does not fall to be aggregated with any other such period by virtue of para (b); and

(b) where a period during which he is on duty is not followed by an interval for rest of not less than 11 hours or (where permitted) of not less than 9½ hours, the aggregate of that period and each successive period until there is such an interval as aforesaid, together with any interval or intervals between periods so aggregated.

Summary of driving periods for crews of goods vehicles

Daily driving period:	8 hours, but may be 9 hours on not more than two days a week, except for drivers of large vehicles (ie motor vehicles with more than one trailer or semi-trailer; or with one trailer or semi-trailer when the permissible maximum weight of the combination exceeds 20 tonnes).
Continuous driving period:	4 hours.
Weekly driving period:	48 hours in any one week.
Fortnightly driving period:	92 hours in any two consecutive weeks.

Rest periods and breaks for all crew members

Daily rest period not less than 11 consecutive hours in a 24 hour period. This may be reduced to 9 hours not more than twice in any one week if taken where the crew is based, or to 8 hours not more than twice in any one week if taken elsewhere than where the crew is based.

Where the vehicle is manned by two drivers and has no bunk the daily rest period shall not be less than 10 consecutive hours in a 27 hour period. If the vehicle is manned by two drivers and has a bunk the daily rest period shall be not less than 8 consecutive hours in a 30 hour period.

The daily rest period must be taken outside the vehicle. If the vehicle has a bunk it may be taken in that bunk provided the vehicle is stationary.

A weekly rest period of 29 hours must be taken in any period of seven consecutive days, which must be immediately preceded or followed by a daily rest period. The weekly rest period may be reduced to not less than 24 hours, provided a rest period equal to the reduction is taken in the same week.

A break of half an hour must be taken after each continuous driving period, but this can be replaced by two 20 minute or three 15 minute periods spread over and immediately after each continuous driving period. Special provision is made for journeys where the distance covered between daily rest periods exceeds 450 km.

Domestic rules

Section 95 of the Transport Act 1968 refers to goods vehicles which are locomotives, motor tractors, articulated vehicles, and motor vehicles constructed or adapted to carry goods other than the effects of passengers; and passenger vehicles which are either public service vehicles or motor vehicles constructed or adapted to carry more than 12 passengers. The domestic rules apply, however, only to journeys made within the United Kingdom by vehicles which are not subject to the EEC rules and are either goods vehicles exceeding 3.5 tonnes permissible maximum weight, or public service vehicles on local regular services under 50 km. There are a number of exceptions for light vehicles.

The hours for the few vehicles operating under these rules are a daily driving period of 10 hours, daily duty time of 11 hours, and a continuous driving period of $5^1/_2$ hours.

DRIVERS' RECORDS

The provisions of Regulation (EEC) 1463/70 are applied by ss97, 97A and 97B of the Transport Act 1968, as amended. These sections require the use of recording equipment ('tachographs') on all commercial vehicles operating under the EEC rules, with a view to 'securing the observance of proper hours or periods of work by persons engaged in the carriage of passengers or goods by road and thereby protecting the public against the risks which arise in cases where the drivers of motor vehicles are suffering from fatigue'.

'Recording equipment' is defined as equipment for recording information as to the use of a vehicle. This is commonly known as a tachograph, which is a device which replaces the speedometer of a motor vehicle and automatically records the time, speed and distance travelled, together with details of the driver's activities, eg driving time, period of work, breaks and rest periods. This is usually done by means of three styli marking a waxed disc, with the work activities being operated manually by means of a mode key. The tachograph disc is officially known as a 'record sheet'.

A tachograph must be fitted and used in all passenger vehicles which are constructed or intended to carry more than 9 passengers including the driver (or 15 on purely national transport operations); and in all goods vehicles exceeding 3.5 tonnes permissible maximum weight. There are a number of exceptions provided by Regulation (EEC) 1463/70 (detailed earlier). Further exemptions, according to type of use, are given by the Community Transport Rules (Exemptions) Regulations 1978, including the transport of animals between farms, the transport of milk, and specialised vehicles designed for door-to-door selling, mobile banking, the purposes of worship, etc.

Tachographs may only be installed and repaired by approved fitters and workshops, and must be sealed after calibration. Record sheets must be issued to vehicle crews by their employers, who must retain them for a year when full. Such sheets (or 'discs') are personal to crew members and dirty or damaged sheets must not be used. Crew members must enter the time, operate the mode switches, insert their names, the date and place where the sheet begins and ends, the registration mark of the vehicle, odometer reading appertaining to the period of use, and the time of any change of vehicle. Tachographs must operate continuously and sheets must be kept for seven days for inspection (or five days in the case of national transport operations).

(Note that EEC rules apply to the keeping of records by 'crew members', ie drivers, driver's mates, and conductors.)

Drivers of vehicles operating under the domestic rules may use tachographs or keep record books.

The Drivers' Hours (Goods Vehicles) (Keeping of Records) Regulations 1987 apply to the driving of goods vehicles where the Community rules are not relevant. They make provision for the issue and keeping of a simplified record book.

Offences and powers of authorised officers

The following offences may be committed in respect of recording equipment under the Transport Act 1968:

(a) Using, causing or permitting a relevant vehicle to be used without having correctly installed recording equipment; or having equipment which does not comply, or which is not used as provided (eg failing to keep a record, operate the switch to indicate periods of duty, or complete a sheet with relevant details) (s97(1)). Defences are provided to cover breakdowns of the equipment, but in such cases records must be kept manually.

(b) Failing, without reasonable cause, to return a record sheet to an employer within 21 days of completion; or, where there are two employers, failing to notify each of the name and address of the other (employers must ensure that sheet, are returned) (s97A).

(c) Failing to comply with a requirement to produce and permit the inspection of any record sheet, and obstructing an authorised officer in the exercise of his powers (s99).

Authorised officers (including constables) may at any time detain and enter any vehicle required to be fitted with recording equipment, demand production of any record sheet, inspect and copy it, and also seize it if it is reasonably believed to have been fraudulently altered. With the exception of police constables in uniform, all such officers must produce their authority.

Chapter 18
Third Party Insurance Liabilities and Registration and Licensing of Vehicles

INSURANCE

Duty to insure

The normal compensation for injury sustained in a road accident is monetary damages, but these are useless if the wrongdoer cannot pay. There must, therefore, be in force in relation to the user of every motor vehicle on a road, unless exempted, a policy of insurance or security in respect of third party risks.

Section 143 of the Road Traffic Act 1988 provides that no person shall use, or cause or permit another person to use, a motor vehicle on a road without there being in force a policy of insurance, or security, covering the use of the vehicle in respect of third party risks. This does not apply, however, to invalid carriages.

(Note that a motor vehicle is a mechanically propelled vehicle intended or adapted for use on roads.)

The following vehicles are exempted from the need for insurance :
  (a) council owned vehicles;
  (b) vehicles owned by a police authority, or driven by or under the direction of a constable;
  (c) vehicles used for salvage purposes under the Merchant Shipping Act 1894;
  (d) army and air force requisitioned vehicles;
  (e) vehicles owned by the London Transport Executive;
  (f) vehicles used under the National Health Service (Scotland) Act 1978 (ss 15 or 16);
  (g) vehicles owned by a person who has deposited £500,000 with the Accountant General of the Supreme Court.

Statutory defence

A person charged with this offence shall not be convicted if he proves that the vehicle did not belong to him and was not in his possession under a contract of hiring or loan, that he was using the vehicle in the course of his employment and that he neither knew, nor had reason to believe, that there was not in force in relation to the vehicle a policy or security.

Proof of insurance cover

The following documents afford proof that the law has been complied with:
  (a)   Certificate of insurance: proof of existence of a policy (Form A for a specific vehicle or vehicles; Form B not specifying a particular vehicle).
  (b)   Cover note: issued as temporary cover while certificate is being prepared (Form C).
  (c)   Certificate of security: proof of the existence of a security issued by an authorised insurer (Form D).
  (d)   Certificate of Deposit: proof that owner has deposited £500,000 with Supreme Court (Form E).
  (e)   Certificate of ownership: proof that vehicle is owned by a local or police authority (Form F).
  (f)   International motor insurance card ('Green Card'): proof that a foreign visitor is covered by insurance.
  (g)   Northern Ireland certificates: proof that a Northern Irish vehicle is covered for its temporary stay in Great Britain.
Note that a policy of insurance is not proof of existing cover.

Production

The certificate must be produced:
  (a)   On the demand of a constable, by any person:
       (i)   driving a motor vehicle on a road; or
       (ii) reasonably believed to have been the driver of a motor vehicle when an accident occurred owing to its presence on a road; or
       (iii) reasonably believed to have committed an offence relating to the use of a motor vehicle on a road.
  (b)   After an accident involving personal injury:
       (i)   to a constable or any person having reasonable cause to demand it; or

(ii)   to a constable or at a police station *as soon as possible* and in any case within 24 hours.

It is an offence to fail to produce a certificate of insurance, but the driver will escape conviction if it is produced within seven clear days at a police station of his choice. (Need not be produced personally.)

Insurance requirements and void conditions (Motor Vehicles (Third Party Risk) Regulations 1972)

A policy of insurance must be issued by an authorised insurer. The policy itself is of no effect unless a certificate has been issued in respect of it.

It must insure persons specified in respect of any liability incurred in respect of the death or bodily injury to any person arising out of the use of the vehicle on a road; and must also cover payment for any emergency, medical or hospital treatment.

A policy is not by law required to cover liability in respect of death or bodily injury in the course of employment or any contractual liability.

Insurers cannot avoid their liability by including in the policy any conditions relating to: age, physical or mental condition of driver; condition of vehicle; number of persons a vehicle carries; weight or physical characteristics; times when or areas where a vehicle is used; carriage of any particular apparatus; carrying of particular identification marks other than identification plates.

Motor Insurers' Bureau

The Motor Insurers' Bureau was set up in 1946 to consider the payment of compensation to third parties in road accidents where the vehicles involved were not insured. Negligence must be established against the driver and this does not, therefore, apply to hit-and-run drivers who cannot be traced. The bureau will, however, consider the making of ex gratia payment in such cases.

REGISTRATION AND LICENSING OF VEHICLES

REGISTRATION

This subject is contained in the Vehicles (Excise) Act 1971 and the Road Vehicles (Registration and Licensing) Regulations 1971.

Before a mechanically propelled vehicle is used or kept on a public road the owner must have the vehicle registered by the Secretary of the State for the Environment. All administrative functions are carried out by the Driver and Vehicle Licensing Agency (DVLA).

A person 'keeps' a vehicle on a public road if he causes it to be there for any period, however short, when it is not in use there. 'Owner' in relation to a vehicle means the person by whom the vehicle is used and kept and the expression 'ownership' shall be construed accordingly.

Each vehicle is given a registration mark and the owner receives a registration document. Any subsequent alteration of the vehicle must be notified in writing forthwith to the Secretary of State and the registration book sent for alteration.

On change of ownership the seller must notify the Secretary of State, in writing, and the buyer must enter his name and address in the registration document and deliver it to the Secretary of State or authorised agents.

Registration mark

Must be fixed in the prescribed manner, ie on a flat rectangular plate or area which is easily distinguishable and unobscured.

Particulars of the owner of a vehicle can be obtained from the Secretary of State for the Environment, ie the Driver and Vehicle Licensing Agency (DVLA) at Swansea.

Registration marks may be white letters on a black background at front and rear, or of reflex reflecting material with black letters on a white background at the front and black letters on a yellow background at the rear. No front plate is required on motor bicycles. Vehicles first used on or after 1 January 1973 must have reflex reflecting plates (with certain exceptions).

Registration document

This document contains the history and description of a vehicle and remains valid until the vehicle is broken up, destroyed or sent permanently out of Great Britain. The owner shall then notify the Secretary of State forthwith and surrender the registration document.

It must be sent to the Secretary of State on alteration of the vehicle or change of the owner's address or change of ownership or when relicensing the vehicle.

A registration document must be produced for inspection at any reasonable time when required by a police officer.

VEHICLE EXCISE DUTY

With certain exceptions no mechanically propelled vehicle shall be used or kept on public roads until the appropriate vehicle excise duty is paid.

A 'public road' is a road repairable at the public expense. The main exceptions are fire brigade vehicles, ambulances, invalid carriages and electrically propelled vehicles and in some cases a licence marked 'nil' is issued.

Where it is alleged that a mechanically propelled vehicle has been used or kept in contravention of the above provisions, the person keeping, the person using the vehicle, or any other person having knowledge, has an obligation to give information when required by a chief officer of police or the Secretary of State. Failure to comply with this requirement is an offence.

Vehicle excise licences are issued on behalf of the Secretary of State, by the DVLA or in certain circumstances may be obtained from an authorised post office.

Issued for a period of six or twelve months on production of the registration document, certificate of insurance and test certificate (where applicable).

Must be fixed to the vehicle in a holder sufficient to protect it from the weather and in the prescribed position, eg on a car it must be in the nearside of the windscreen.

Offences

(a) Not having registration marks properly fixed to front and rear of motor vehicle (reg 9 and s22).

(b) Using a motor vehicle on a road with registration mark obscured or not easily distinguished (reg 18).

(c) Failing to notify change of ownership of vehicle (reg 12).

(d) Using or keeping a motor vehicle on a public road without a proper excise licence (s8).

(e) Forging, fraudulently altering, lending or allowing another person to use an excise licence (s26).

(f) Failing to display a current excise licence in the prescribed manner (s12).

Note: Careful examination of vehicle excise licence can result in detection of many offences, eg theft of motor vehicle, theft of the licence, fraudulent use of the licence. The keeper of an unlicensed vehicle commits offences against both s8 and s12.

For the purpose of fraudulent use of an excise licence 'fraudulent ' is not confined to economic loss but includes deceiving a police officer into thinking that a vehicle is licensed. An expired licence is a licence for this offence.

TRADE LICENCES

A trade licence is a special type of reduced-rate vehicle excise licence issued only to motor traders and vehicle testers. The relevant legislation is s16 of the Vehicles (Excise) Act 1971 and the Road Vehicles (Registration and Licensing) Regulations 1971.

A 'motor trader' means a manufacturer or repairer of, or dealer in, mechanically propelled vehicles; and a person shall be treated as a dealer in such vehicles if he carries on a business consisting wholly or mainly of collecting and delivering mechanically propelled vehicles and not including any other activities except activities as a manufacturer or repairer of, or dealer in such vehicles.

A 'vehicle tester' means a person, other than a motor trader, who regularly in the course of his business engages in the testing on roads of mechanically propelled vehicles belonging to other persons.

Trade plates

The issuing authority supplies a set of two 'trade plates' with every trade licence. The trade licence is displayed on the plate attached to the front of the vehicle and the other plate attached to the rear of the *same* vehicle. Trade plates remain the property of the issuing authority and must be returned when the licence expires. Fees are charged for replacing trade plates lost or damaged.

Use of vehicles

Trade licences may only be used by the following persons and on certain vehicles.

A 'motor trader' may use a trade licence on any vehicles *temporarily* in his possession in the course of his business as a motor trader.

A 'vehicle tester' may use a trade licence on a vehicle submitted to him for test, provided such a vehicle does not belong to him.

Recovery vehicle

The Road Vehicle (Registration and Licensing) (Amendment) Regulations 1987 introduced a new taxation class of recovery vehicle on 1 January 1988. Trade licences can no longer be used for such vehicles.

A recovery vehicle may be used for the recovery or removal of disabled vehicles, for repairing them at the place where they became disabled or to which they have been moved in the interests of safety, or for drawing or carrying one trailer which had been drawn by or was on the disabled vehicle.

Under the Recovery Vehicles (Prescribed Purposes) Regulations 1988, 'recovery vehicle' means a vehicle which is constructed or permanently adapted primarily for the purposes of lifting, towing and transporting not more than two disabled vehicles.

Restrictions on use (reg 34)

No person (other than the licence holder) shall use on a public road a vehicle exhibiting a trade plate or trade licence, but this is not to apply to a person driving with the consent of the licence holder if the vehicle is being used by the licence holder under the licence.

Permitted purposes (reg 35)

A motor trader shall not use a motor vehicle on a public road under a trade licence unless it is in his *temporary* possession in the course of his business as such, or for a purpose other than a business purpose and other than one of the following:

(a) test or trial of vehicle (or equipment or accessories) in course of construction or repair, or after completion of either;

(b) to and from a public weighbridge to place of registration or inspection;

(c) test or trial for publicity purposes or for a prospective purchaser or proceeding to or from place of test or trial;

(d) delivery to take place where intending purchaser intends to keep it;

(e) for demonstrating the operation of the vehicle or its equipment or accessories before being handed over to purchaser;

(f) delivery to parts of his own premises or premises of another manufacturer, dealer or repairer, and removing it directly back again to his own premises;

(g) going to and coming from a workshop for refitting of body or special equipment or accessory, painting or repair;

(h) proceeding from premises of manufacturer, repairer or dealer, to railway station, aerodrome or wharf (for transport) or vice versa;

(i) journey to and from storage place, garage or salesroom where vehicle is to be or has been stored or offered for sale;

(j) to and from place of testing or where it is to be broken up or dismantled.

Conveyance of loads (reg 38)

The only loads that may be carried on a vehicle using a trade licence are:
(a) Those loads necessary for testing or demonstrating the vehicle, its accessories and equipment. Such loads have to be returned to the place of loading, except in the case of accident or mechanical breakdown.
(b) Parts, accessories or equipment carried for the purpose of being fitted to the vehicle conveying them; or to a trailer which is to be used with that vehicle.
(c) When load is built in as part of the vehicle or permanently attached thereto.
(d) A trailer.

Carriage of passengers (reg 40)

The following classes of people only can be carried on a vehicle or trailer used under a trade licence:
(a) Driver, who must be the holder of the licence or his employee.
(b) Any other person driving with the consent of the licence holder, provided he is accompanied by the licence holder or his employee.
(c) Person required by the Road Traffic Act 1988 to be on the vehicle or trailer.
(d) Person making a statutory inspection of the vehicle or trailer.
(e) Person in a disabled vehicle being towed.
(f) Holder of licence, or employee, if presence is necessary for the purpose for which the vehicle is being used.
(g) Employee of the holder of the licence going to a place to drive vehicles for his employer, in the course of his business as a motor trader.
(h) Purchaser (or prospective purchaser) or his servant, or agent or any person requested to accompany him.
(i) Member of the Press or any person interested in promoting publicity in regard to the vehicle or trailer.
(In (h) and (i) above, persons must be accompanied by the holder of the licence, or his employee (unless the vehicle is constructed to carry only one person).)

HACKNEY CARRIAGES

Public hackney carriage

A hackney carriage is a vehicle which stands or plies for hire in the streets, the driver putting the whole carriage at the disposal of the hirer, and the vehicle, if a motor vehicle, being adapted to carry less than eight passengers.

The Town Police Clauses Act, 1847 (now incorporated in the Public Health Act 1875) which extends to town, urban districts and certain rural districts, prescribes conditions under which these vehicles operate. These conditions may be reinforced by byelaws.

The vehicles ply for hire from an authorised stand in a street or public place and are licensed and controlled by the local authority who sometimes delegate their authority to the police.

Hackney carriage plates

When the vehicle is licensed at hackney carriage rate (less than full private rate of duty) there shall be displayed on the vehicle a semi-circular plate bearing the words 'Hackney Carriage' and the number of seats, unless the local authority has prescribed a mark to be carried indicating that the vehicle is so licensed (Vehicles (Excise) Act 1971, s21).

Do not confuse with private hire vehicles which may not ply for hire but are available from premises only. None of the above restrictions applies.

Chapter 19
Miscellaneous Traffic Matters

POWERS OF ARREST UNDER THE ROAD TRAFFIC ACT 1988

Section 1 - causing death by dangerous driving. This is an arrestable offence by virtue of its penalty and the power of arrest is under s24 of the Police and Criminal Evidence Act 1984.

Section 3a - causing death by careless driving when under influence of drink or drugs. This is also an arrestable offence under s24 of the 1984 Act.

Section 4(6) and (7) - driving or being in charge when under influence of drink or drugs. A constable may arrest a person without warrant if he has reasonable cause to suspect that that person is or has been committing an offence under this section. For the purpose of arresting a person under this power, a constable may enter (if need be by force) any place where that person is or the constable, with reasonable cause, suspects him to be.

Section 6(5) and (6) - breath tests. A constable may arrest a person without warrant if:
  (a) as a result of a breath test he has reasonable cause to suspect that the proportion of alcohol in that person's breath or blood exceeds the prescribed limit, or
  (b) that person has failed to provide a specimen of breath for a breath test when required to do so in pursuance of this section and the constable has reasonable cause to suspect that he has alcohol in his body,
but a person shall not be arrested by virtue of this subsection when he is at a hospital as a patient.
  A constable may, for the purpose of requiring a person to provide a specimen of breath when an accident has occurred owing to the presence of a motor vehicle on a road or other public place, in a case where he has reasonable cause to suspect that the accident involved injury to another

person; or of arresting him *in such a case* under sub s(5) above, enter (if need be by force) any place where that person is or where the constable, with reasonable cause, suspects him to be.

Section 103(3) - driving while disqualified. A constable in uniform may arrest without warrant any person driving a motor vehicle on a road whom he has reasonable cause to suspect of being disqualified.

Police and Criminal Evidence Act 1984

Section 24

Causing the death of another person by driving a motor vehicle on a road dangerously (Road Traffic Act 1988, s1) is an arrestable offence, as is causing death by careless driving when under influence of drink or drugs (s3A).

Section 25

Full details of the general arrest conditions are given in Chapter 5. Briefly, however, a constable may arrest a person whom he reasonably suspects of committing or attempting *any* non-arrestable offence, if it appears to him that the service of a summons is impracticable or inappropriate because the person does not provide a satisfactory name or address, or it is believed that arrest is necessary to prevent physical harm being caused, loss or damage to property, or an unlawful obstruction of the highway.

This power could be useful in the case of any traffic offence where the offender refuses to give his name or address, or has no fixed abode, or does not live in this country.

TRAFFIC OFFENCES PUNISHABLE WITH IMPRISONMENT

Road Traffic Regulation Act 1984

Section 115(1) - mishandling or faking parking documents. (2 years)

Road Traffic Act 1988

Section 1	causing death by dangerous driving. (5 years)
Section 2	dangerous driving. (2 years)
Section 3A	causing death by careless driving, when under influence of drink or drugs. (5 years)

Section 4(1)	driving or attempting to drive when unfit to drive through drink or drugs. (6 months)
Section 4(2)	being in charge of a mechanically propelled vehicle when unfit to drive through drink or drugs (3 months)
Section 5(1)(a)	driving or attempting to drive with excess alcohol in breath, blood or urine. (6 months)
Section 5(1)(b)	being in charge of a motor vehicle with excess alcohol in breath, blood or urine. (3 months)
Section 7	failing to provide specimen for analysis or laboratory test. (6 months if to ascertain ability to drive, etc; 3 months in any other case)
Section 22A	causing danger to road users. (7 years)
Section 103(1)(b)	driving while disqualified. (6 months)
Section 170(4)	failing to stop after accident and give particulars or report accident. (6 months)
Section 173	forgery, etc. of licences, test certificates, certificates of insurance and other documents and things. (2 years)

DUTY TO GIVE NAME AND ADDRESS

Any person driving a motor vehicle on a road (other than an invalid carriage), or believed to have been the driver when an accident occurred, or believed to have committed an offence in relation to the use of the vehicle on a road, must, on being required by a constable, give his name and address and that of the owner of the vehicle, and failure is an offence (Road Traffic Act 1988, s165).

POWER TO STOP VEHICLES

A person driving a motor vehicle on a road and a person riding a cycle on a road must stop on being so required by a constable in uniform, and failure is an offence (Road Traffic Act 1988, s163).

DUTY OF KEEPER TO GIVE IDENTITY OF DRIVER

Where the driver of a motor vehicle or pedal cycle is alleged to be guilty of an offence relating to use of the vehicle on a road, the keeper and any other person shall give such information as may be required by or on behalf of a chief officer of police as to the identity of the driver (Road Traffic Act 1988, s172, and Road Traffic Regulation Act 1984, s84).

ACCIDENTS

Duty of driver to stop, report accident and give information or documents (Road Traffic Act 1988, s170)

In a case where, owing to the presence of a motor vehicle on a road, an accident occurs by which :
- (a) personal injury is caused to a person other than the driver of that mechanically propelled vehicle; or
- (b) damage is caused to - (i) a vehicle other than that motor vehicle or a trailer drawn by that mechanically propelled vehicle, or (ii) an animal other than an animal in or on that motor vehicle, or (iii) any other property constructed on, fixed to, growing in or otherwise forming part of the land on which the road.in question is situated or land adjacent to such land;

the driver of the mechanically propelled vehicle must stop and, if required to do so by any person having reasonable grounds for so requiring, give his name and address and also the name and address of the owner and the identification marks of the vehicle. If for any reason the driver of the mechanically propelled vehicle does not give his name and address, he must report the accident. A person who fails to comply is guilty of an offence.

If, in a case where personal injury is caused to a person other than the driver of a mechanically propelled vehicle, the driver of the motor vehicle (other than an invalid carriage) does not at the time of the accident produce a certificate of insurance or security to a constable or to some person who, having reasonable grounds for so doing, has required him to produce it, the driver must report the accident and produce such a certificate or other evidence. A person who fails to comply with this duty is guilty of an offence, but he shall not be convicted by reason only of a failure to produce a certificate or other evidence if, within 7 days after the occurrence of the accident, he produces it at a police station specified by him at the time the accident was reported.

To comply with a duty to report an accident or to produce evidence of insurance, the driver must do so at a police station or to a constable as soon as is reasonably practicable and, in any case within 24 hours of the occurrence of the accident.

(Note that if the driver stops and gives his name and address and, in the case of personal injury to another person, produces evidence of insurance, there is no need to report any accident.).

'Animal' means horse, cattle, ass, mule, sheep, pig, goat or dog. 'Road', in relation to England and Wales, means any highway and any other road to which the public has access, and includes bridges over which a road passes.

Police action

When called to a street accident, a police officer must first give consideration to the prevention of further accidents and to any injured persons.
Excitement and agitation may arise among the parties involved; the
constable must remain cool and impartial. He should always remember the
importance of identification, and the manner of treatment of casualties, as
well as the need to exercise particular care when casualties are taken to
different hospitals. The necessary relatives should also be remembered.

The duties of the police when accidents occur in the streets are to:

   (a)   attend promptly to the injured, if necessary obtaining medical aid
or having them removed to hospital;

   (b)   ensure that adequate measures are taken to prevent further accidents arising from any obstruction, especially on roads carrying
fast moving traffic;

   (c)   enquire for witnesses, especially independent witnesses;

   (d)   obtain help if necessary, eg from the station, or traffic patrol car as
appropriate;

   (e)   prevent obstruction or danger being caused by the vehicle concerned;

   (f)   take particulars in the appropriate accident report book as necessary;

   (g)   consider whether any blame attaches to any person and, if so, take
any additional particulars and action that may be necessary.

Payment for hospital treatment

Emergency treatement of persons involved in road traffic accidents is
payable by the person using the vehicle at the time to a doctor or hospital.
Information must be provided by a chief officer of police on the request of
a claimant. (Road Traffic Act 1988, ss157-159 and Road Traffic Accidents
(Payments for Treatment) Order 1991.)

**REQUIREMENT OF WARNING OF PROSECUTIONS FOR
CERTAIN OFFENCES (ss 1 and 2, Road Traffic Offenders Act
1988)**

Where a person is prosecuted for an offence of dangerous or careless
driving or cycling, failing to comply with traffic directions or traffic signs,
leaving a vehicle in a dangerous position, or exceeding a speed limit, he is
not to be convicted unless:

(a) he was warned at the time the offence was committed that the question of prosecuting him for one or other of the relevant offences would be taken into consideration, or

(b) within 14 days of the commission of the offence a summons was served on him, or

(c) within 14 days of the commission of the offence a notice of the intended prosecution specifying the nature of the alleged offence and the time and place where it is alleged to have been committed, was served on him or, in the case of a motoring offence, served on him or on the registered keeper of the vehicle.

A notice shall be deemed to have been served if it was sent by registered post or recorded delivery to his last known address, notwithstanding that it was returned as undelivered or for any other reason not received.

These requirements do not apply in relation to an offence:

(a) if, at the time of the offence or immediately after it, an accident occurs owing to the presence on a road of the vehicle in respect of which the offence was committed;

(b) in respect of which a fixed penalty notice had been given or fixed;

(c) in respect of which a notice has been given to him for production at a police station.

Failure to comply with these requirements is not a bar to conviction where the court is satisfied that neither the name and address of the accused nor that of the registered keeper could with reasonable diligence have been ascertained in time for a summons or notice to be served or sent; or the accused contributed by his own conduct to the failure.

THE HIGHWAY CODE

The Highway Code comprises directions for the guidance of persons using the road. It is freely available and should be studied by all police officers.

Section 38 of the Road Traffic Act 1988 states:

A failure on the part of a person to observe a provision of the Highway Code shall not of itself render that person liable to criminal proceedings, but any such failure may in any proceedings (whether civil or criminal and including proceedings under the Traffic Acts, the Public Passenger Vehicles Act 1981 or ss18-23 of the Transport Act 1985) be relied upon by any party to the proceedings as tending to establish or to negative any liability which is in question in those proceedings.

BEING TOWED BY, GETTING ON TO, OR TAMPERING WITH A MOTOR VEHICLE

(a) No person shall without lawful authority or reasonable cause:
- (i)   get on to a motor vehicle or tamper with the brake or other part of its mechanism while it is on a road or on a parking place provided by the local authority (s25), or
- (ii) take or retain hold of or get on to a motor vehicle or trailer while in motion on a road for the purpose of being carried (s26(1));

(b) No person shall take or retain hold of a motor vehicle or trailer while in motion on a road for the purpose of being drawn (s26(2)).

(Note also the offence of interference with vehicles under s9 of the Criminal Attempts Act 1981, dealt with later.)

WEIGHING OF MOTOR VEHICLES

No person shall fail to comply with a request made by a constable authorised in writing or other person similarly authorised to weigh a motor vehicle or trailer of which he is in charge, but there is no authority to unload the vehicle or trailer; and if the vehicle is more than five miles from a weighbridge and the weight is within the limits authorised, the highway authority shall compensate for any loss occasioned by the journey (Road Traffic Act 1988, s78).

HAZARDOUS SUBSTANCES (Dangerous Substances (Conveyance by Road in Road Tankers and Tank Containers) Regulations 1981)

These Regulations require the carrying of informative notices on tank vehicles carrying dangerous substances, so that the emergency services can safely and quickly deal with incidents involving chemical hazards. Carriers of dangerous substances are required to put a 'composite sign' on their tank vehicles which is divided into five parts containing the following information:

(a) The Hazchem Code. The code symbols displayed give information to emergency services which is interpreted by means of a card supplied to them.

(b) UN Number. This identifies the chemical carried.

(c) Specialist advice - Telephone Number. Giving the number of a telephone manned when the vehicle is in transit giving access to specialist advice.

(d) Warning Diamond. The internationally agreed warning notice.
(e) Manufacturer. The manufacturer's name or house symbol.

MOTORWAYS

Legislation and definitions

Schedule 4 of the Highways Act 1980 divides vehicles into 11 classes. Only those of Class I and Class II are permitted to be driven on special roads or motorways, except in emergencies.

The Motorway Traffic(England and Wales) Regulations 1982 provide the rules which drivers of vehicles on motorways must comply with.

'Carriageway' means that part of a motorway which -(i) is provided for the regular use of vehicle motor traffic along the motorway; and (ii) where a hard shoulder is provided, has the approximate position of its left-hand or near-side marked with a solid white line.

'Central reservation' means that part of a motorway which separates the carriageway to be used by vehicles travelling in one direction from the carriageway to be used by vehicles travelling in the opposite direction.

'Hard shoulder' means a part of the motorway which is adjacent to and situated on the left hand or near side of the carriageway when facing in the direction in which vehicles may be driven and which is designed to take the weight of a vehicle.

'Verge' means any part of a motorway which is not a carriageway, a hard shoulder, or a central reservation.

Regulations

The following regulations are applicable to drivers of vehicles on motorways:

5 - *Vehicles to be driven on the carriageway only.* No vehicle shall be driven on any part of a motorway which is not a carriageway.

6 - *Direction of driving.* Signs prohibiting entry to the carriageways must be complied with. Vehicles must be driven so that the central reservation is on the right-hand or offside of the driver. U-turns must not be made.

7 - *Restriction on stopping.* Vehicles may only stop or remain at rest on a carriageway where it is necessary: (i) by reason of a breakdown or mechanical defect or lack of fuel, oil or water required by the vehicle; or (ii) by reason of any accident, illness or other emergency; or (iii) to permit any person carried in or on the vehicle to recover or move any object which has fallen on the motorway; or (iv) to permit any person in or on the vehicle to give help in any of the foregoing circumstances. In these circumstances the vehicle must be moved to the hard shoulder as soon as reasonably practicable and must not be allowed to remain there longer than is necessary.

8 - *Restriction on reversing.* Vehicles must not be reversed on a carriageway, except when it is necessary to reverse in order to turn or to connect with another vehicle.

9 - *Restriction on the use of hard shoulder.* Vehicles must not be driven or moved or stop on any hard shoulder, except in accordance with reg 7.

10 - *Vehicles not to use the central reservation or verge.* Vehicles must not be driven or stop or remain at rest on a central reservation or verge.

11 - *Vehicles not to be driven by learner drivers.* A provisional licence holder who has not passed a test must not drive on a motorway.

12 - *Restriction on the use of right-hand or offside lane.* Motor vehicles other than motor cars not exceeding 7.5 tonnes maximum gross weight, heavy motor cars constructed and used solely to carry passengers and not exceeding 12 metres in length, and motor vehicles drawing trailers, must not be driven in the right-hand or offside lane of a motorway with three lanes of traffic moving in the same direction. This does not apply when it is necessary to pass a vehicle with a load of exceptional width and it is impossible to pass without driving in the right-hand lane.

13 - *Restrictions affecting persons on foot on a motorway.* No person on foot must go on a motorway except when necessary to get to a verge or to comply with regulations, or to remove an object or give help as in reg 7.

14 - *Animals on motorways.* The person in charge of a vehicle must ensure, so far as is practicable, that an animal is not removed from

or allowed to leave the vehicle on the motorway, and if it escapes or has to be removed from, or allowed to leave a vehicle, it is confined to the hard shoulder, kept on a lead and under proper control.

15 - *Use of motorways by excluded traffic*. Motor vehicles other than those in Classes I and II may use a motorway for maintenance purposes and in cases of emergency. The chief officer of police of an area may authorise use by excluded traffic in an emergency.

16 - *Exceptions and relaxations*. The above restrictions do not apply to anything permitted or directed by a constable in uniform, to emergency services, or for specified maintenance purposes.

PARKING BY DISABLED PERSONS

The Local Authorities' Traffic Orders (Exemptions for Disabled Persons) (England and Wales) Order 1986 provides that where a local traffic order prohibits the waiting of vehicles in a road, it shall also include an exemption for any disabled person's vehicles which displays a disabled person's badge. The exemption shall be (i) where the period of prohibition is of three hours' duration or less, the whole of the period; (ii) where the period of prohibition is of more than three hours, a period of three hours.

In all cases a disabled person's badge must be displayed in the relevant position, and for the purposes of (ii) above, a parking disc coloured orange on which is marked the time at which the period of waiting began. The vehicle must have been driven by a disabled person, or used for carrying disabled persons or passengers, immediately before or after the period of waiting.

TRAFFIC WARDENS (Road Traffic Regulation Act 1984)

Police authorities may appoint traffic wardens to assist the police in the duties normally undertaken by the police in connection with the control and regulation of traffic and the enforcement of road traffic law.

The Functions of Traffic Wardens Order 1970, as amended, provides that traffic wardens may be employed to enforce the law with respect to an offence:

   (a) by a vehicle left or parked without obligatory lights or reflectors;

   (b) by a vehicle obstructing a road or waiting, or being left or parked, or being loaded or unloaded in a road;

   (c) in connection with street parking places, where charges are made;

(d)   committed in contravention of the Vehicles (Excise) Act 1971.

Traffic wardens can also be used for the control and regulation of traffic at road junctions and places which are, or are likely to be, congested with traffic; and any other functions normally undertaken by the police in relation to traffic control. They must wear such uniforms as the Secretary of State determines and must not act as traffic wardens when not in uniform.

Traffic wardens may also act as school crossing patrols if the patrols are appointed by the police. If school crossing patrols are appointed by the local authority, a traffic warden may do school crossing duty but his powers are then those of a traffic warden only.

Traffic wardens may exercise the functions conferred on constables in respect of offences to which the fixed penalty procedure applies (other than for leaving a vehicle in a dangerous position or obstruction).

SCHOOL CROSSING PATROLS (Road Traffic Regulation Act 1984, ss 26-28)

Local authorities and the police are empowered to appoint school crossing patrols where children cross roads to and from school between 8.00 am and 5.30 pm, or when going from one part of a school to another.

Such person, when in uniform and exhibiting a prescribed sign at a place where children on their way to or from school are crossing or seeking to cross the road, has power to require persons driving or propelling vehicles on a road to stop.

Offences are committed by drivers who fail to stop on being required by a school crossing patrol exhibiting the prescribed sign, or who start again while the sign is still displayed.

FIXED PENALTY OFFENCES (Road Traffic Offenders Act 1988)

Where a constable in uniform has reason to believe that a person is committing a fixed penalty offence, he may give him a fixed penalty notice.

In the case of an offence involving obligatory endorsement, a notice may not be given unless the person produces and surrenders his licence and the constable is satisfied that he would not be liable to be disqualified (ie not more than 12 penalty points) (s54). If a licence is not produced a notice may be given which can be exchanged for a fixed penalty notice at a police station of his choice within 7 days.

In the case of a non-endorseable fixed penalty offence committed in respect of a stationary vehicle, a fixed penalty notice may be fixed to the vehicle (s62).

It is an offence to remove or interfere with a notice fixed to a vehicle, unless this is done by or under the authority of the driver or person in charge or liable for the offence.

Part 3
Crime

Chapter 20
Principles of Criminal Liability

Meaning of crime

A crime is usually defined as an act of disobedience of the law forbidden under pain of punishment. Generally a crime affects the interests of the community, while a civil wrong (or tort) affects only an individual.

Possibly the best way to distinguish between crimes and torts for police purposes is the element of punishment. Criminal offences are punishable by the State by means of fines or imprisonment; whereas the redress for a civil wrong is usually compensation by way of damages.

A further complication has been introduced, however, by the use of the word crime in a narrow sense to mean only indictable offences.

Elements of crime

Most crimes require a criminal state of mind or an intention to commit a criminal act. This guilty state of mind is known as *mens rea* and must be proved by the prosecution. Many minor statutory offences, however, are absolute offences and are punishable without evidence of *mens rea*.

The other element is the *actus reus,* which is the physical, wilful act or omission.

Common law and statute law

The law of England and Wales may be divided into two kinds: common law and statute law.

The common law is made up of certain rules of conduct which have been regarded as law from time immemorial by custom and general agreement. This law is unwritten but accepted and approved of by the courts.

Some offences against the common law are also offences punishable by statute, eg assaults. Other examples of offences against the common law are murder, manslaughter, and attempts to commit certain offences.

Statute law is the law enacted in Acts of Parliament. On receiving the Royal assent a Bill becomes an Act.

Apart from Public General Acts there are also Local Acts. These are laws of limited jurisdiction, eg the Stockport Corporation Act 1972 enacted for local government purposes in the Borough of Stockport.

Various statutes enable delegated legislation to be made, ie statutory instruments or byelaws.

Statutory Instruments are Regulations, Orders, Rules or Directions made under powers conferred by an Act on a Secretary of State or other Minister of the Crown. An example is the Road Vehicles (Construction and Use) Regulations made by the Secretary of State for the Environment under the Road Traffic Act 1988.

Byelaws are made by local authorities under various statutes, eg the Local Government Act 1972. On being approved by the Minister of the Crown specified in the enabling Act, byelaws may be enforced summarily.

Malice

Where malice is mentioned in a statute it must not be taken in the old sense of wickedness, but as meaning an actual intention to do the particular kind of harm done, or recklessness as to whether such harm should occur.

Motive

Motive is a person's reason for acting as he did, eg for financial gain or because he has a starving family. It must not be confused with intent, which has to do with the result of a person's act.

Exemption from criminal liability

The following are exempt from liability in respect of any offences they may commit:

(a) The Queen; it is a maxim of law that the sovereign can do no wrong.

(b) Foreign sovereigns and ambassadors; while resident in this country these persons do not come under the jurisdiction of English courts. These diplomatic privileges are extended to all members of embassy staff. If offences are committed the offender may be requested to leave the country.

(c) Corporations; a corporation or company cannot be dealt with as an individual as it cannot be imprisoned. It can, however, be prosecuted for offences which are punishable with a fine. Section 36 of the Magistrates' Courts Act 1980 gives the procedure in relation to indictable offences.

(d) Children; under 10 years of age children cannot be punished for any offence, but may be dealt with as being in need of care. Between the ages of 10 and 14 children may be tried but may not be found guilty without proof of guilty knowledge.

Defences and excuses for crime

(a) Insanity (the test for which is laid down in the M'Naghten Rules).
(b) Drunkenness. Only an excuse if involuntary.
(c) Ignorance or mistake. Ignorance of the law is not an excuse, but an honest and reasonable mistake may excuse a crime if there is no unlawful intent. This does not apply to absolute offences.
(d) Accident.
(e) Duress (compulsion or coercion). Direct physical compulsion may excuse a crime, but not threats.
(f) Married women. It is a defence for a woman charged with any offence except treason or murder to prove that it was committed under coercion of her husband.

Vicarious liability

The legal responsibility of a person for the illegal acts of another, usually in a master/servant situation.

Attempts

An attempt to commit a crime is an act done which if not interrupted would result in the actual commission of the crime. Before a person may be convicted of an attempt, he must be shown to have an intention to commit the act and to have taken some step towards its commission.

Under the Criminal Attempts Act 1981, if, with intent to commit an *indictable* offence, a person does an act which is more than merely preparatory to its commission, he will be guilty of attempting to commit it. A person may be guilty of attempting to commit an offence to which this applies even though the facts are such that the commission of the offence is impossible. The penalty for an attempt under this Act is basically the same as for the principal offence.

A number of statutes create offences of attempting to commit summary offence.

Incitement

Inciting or urging another person to commit a crime is a common law misdemeanour. The crime does not have to be committed for a charge of inciting to be laid.

Certain incitements are specially catered for by statute, such as: incitement to murder: Offences against the Person Act 1861, s4; inciting a woman to cause her own miscarriage: Offences against the Person Act 1861, s58; inciting members of HM Forces to mutiny: Incitement to Mutiny Act 1797, s1; and, inciting a girl under 16 to commit incest: Criminal Law Act 1977, s54.

Chapter 21
Classification of Crimes and Parties to Crime

Classification

Crimes may be classified according to mode of trial, in which they fall into one of the following categories:
- (a) Indictable offences. Triable only on indictment before a jury at a Crown Court.
- (b) Summary offences. No right of trial by jury. Must be tried by magistrates in courts of summary jurisdiction.
- (c) Offences triable either way, ie either summarily or on indictment at the discretion of the magistrates.

Arrestable offences—Police and Criminal Evidence Act 1984

Briefly these are offences for which the penalty is fixed by law, or for which the penalty is imprisonment for five years, and certain statutory offences. (See Chapter 5 for full details.)

Remember also that certain statutory powers of arrest are preserved.

Throughout this book all powers of arrest are indicated where applicable.

Assisting persons who have committed arrestable offences

Section 4 of the Criminal Law Act 1967 provides that where a person has committed an arrestable offence, any other person who, knowing or believing him to be guilty of the offence or some other arrestable offence, does, without lawful authority or reasonable excuse, any act with intent to impede his apprehension or prosecution shall be guilty of an offence.

The consent of the DPP is necessary before proceedings are taken.

Concealing arrestable offences or giving false information

Where a person has committed an arrestable offence, any other person who, knowing or believing that the offence or some other arrestable offence has been committed, and that he has information which might be of material assistance in securing the prosecution or conviction of an offender for it, accepts or agrees to accept for not disclosing that information any consideration other than the making good of loss or injury caused by the offence, or the making of reasonable compensation for that loss or injury, commits an offence (Criminal Law Act 1967, s5(1)).

Where a person causes any wasteful employment of the police by knowingly making to any person a false report tending to show that an offence has been committed or to give rise to apprehension for the safety of any persons or property or tending to show that he has information material to any police enquiry, he commits an offence (Criminal Law Act 1967, s5(2)).

The consent of the DPP is required for both the above offences.

Principals, aiders, abettors, counsellors and procurers

The actual offender in the commission of a crime is the principal. Other persons may be dealt with as accessories by aiding and abetting, or counselling or procuring its commission.

Section 8 of the Accessories and Abettors Act 1861 provides that any person who aids, abets, counsels or procures the commission of an indictable offence is liable to be punished as a principal.

Section 44 of the Magistrates' Courts Act 1980 states that a person who aids, abets, counsels or procures the commission of a summary (or either way) offence, shall be guilty of a like offence.

Conspiracy—Criminal Law Act 1977

If a person agrees with any other person or persons that a course of conduct shall be pursued which will necessarily amount to or involve the commission of any offence or offences by one or more of the parties to the agreement if the agreement is carried out in accordance with their intentions, he is guilty of conspiracy (s1).

An intended victim cannot be guilty of conspiracy; nor a person who conspires only with his spouse, a person under the age of criminal responsibility, or an intended victim.

The offence of conspiracy at common law has been abolished with the exception of conspiracy to corrupt public morals or to outrage public

decency where the agreement relates to conduct which would not constitute an offence if carried out by a single person.

Section 12 of the Criminal Justice Act 1987 provides that if a person
agrees with any other person that a course of conduct shall be pursued
which will amount to or involve the commission of an offence or offences
by one or more of the parties to the agreement if it is carried out, the fact
that it will do so shall not preclude a charge of conspiracy to defraud being
brought against each of them.

Chapter 22
Offences against the Public Peace

BREACH OF THE PEACE

At common law the police have a duty to keep the peace, particularly in public places. In pursuance of this duty, and in order to prevent breaches of the peace, the police may take such action as the clearing of streets and closing of meetings (see Chapter 5 for definition of breach of the peace and powers of arrest.)

PUBLIC ORDER OFFENCES (Part I, Public Order Act 1986)

Riot (s1)

Where 12 or more persons who are present together use or threaten unlawful violence for a common purpose and the conduct of them (taken together) is such as would cause a person of reasonable firmness present at the scene to fear for his personal safety, each of the persons using unlawful violence for the common purpose is guilty of riot.

It is immaterial whether or not the persons use or threaten violence simultaneously and the common purpose may be inferred from conduct. No persons of reasonable firmness need actually be present. The offence may be committed either in public or in private places. The penalty is imprisonment for not exceeding ten years - arrestable offence.

Prosecution for riot or incitement to riot may only be instituted by or with the consent of the DPP.

Where buildings are damaged or destroyed by riot, the Riot (Damages) Act 1886 provides that compensation shall be paid by the police authority.

Violent disorder (s2)

Where three or more persons who are present together use or threaten unlawful violence and the conduct of them (taken together) is such as would cause a person of reasonable firmness present at the scene to fear for his personal safety, each of the persons using or threatening unlawful violence is guilty of violent disorder.

It is immaterial whether the persons' threaten violence simultaneously and no person of reasonable firmness need actually be present. The offence may be committed either in public or private. Maximum penalty is five years' imprisonment - arrestable offence.

Affray (s3)

Where a person uses or threatens unlawful violence towards another and his conduct is such as would cause a person of reasonable firmness present at the scene to fear for his personal safety.

Where two or more persons use or threaten the unlawful violence, it is their conduct taken together that must be considered. A threat cannot be made by the use of words alone. No person of reasonable firmness need actually be present. The offence may be committed in private as well as public places. A constable may arrest without warrant anyone he reasonably suspects is committing affray.

Fear or provocation of violence (s4)

Using towards another person threatening, abusive or insulting words or behaviour, or distributing or displaying to another person any writing, sign or other visible representation which is threatening, abusive or insulting, with intent to cause that person to believe that immediate unlawful violence will be used against him or another by any person, or to provoke the immediate use of unlawful violence by that person or another, or whereby that person is likely to believe that such violence will be used or it is likely that such violence will be provoked.

This offence may be committed in a public or a private place, but not by a person inside a dwelling to another person in that or another dwelling. A constable may arrest without warrant anyone he reasonably suspects is committing this offence.

Harassment, alarm or distress (s5)

Using threatening abusive or insulting words or behaviour, or disorderly behaviour, or displaying any writing, sign or other visible representation which is threatening, abusive or insulting, within the hearing or sight of a person likely to be caused harassment, alarm or distress thereby.

This offence may be committed in public or private, but not by a person inside a dwelling to another person in that or another dwelling. A constable may arrest a person without warrant if he engages in offensive conduct and, after being warned to stop, engages in further offensive conduct immediately or shortly afterwards. 'Offensive conduct' means conduct the constable reasonably suspects to constitute this offence.

Notes on the foregoing offences

A person is guilty of riot only if he intends to use violence or is aware that his conduct may be violent, and a similar mental element is necessary for the offences under ss 2,3,4 and 5.

Impairment of awareness by intoxication may be ignored, unless the person shows that his intoxication was not self-induced or was caused solely by medical treatment. 'Intoxication' may be caused by drink, drugs or other means, or by a combination of means. 'Dwelling' means any structure or part of a structure occupied as a person's home or as other living accommodation (whether the occupation is separate or shared with others) but does not include any part not so occupied, and for this purpose 'structure' includes a tent, caravan, vehicle, vessel or other temporary or movable structure.

'Violence' means any violent conduct, so that - (a) except in the context of affray, it includes violent conduct towards property as well as violent conduct towards persons, and (b) it is not restricted to conduct causing or intended to cause injury or damage but includes any other violent conduct (for example throwing at or towards a person a missile of a kind capable of causing injury which does not hit or falls short).

UNIFORMS AND TRAINING (Public Order Act 1936)

Prohibition of uniforms in connection with political objects (s1)

In any public place or at any public meeting, wearing uniform signifying an allegiance with any political organisation or with the promotion of any political object.

If the chief officer of police is satisfied that the wearing of such uniform on a special occasion will not involve risk of public disorder he may, with the consent of the Secretary of State, permit it to be worn. A constable may without warrant arrest any person reasonably suspected to be committing this offence.

Prohibition of quasi-military organisations (s2)

Members or adherents of any association of persons being organised or trained or equipped for the purpose of enabling them to be employed in usurping the functions of the police or the armed forces, or for the use or display of physical force in promoting any political object, or in such manner as to arouse reasonable apprehension that they are organised for that purpose.

Consent of Attorney General required for prosecution.

RACIAL HATRED (Part III, Public Order 1986)

'Racial hatred' means hatred against a group of persons in Great Britain defined by reference to colour, race, nationality (including citizenship) or ethnic or national origins. Proceedings may only be instituted by or with the consent of the Attorney General.

Use of words or behaviour or display of written material (s18)

Using threatening, abusive or insulting words or behaviour, or displaying any written material which is threatening, abusive or insulting, intending thereby to stir up racial hatred or having regard to all the circumstances racial hatred is likely to be stirred up thereby.

This offence may be committed in a public or a private place, but not by a person inside a dwelling to other persons in that or another dwelling. A constable may arrest without warrant anyone he reasonably suspects is committing the offence.

Publishing or distributing written material (s19)

Publishing or distributing written material which is threatening, abusive or insulting, intending thereby to stir up racial hatred, or having regard to all the circumstances racial hatred is likely to be stirred up thereby.

Other offences involving intent to stir up racial hatred

Section 20.   Public performance of play.
Section 21.   Distributing, showing or playing a recording.
Section 22.   Broadcasting or including programme in cable pro-
               gramme service.
Section 23.   Possession of racially inflammatory material.

MISCELLANEOUS OFFENCES (Part V, Public Order Act 1986)

Contamination of or interference with goods with intention of causing public alarm or anxiety, etc (s38)

Contaminating or interfering with goods, or making it appear that goods have been contaminated or interfered with, in a place where such goods are consumed, used, sold or otherwise supplied; with the intention of causing public alarm or anxiety, injury to members of the public consuming or using the goods, or economic loss to any person by reason of the goods being shunned by members of the public or by steps taken to avoid any such alarm or anxiety, injury or loss.

Threatening that he or another will do, or claiming to have done, any such act.

With a view to the commission of such an offence, being in possession of materials to be used for contaminating or interfering with goods, or goods which have, or appear to have, been contaminated or interfered with.

The maximum penalty is ten years' imprisonment, so these are arrestable offences. 'Goods' includes substances whether natural or manufactured and whether or not incorporated in or mixed with other goods.

Power to direct trespassers to leave land (s39)

If the senior police officer at the scene reasonably believes that two or more persons have entered land as trespassers with the common purpose of residing there; that reasonable steps have been taken by or on behalf of the occupier to ask them to leave; and that any of them has caused damage to property on the land, used threatening, abusive or insulting words or behaviour towards the occupier or a member of his family or employee, or that they have brought 12 or more vehicles on to the land, he may direct those persons, or any of them, to leave the land.

A person knowing that such a direction has been given to him who fails to leave the land as soon as reasonably practicable, or having left enters again as a trespasser within a period of three months, commits an offence.

A constable in uniform who reasonably suspects that a person is committing this offence may arrest him without warrant. 'Land' does not include buildings other than agricultural buildings, or scheduled monuments, or land forming part of a highway. 'Vehicle' includes a caravan.

PUBLIC MEETINGS, PROCESSIONS AND ASSEMBLIES

It is an offence under s1 of the Public Meetings Act 1908 to act in a disorderly manner at a lawful public meeting to prevent the transaction of the business for which the meeting is called. At the request of the chairman, a constable who reasonably suspects anyone of this offence may require that person to declare his name and address.

Part II of the Public Order Act 1986 provides that not less than six days' advance notice must be given to the police of public processions (unless it is not reasonably practicable to give such notice). An offence is committed by the organisers if they fail to comply. Note that this does not apply to customarily held processions or funerals.

The senior officer at the scene may impose conditions in respect of a public procession or assembly, which he reasonably believes may result in serious public disorder, serious damage to property, or serious disruption to the life of the community. Offences are committed by the organisers or other persons who fail to comply with the conditions, or who incite others to do so. A constable in uniform may arrest without warrant anyone reasonably suspected of committing the offence.

If at any time the chief officer of police reasonably believes that conditions which may be applied to the holding of public processions will not be sufficient to prevent serious public disorder, he must apply to the district council for an order prohibiting processions for a period not exceeding three months. (In London, the Commissioners of the City of London or the Metropolis may do this with the consent of the Secretary of State).

ACTS OF TERRORISM OR PROSCRIBED ORGANISATIONS

The Prevention of Terrorism (Temporary Provisions) Act 1989 deals with persons belonging to proscribed organisations, ie the Irish Republican Army and the Irish National Liberation Army. The following offences are provided:

Section 2 - membership, support and meetings. It is an offence to belong or profess to belong to a proscribed organisation; to solicit or invite support for a proscribed organisation, other than with money or property; or to arrange or assist in the arrangement or management of, or address any meeting of three or more persons, knowing that the meeting is to support or further the activities of a proscribed organisation or to be addressed by a member. Maximum penalty is 10 years' imprisonment - an arrestable offence.

Section 3 - display of support in public. Committed by any person who in a public place wears any item of dress, or wears, carries or displays apprehension that he is a member or supporter of a proscribed organisation.

Section 8 - offences in respect of exclusion orders. Failing to comply with an exclusion order made by the Secretary of State, or being concerned in facilitating the entry of such a person into Great Britain, or knowingly harbouring such a person. Maximum penalty 5 years' imprisonment - an arrestable offence.

Section 9 - contributions towards acts of terrorism. A person is guilty of an offence if he:

(a) solicits or invites any person to give, lend or otherwise make available, any money or other property, or receives or accepts any money or property, intending that it will be used in connection with acts of terrorism;

(b) gives, lends or otherwise makes available, any money or property, or enters into an arrangement whereby money or other property is made available, knowing or having reasonable cause to suspect that it will be used in acts of terrorism.

Other offences are - contributions to resources of proscribed organisations (s10), and assisting in retention or control of terrorist funds (s11).

A constable may arrest without warrant a person whom he reasonably suspects to be guilty of an offence under ss9,10 or 11; a person concerned in the commission, preparation or instigation of acts of terrorism; or a person subject to an exclusion order. A person arrested shall not be detained in right of the arrest for more than 48 hours, but the Secretary of State may extend the period by up to a further five days.

'Terrorism' means the use of violence for political ends and includes the use of violence for the purpose of putting the public or any section of the public in fear.

OFFENCES AT SPORTING EVENTS

SPORTING EVENTS (CONTROL OF ALCOHOL ETC) ACT 1985, AS AMENDED BY THE PUBLIC ORDER ACT 1986

Offences in connection with alcohol on coaches and trains (s1)

Knowingly causing or permitting intoxicating liquor to be carried on a public service vehicle or railway passenger vehicle, being used for the principal purpose of carrying passengers for the whole or part of a journey to or from a designated sporting event.

Possessing intoxicating liquor while on a vehicle to which the section applies.

Being drunk on a vehicle to which this section applies.

Alcohol on certain other vehicles (s1A)

This applies the three offences in s1 to motor vehicles which are not public service vehicles but are adapted to carry more than eight passengers, and being used to carry two or more passengers.

Offences in connection with alcohol containers, etc at sports grounds (s2)

Possessing intoxicating liquor or an article capable of causing injury to a person struck by it at any time during the period of a designated sporting event. This applies to any bottle, can or other portable container which is for holding any drink, and is of a kind which, when empty, is normally discarded or returned to the supplier, or part of such an article.

Being drunk in or while trying to enter a designated sports ground at any time during the period of the event.

Fireworks etc (s2A)

Possessing any article or substance whose main purpose is the emission of a flare for purposes of illuminating or signalling or the emission of smoke or a visible gas; and in particular distress flares, fog signals, and pellets and capsules intended to be used as fumigators or for testing pipes, or a firework, at any time during the period of a designated sporting event when in the areas of, or trying to enter a designated sports ground.

Powers of enforcement (s7)

A constable may, at any time during the period of a designated sporting event, enter any part of the ground for the purpose of enforcing the provisions of this Act; search a person he has reasonable grounds to suspect is committing or has committed an offence, and may arrest such a person; and may stop and search a public service vehicle, a railway passenger vehicle or a vehicle within the meaning of s1A, if he has reasonable grounds to suspect that an offence under s1 or 1A is being or has been committed.

FOOTBALL (OFFENCES) ACT 1991

Throwing of missiles (s2)

At a designated football match, throwing anything at or towards the playing area, any area adjacent to the playing area to which spectators are not generally admitted, or any area in which spectators or other persons may be present, without lawful authority or lawful excuse (which shall be for him to prove).

Indecent or racialist chanting (s3)

Taking part at a designated football match in chanting of an indecent or racialist nature. 'Chanting' means the repeated uttering of any words or sounds in concert with one or more others. 'Of a racialist nature' means consisting of or including matter which is threatening, abusive or insulting to a person of his colour, race, nationality (including citizenship) or ethnic or national origins.

Going onto the playing area (s4)

At a designated football match, going onto the playing area, or any area adjacent to the playing area to which spectators are not generally admitted, without lawful authority or lawful excuse (which shall be for him to prove).

Definition and power of arrest

A 'designated football match' means an association football match designated, or of a description designated, for the purposes of this Act by order of the Secretary of State. References to things done at a designated football match include anything done at the ground within two hours before the start of the match and ending one hour after it ends, or within that period before and after the advertised starting time.

Any offence under this Act is an arrestable offence under s24(2) of the Police and Criminal Evidence Act 1984.

Chapter 23
Offences against Public Morals and Public Policy

Bigamy

Whoever, being married, goes through a ceremony of marriage with any other person during the life of his or her spouse, is guilty of bigamy (Offences against the Person Act 1861, s57). Maximum penalty seven years' imprisonment - arrestable offence.

The essential ingredients of this offence are: the existence of a valid marriage, its subsistence at the time of the second ceremony, and evidence of the celebration of the second ceremony. Proof of the identity of the parties concerned is also required, and evidence that the first husband or wife was alive when the second marriage took place.

Bribery

Bribery is the offering to, or the receiving by, any person of any undue reward in order to influence him to do, or to reward him for doing, an act or making an omission contrary to the rules of honesty and integrity.

Both the offerer and taker are equally guilty; if the bribe is not accepted the offer still constitutes an offence.

At common law it is a misdemeanour to bribe any public officer or for such an officer to accept a bribe.

The Public Bodies Corrupt Practices Act 1889 and the Prevention of Corruption Act 1906 create the following offences:

(a) for any agent to corruptly accept, or attempt to obtain from any person for himself, or for another person, any gift or consideration as an inducement or reward for doing or not doing any act in relation to his principal's affairs or business or for showing or not showing favour or disfavour to any person in relation to his principal's affairs or business;

 (b) for any person to corruptly offer, to give or agree to give any gift or consideration to any agent for the like reason;

 (c) for any person to knowingly give to any agent or for any agent to knowingly use with intent to deceive his principal, any receipt, account or document which is false or incorrect in any material particular and which to his knowledge is intended to mislead the principal.

A constable is an agent for the purpose of this Act. No prosecution may be instituted without the consent of the Attorney General.

It is also an offence under s178 of the Licensing Act 1964, for the holder of a justices' licence to bribe or attempt to bribe a constable.

Embracery

An attempt by bribery or other corrupt means to influence or corrupt a jury, which is a common law misdemeanour.

Obscene publication

The Obscene Publications Acts 1959 and 1964 prohibit the publication of obscene articles whether for gain or not, and the possession of obscene articles for publication for gain.

Article means anything containing or embodying matter to be read or looked at or both, any sound record, film, or the record of a picture or pictures, whether intended to be used alone or as one of the set, or for the reproduction or manufacture of such articles.

Publish means to distribute, circulate, sell, let or hire, give, lend, offer for sale, or let on hire, or to show, play or project any article to be looked at or heard.

Obscene: an article is obscene if its effect or the effect of any one of its items is, if taken as a whole, such as would tend to deprave and corrupt persons who are likely to read, see or hear the matter contained or embodied in it.

Other obscenity offences

The following are statutory offences involving obscenity:

 (a) Wilfully exposing to view in any road or public place any obscene print, picture, or other publication (Vagrancy Act 1824, s4).

 (b) Exhibiting, distributing or offering for sale profane, indecent, or obscene literature or pictures, in streets to the annoyance, danger

or obstruction of residents or passengers (Town Police Clauses Act 1847, s28 - where it applies).
(c) Exhibiting or distributing indecent or obscene matter in a public highway (Indecent Advertisements Act 1889). Advertisements relating to venereal disease are deemed indecent for the purposes of this Act (except where used by Public Health Authorities or by a person authorised by the Secretary of State).
(d) Sending or attempting to send indecent literature through the post (Post Office Act 1953, s11).
(e) Sending by means of a public telecommunications system, a message or other matter that is grossly offensive or of an indecent, obscene or menacing character (Telecommunications Act 1984, s43(1)).

PROTECTION OF CHILDREN ACT 1978

This Act makes it an offence for a person -
(a) to take, or permit to be taken, any indecent photograph of a child (meaning a person under the age of 16); or
(b) to distribute or show such indecent photographs; or
(c) to have in his possession such indecent photographs, with a view to their being distributed or shown by himself or others; or
(d) to publish or cause to be published any advertisement likely to be understood as conveying that the advertiser distributes or shows such indecent photographs, or intends to do so.

Proceedings shall not be instituted except by or with the consent of the DPP.

Where a person is charged with an offence under (b) or (c) above, it shall be a defence for him to prove-
(a) that he had a legitimate reason for distributing or showing the photographs or (as the case may be) having them in his possession; or
(b) that he had not himself seen the photographs and did not know, nor had any cause to suspect, them to be indecent.

POSSESSION OF INDECENT PHOTOGRAPH OF CHILD (s160, Criminal Justice Act 1988)

It is an offence for a person to have any indecent photograph of a child under 16 in his possession. Defence to prove legitimate reason for possession; that he had not seen the photograph and did not know or suspect it to be indecent; or that the photograph was sent without prior request and not kept for an unreasonable time.

CHILDREN AND YOUNG PERSONS (HARMFUL PUBLICATIONS) ACT 1955

This Act applies to any book, magazine or other like work which is of a kind likely to fall into the hands of children or young persons and consists wholly or mainly of stories told in pictures portraying the commission of crimes, acts of violence or cruelty, or incidents of a repulsive or horrible nature, in such a way that it would tend to corrupt a child or young person into whose hands it might fall.

A person who prints, publishes, sells or lets on hire, or has in his possession any such work for these purposes, shall be guilty of an offence. It is a defence for a person to prove that he had not examined the contents of the work and had no reasonable cause to suspect that the Act applied to it. Consent of the Attorney General required for a prosecution.

UNSOLICITED GOODS AND SERVICES ACT 1971

It is an offence for a person to send or cause to be sent to another person any book, magazine or leaflet (or advertising material for any such publication) which he knows, or ought reasonably to know, is unsolicited and which describes or illustrates human sexual techniques. Consent of DPP required for a prosecution.

INDECENT DISPLAYS (CONTROL) ACT 1981

If any indecent matter is publicly displayed the person making the display and any person causing or permitting it to be made shall be guilty of an offence. Any matter which is displayed in or so as to be visible from any public place is deemed to be publicly displayed.

'Public place' means any place to which the public have or are permitted to have access (whether on payment or otherwise) while that matter is displayed except:

(a) a place to which the public are permitted to have access only on payment which is or includes payment for that display; or

(b) a shop or any part of a shop to which the public can only gain access by passing beyond an adequate warning notice reading: 'Warning. Persons passing beyond this notice will find material on display

which they may consider indecent. No admittance to persons under
18 years of age.';
but the exclusions shall only apply where persons under the age of 18 years
are not permitted to enter while the display in question is continuing.

'Matter' includes anything capable of being displayed, except that it
does not include an actual human body or any part thereof.

Chapter 24
Offences against the Person

HOMICIDE

Homicide is the killing of a human being, by a human being. It may be either culpable, or non-culpable.

(a) Culpable homicide is of six kinds:

    (i) Murder: where a person of sound memory and discretion unlawfully killeth any reasonable creature in being, under the Queen's peace, with malice aforethought, either express or implied, the death following within a year and a day.

    Express malice means an intention to kill, or inflict some bodily injury likely to result in death, or grievous bodily harm. Implied malice means the intentional performance of a wrongful act which the offender must have contemplated would be likely to cause death or serious bodily harm. The punishment for murder is life imprisonment by virtue of the Murder (Abolition of Death Penalty) Act 1965; except for a person under 18 at the time the offence was committed, who shall be sentenced to be detained during Her Majesty's pleasure.

    (ii) Manslaughter: which is the unlawful killing of a human being without malice aforethought, either express or implied. It may be voluntary, eg where death results from an assault made under provocation; or involuntary, eg where death results accidentally from an unlawful act or omission.

    It shall be manslaughter for a person acting in pursuance of a suicide pact to kill the other or be a party to the other being killed by a third person (Homicide Act 1957).)

    (iii) Causing death by dangerous driving (dealt with earlier).

    (iv) Causing death by careless driving when under influence of drink or drugs (dealt with earlier).

    (v) Causing death by aggravated taking of a mechanically propelled vehicle (see later).

(vi) Infanticide (see later).

(b) Non-culpable homicide is of two kinds:

(i) Justifiable; as in the lawful execution of a criminal, or when such force as is reasonable in the circumstances is used in the prevention of a forcible and atrocious crime, or in a case of necessity in killing a person who resists or prevents a constable in the execution of his duty.

(ii) Excusable; ie misadventure or accident, or reasonable self-defence in a sudden quarrel, provided that the force used is not out of proportion to the attack, and there is no other means of resistance or escape.

Genocide

By the Genocide Act 1969, a person is guilty of this offence if, with intent to destroy a national, ethnic, racial or religious group, he kills, causes serious bodily or mental harm, deliberately inflicts conditions of life calculated to bring about physical destruction, or imposes measures intended to prevent births, on the group, or forcibly transfers children of the group to another group.

Aiding and abetting suicide

It is an offence for a person to aid, abet, counsel or procure the suicide of another or an attempt by another to commit suicide (Suicide Act 1961, s2, penalty 14 years' imprisonment - arrestable offence).

Soliciting murder

Whosoever shall solicit, encourage, persuade, or endeavour to persuade, or shall propose to any person, to murder any other person, shall be guilty of an offence (Offences against the Person Act 1861, s4).

Threats to kill

A person who, without lawful excuse, makes to another a threat intending that that other would fear it would be carried out, to kill that other or a third person, shall be guilty of an offence (Offences against the Person Act 1861, s16).

Child destruction

The Infant Life Preservation Act 1929 makes it an offence for a person with intent to destroy the life of a child capable of being born alive, by any wilful act to cause the child to die before it has had an existence independent of its mother. (Life imprisonment - arrestable offence.)

Evidence of pregnancy for at least 28 weeks is proof that the child was capable of being born alive.

Concealment of birth

Section 60 of the Offences against the Person Act 1861 makes it an offence for any person, who, when a child has been born (alive or dead), endeavours to conceal the birth by any *secret* disposition of the dead body of the child.

Abortion

The premature expulsion of the contents of the pregnant womb. If attempted or procured unlawfully it is criminal.

The following are statutory offences relating to criminal abortion:

(a) Committed by a pregnant woman who administers to herself any poison or noxious thing or uses on herself any instrument or any other means, with intent to procure her own miscarriage (Offences against the Person Act 1861, s58, life imprisonment - arrestable offence).

Note that the woman must be pregnant, but the offence is still committed even if the operation is not successful.

(b) Committed by a person who, with intent to procure the miscarriage of any woman (whether pregnant or not), administers to her or causes her to take any poison or other noxious thing or uses any instrument upon her or uses other means (Offences against the Person Act 1861, s58, life imprisonment - arrestable offence).

Note that it is not necessary that women be actually pregnant; the intent is sufficient.

(c) Committed by a person who supplies or procures any poison or other noxious thing or any instrument knowing that the same is intended to be used with intent to procure the miscarriage of any woman (whether pregnant or not) (Offences against the Person Act, 1861, s59, five years' imprisonment - arrestable offence).

Note: Guilty knowledge as to the intention must be proved. It is not necessary that the woman is actually pregnant.

Under the Abortion Act 1967, a person is not guilty of an offence when the pregnancy is terminated by a registered medical practitioner, after two medical practitioners have stated that they are of the opinion that continued pregnancy would involve risk to the mother's health or substantial risk of abnormality of the child.

INFANTICIDE (Infanticide Act 1938)

Where a woman by any *wilful act or omission* causes the death of her child, being under the age of 12 months, but at the time of the act or omission the balance of her mind was disturbed by reason of her not having fully recovered from the effects of giving birth to the child, or the effect of lactation. (Penalty as for manslaughter.)

RAPE AND OTHER SEXUAL OFFENCES

Offences involving unlawful sexual intercourse

Briefly, a man commits an offence if he has sexual intercourse with a woman who is either unwilling, under the age of 16 years, mentally defective, or a blood relative.

Rape

Section 1 of the Sexual Offences Act 1956 states that it is an arrestable offence for a man to rape a woman; and that a man who induces a married woman to have sexual intercourse with him by impersonating her husband commits rape. The maximum penalty for rape and attempted rape is life imprisonment.

The Sexual Offences (Amendment) Act 1976 defines the offence by saying that for the purposes of the above, a man commits rape if:

(a) he has unlawful sexual intercourse with a woman who at the time of the intercourse does not consent to it; and

(b) at that time he knows that she does not consent to intercourse or he is reckless as to whether she consents to it;

and references to rape in other enactments shall be construed accordingly.

Penetration must be proved or the offence will be attempted rape or indecent assault.

In practice (though not in law) corroboration is necessary to secure a conviction. This is usually obtained by showing 'recent complaint'.

A boy under 14 years cannot be convicted of rape, or any other offence involving sexual intercourse, as it is presumed that such a person is incapable of the act. He may, however, be charged with indecent assault.

No matter shall be published in England and Wales which is likely to lead members of the public to identify a person as the complainant or the accused in a rape offence. At a trial no questions shall be asked about any sexual experience of the complainant with a person other than the defendant, except with the leave of the judge.

'Rape offence' means any of the following, namely rape, attempted rape, aiding, abetting, counselling and procuring rape or attempted rape, incitement to rape, conspiracy to rape and burglary with intent to rape.

Procuration (Sexual Offences Act 1956)

Procuration is having sexual intercourse with a woman by deliberately lowering her resistance, so that she is less capable of exercising true judgement, in order to obtain consent. It differs from rape in that for rape a woman's resistance is completely overcome by threats of personal violence, by deception, or by rendering her insensible, so that no true consent is given.

It is an offence for a person to procure or attempt to procure any woman to have unlawful sexual intercourse in any part of the world:
- (a) by threats or intimidation, eg to expose a theft or an illicit sexual relationship (s2);
- (b) by false pretences, eg a married man pretending to be single and in a position to marry (s3);
- (c) by administering any drug or thing with intent to stupefy or overpower, eg plying with alcohol or encouraging the smoking of cannabis (s4);
- (d) if the woman (girl) is under 21 (s23 - arrestable offence).

These offences may be committed by any person, male or female (penalty two years' imprisonment). Remember that 'unlawful' simply means out of wedlock.

Defilement (Sexual Offences Act 1956, ss 5 and 6)

A male who has unlawful sexual intercourse with a girl under 13 commits an arrestable offence as the penalty is life imprisonment (seven years for an attempt).

A male who has unlawful sexual intercourse with a girl under 16 commits an offence. (Penalty two years.) The man has a statutory defence if he is under 24 years, has not previously been charged with a like offence and has reasonable cause in his belief that the girl is 16 years or over. (This defence is *not* applicable where the girl is under 13.)

Consent is immaterial and, if the intercourse is against the girl's will, the offence of rape is also committed.

Seduction or prostitution (Sexual Offences Act 1956, s28)

It is an offence for any person having custody, charge or care of a girl under 16 years to cause or encourage her seduction or prostitution. (This includes unlawful sexual intercourse and indecent assault - penalty two years' imprisonment.)

A similar offence is committed under s29 if the woman (of any age) is a defective.

Sexual intercourse with mental defectives (Sexual Offences Act 1956 and Mental Health Act 1959)

Defective means a person suffering from severe subnormality, ie subnormality of such a nature that the person is incapable of living an independent life, or of guarding herself against serious exploitation.

(a) It is an offence for a man to have unlawful sexual intercourse with a woman who is defective: Sexual Offences Act 1956, s7.

(b) For any person to procure a mental defective (female) to have intercourse anywhere is an offence under s9 of the Sexual Offences Act 1956.

Note: A person is not guilty of such offences if he does not know and has no reason to suspect the woman to be a defective.

(c) For a man to have unlawful sexual intercourse with a patient suffering from mental disorder, who is subject to his guardianship or in his legal custody or care; or

(d) For a man who is a manager of or on the staff of a hospital, or mental nursing home, to have unlawful sexual intercourse with a woman who is for the time being receiving treatment there for mental disorder are offences against s128 of the Mental Health Act 1959.

Note: A person is not guilty of such offences if he does not know and has no reason to suspect her to be a mentally disordered person. Reference to unlawful sexual intercourse with a woman was extended by the Sexual Offences Act 1967 to include buggery or gross indecency with a man.

The consent of the DPP is required for proceedings in (b), (c) and (d) and he should be informed of offences under (a).

Incest (Sexual Offences Act 1956, ss10 and 11)

It is an offence for a man to have sexual intercourse with a woman whom he knows to be his granddaughter, daughter, sister or mother.

It is an offence for a female of 16 years or over to allow a man she knows to be her grandfather, father, brother, or son to have sexual intercourse with her by her consent.

This includes 'half' brothers and sisters, and it does not matter that the relationship is not through lawful wedlock. 'Step' brothers and sisters are not blood relations.

Note: (a) If against will of female the offence will be rape.
     (b) If the girl is under 13 years, penalty may be life imprisonment.
     (c) If the girl is a juvenile the court may consider her as being in need of care.
     (d) The sanction of Attorney General required for prosecution unless taken by or for Director of Public Prosecutions.

(Maximum penalty, life imprisonment if with a girl under 13, otherwise seven years - arrestable offences.)

UNNATURAL OFFENCES

Buggery

Buggery (Sexual Offences Act 1956, s12) is sexual intercourse between males or between male and female in an unnatural manner (ie per anus); or sexual intercourse between male or female with an animal (bestiality) in any manner whatsoever.

Buggery is an arrestable offence. (Penalty: life imprisonment if with a boy under 16, a woman or an animal; ten years if with male of or over 16 without consent; five years if accused of or over 21 and other man under that age and has consented.)

Assault with intent to commit buggery is an offence under s16 (penalty ten years' imprisonment - arrestable offence).

(See section headed 'Homosexual acts' re consenting adults in private.)

Gross indecency (Sexual Offences Act 1956, s13)

It is an offence for a male person to commit an act of gross indecency with another male person, or be a party to the commission by a male person of an act of gross indecency with another male person or to procure the commission by a man of an act of gross indecency with another male person. (Penalty for a man of or over 21 with a man under that age, five years' imprisonment; otherwise two years.)

Soliciting and importuning (Sexual Offences Act 1956, s32)

It is an offence for a man to persistently solicit or importune in a public place for immoral purposes. (Penalty two years' imprisonment.)

Homosexual acts

It is not an offence in the following circumstances for a man to commit a homosexual act with another man, or be party to the commission of such an act (Sexual Offences Act 1967, s1(1)), if:

(a) the act is committed in private;
(b) both parties consent;
(c) two persons only are present;
(d) both parties have attained the age of 21 years. (Note: *not* 'over 21'.)

Any homosexual act committed outside the scope of the above provisos is an offence, burden of proof on prosecution.

These conditions do not apply to homosexual acts between crew members of UK merchant ships on board UK merchant ships.

A homosexual act between male persons is *not* committed in private if more than two persons take part or are present, or the meeting is in a lavatory to which the public have access whether on payment or otherwise.

The presumed incapacity in law of boys under 14 years as to sexual intercourse extends to buggery and they are deemed incapable of being accomplices. A boy under 16 years or a mental defective cannot give consent to buggery, attempted buggery, or gross indecency, but a person shall not be convicted if he proves a probability that he did not know and had no reason to suspect he was a mental defective.

No proceedings shall be commenced after the expiration of 12 months from the date of the following offences:

(a) Gross indecency.
(b) Soliciting and importuning a man for homosexual acts.
(c) Buggery by a man with another man, not amounting to an assault, and not including an offence by a man with a boy under the age of 16 years.

The consent of the DPP is necessary to proceedings in cases of buggery and gross indecency when either person is under 21 years of age. This does not prevent arrest without warrant or execution of warrant or power to remand in custody or on bail.

INDECENCY

Indecent language and behaviour

Any gross outrage on public decency is a common law misdemeanour, but it is better to deal with such offences under statutes or byelaws where relevant legislation is available.

To sing obscene or profane songs or to use language of a similar nature in any street or public place to the annoyance, danger or obstruction of residents or passengers is an offence against s28 of the Town Police Clauses Act 1847.

It is an offence to send an indecent, obscene or menacing message by telephone under the Post Office Act 1969.

Indecent exposure

Vagrancy Act 1824, s4
It is a summary offence for any person *wilfully, openly, lewdly* and *obscenely* to expose *his* person with intent to insult a female.

The act must be wilful, not by mistake or through carelessness. It may be committed anywhere either in public or private. Note carefully the four qualifying words. The word 'person' refers to the penis and no other parts of the body in the section.

Town Police Clauses Act 1847, s28
It is a summary offence wilfully and indecently to expose the person in any street or public place to the annoyance of residents or passengers.

Under this Act it is not necessary to prove intent to insult a female. The offence may be committed by a male or female.

Common law
To publicly expose the naked person is a nuisance and is indictable as a common law misdemeanour. It must be to more than one person and it is not necessary to show that anyone was offended. (Arrestable offence.)

Indecency with children (Indecency with Children Act 1960)

It is an offence for *any person* to commit an act of gross indecency with or towards a child under the age of 14 years or to incite such a child to do such an act with him or any other person. Penalty: two years' imprisonment. This offence is included in Sch 1 to the Children and Young Persons Act

1933. It covers circumstances involving a child which do not amount to an indecent assault (ie where there is no hostile touching or threat).

Abduction

Abduction means to take away by force or by fraud. The offences are covered by the Sexual Offences Act 1956, and may be put under the following four headings:

(1) Abduction of woman regardless of age . . . . (s 17)
(2) Abduction of unmarried girls under 18 years of age . . . . . (s 19)
(3) Abduction of unmarried girls under 16 years of age . . . . . (s 20)
(4) Abduction of female defectives regardless of age . . . . (s 21)

The offences are dealt with individually as follows:

Section 17. Abduction of a woman by force or for the sake of her property.

It is an offence for a person to take away or detain a woman against her will with the intention that she shall marry *or* have unlawful sexual intercourse with that, or any other, person *if* she is so taken away or detained either by force or for the sake of her property or expectation of property. (Penalty 14 years - arrestable offence.)

Section 19. Abduction of an unmarried girl under 18 years.

It is an offence, subject to the exceptions mentioned in this section, for a person to take an unmarried girl under the age of 18 out of the possession of her parent or guardian *against HIS will* if she is so taken with the intention that she shall have unlawful sexual intercourse with men or with a particular man. (Penalty two years.)

Section 20. Abduction of unmarried girl, under 16 years.

It is an offence for a person, acting without lawful authority or excuse to take an unmarried girl, under the age of sixteen out of the possession of her parent or guardian, *against HIS will* (ie the parent or guardian). (Penalty two years.)

Note that the taking need not be by force, either actual or constructive, and it is immaterial whether the girl consents or not.

Section 21. Abduction of female defective.

It is an offence for a person, subject to the exception mentioned in this section, to take a woman who is a defective out of the possession of her parent or guardian against his will, if she is so taken with the intention that she shall have unlawful sexual intercourse with men or with a particular man. (Penalty two years.)

The exception mentioned in the above section states that a person is not guilty of an offence under this section because he takes such a woman out of the possession of her parent or guardian if he does not know and has no reason to suspect her to be a defective.

PROSTITUTION

Definition and purpose of legislation

A prostitute is any person who for reward offers *his or her* body commonly for sexual connection or for acts of lewdness.

The object of the legislation regarding prostitution is to prevent loitering or soliciting for the purpose of prostitution; the assembling of prostitutes in places of public resort; trading in prostitution; and the habitual use of premises for prostitution.

Loitering or soliciting for the purposes of prostitution (Street Offences Act 1959)

It is an offence for a *common* prostitute to loiter or solicit in a street or public place for the purposes of prostitution. A constable may arrest without warrant anyone he finds in a street or public place and suspects, with reasonable cause, to be committing this offence.

A common prostitute is a *woman* who is a convicted prostitute, or who has been cautioned twice.

The Home Office have recommended that, where a woman has not previously been convicted of loitering or soliciting for the purposes of prostitution, she should be cautioned as to her conduct on two occasions, and such formal cautions should be recorded, before she is charged with this offence.

If a woman complains about a caution and it appears that the officer who administered the caution was mistaken, any entry in the 'register of cautions' should be expunged. If the woman desires a more formal withdrawal, she may apply within 14 days to a magistrates' court for an order that the caution should not be recorded, or, if recorded, shall be expunged.

Places of public resort and refreshment

The holder of a justices' licence commits an offence if he knowingly allows his licensed premises to be the habitual resort or meeting place of reputed prostitutes; but prostitutes may remain on the premises for the time necessary to obtain reasonable refreshment. (Section 175, Licensing Act 1964.)

Keepers of late night refreshment houses also commit an offence if they knowingly allow prostitutes to assemble or continue on their premises.(Section 9, Late Night Refreshment House Act 1969.)

Trading in prostitution (Sexual Offences Act 1956)

It is an offence for any man knowingly to live wholly or in part on the earnings of prostitution (Sexual Offences Act 1956, s30), or for any woman, for the purposes of gain, to exercise control, direction or influence over a prostitute's movements (s31). Punishment - seven years' imprisonment - arrestable offence.

It is also an arrestable offence to procure a woman to become a common prostitute (s22).

Kerb crawling (Sexual Offences Act 1985, s1)

It is an offence for a man to solicit a woman (or different woman) from a motor vehicle in a street or public place, or while in the immediate vicinity of a motor vehicle that he has just got out of or off, persistently or in such manner or in such circumstances as to be likely to cause annoyance to the woman solicited, or nuisance to other persons in the neighbourhood.

Habitual use of premises for prostitution (Sexual Offences Act 1956, s33)

It is an offence for a person to keep a brothel, or to manage or act or assist in the management of a brothel.

A brothel is a house, room or other place, used by persons of opposite sexes for the purposes of illicit sexual intercourse and/or acts of lewdness, or used by male persons for the purpose of illicit lewd homosexual practices.

If the holder of a justices' licence permits his premises to be used as a brothel he commits an offence, and upon conviction shall forfeit his licence.

ASSAULTS AND WOUNDINGS

Assaults

An assault is any intentional or reckless act which causes another person to apprehend immediate, unlawful personal violence.

A battery is the actual application of unlawful force to another. It is possible to have an assault without a battery or a battery without an assault, but in practice the word 'assault' is normally used to include a battery.

Justifiable assaults

Where only sufficient force to achieve the purpose is used, an assault is justifiable in the following circumstances:
  (a) Furtherance of a legal duty, eg lawful arrest.
  (b) Administering lawful correction, eg parent punishing his child.
  (c) Self-defence, or defence of spouse, parent, child, master or servant.
  (d) Defence of property.

Types of assault

An assault is an indictable common law misdemeanour which may be rendered more serious by the circumstances accompanying it. There are also the following statutory assaults:
  (a) Common assault: s39 of the Criminal Justice Act 1988. It is a summary offence to assault or beat any person. The police may arrest to prevent a breach of the peace, if seen committing.
  (b) Aggravated assault: s 43 of the Offences against the Person Act 1861. This is not a separate offence, but where the victim of common assault is a boy not more than 14, or any female, and the assault is aggravated by VIOLENCE the summary court can impose a heavier penalty under this section.
  (c) Actual bodily harm: s47 of the Offences against the Person Act 1861. Provides punishment for trial on indictment, where the assault results in actual bodily harm, ie interferes with the health or comfort of victim, but not amounting to grievous bodily harm. (Arrestable offence.)
  (d) Assault with intent to resist arrest: s33 of the Offences against the Person Act 1861.
  (e) Assault on police: s51 of the Police Act 1964. A number of offences are created by this section, including assaulting, wilfully resisting, or obstructing a constable in the execution of his duty, or a person assisting a constable. The duty must be lawful one.
A constable may arrest when an assault is committed in his presence. He should, however, exercise this power with discretion. The main points to consider are the seriousness of any injury sustained and the likelihood of any injury sustained and the likelihood of a repetition of the offence.

Woundings

Grievous bodily harm: Offences against the Person Act 1861, s20
Unlawfully and maliciously to wound, or inflict grievous bodily harm on any person, with or without any instrument. (Penalty five years' imprisonment - arrestable offence.)

Grievous bodily harm with intent: Offences against the Person Act 1861, s18
Unlawfully and maliciously to wound, or cause grievous bodily harm to any person *with intent to* cause grievous bodily harm to any person, *or* prevent or resist the lawful arrest or detention of any person. (Penalty life imprisonment - arrestable offence.)

Definitions

'Wound': the whole skin must be broken, bruising is not enough.
'Grievous bodily harm': means really serious bodily harm.
'Maliciously' means: (i)   an actual intention to do the particular harm that was in fact done, or
(ii) recklessness as to whether that particular harm should occur or not. The accused must have foreseen that harm might be done and has gone on to take that risk.
'Unlawfully': means that which is not permitted by law.
'Intent' : means the actual intent of the accused. The court will decide whether he intended or foresaw the result of his actions by considering all the evidence.

Indecent assaults (Sexual Offences Act 1956, ss14 and 15)

Section 14. It is an arrestable offence for a person to indecently assault a female. Penalty - ten years' imprisonment.

Section 15. It is an arrestable offence to indecently assault a male. Penalty - ten years' imprisonment.

An indecent assault is an assault accompanied by circumstances of indecency. Evidence of an assault is required plus evidence of an indecent act. Remember that an assault may be by threat only and does not require a battery. Touching of bare flesh or of sexual parts is not necessary; indecent circumstances are sufficient.

A girl under 16, or a mental defective, cannot in law consent to such an assault and consent cannot be given to an assault likely to cause bodily harm.

An indecent assault may be complete in itself or may be committed in an attempt at sexual intercourse. A boy of 14 years is legally deemed incapable of sexual intercourse but if 10 years of age or over can commit an indecent assault.

BLACKMAIL (Theft Act 1968, s21)

A person is guilty of blackmail if with a view to gain for himself or another or with intent to cause loss to another, he makes any unwarranted demand with menaces, unless he does so in the belief that he has reasonable grounds for making the demand, *and* that the use of menaces is a proper means of reinforcing the demand.

The nature of the act or omission demanded is immaterial, and it is also immaterial whether the menaces relate to action to be taken by the person making the demand.

(Penalty : 14 years' imprisonment - arrestable offence.)

Note: That s34 of the Act states that 'gain' and 'loss' are to be construed as extending only to gain or loss in money or other property but as extending to any such gain or loss whether temporary or permanent; and

(i)   'gain' includes gain by keeping what one has as well as a gain by getting what one has not; and

(ii)   'loss' includes a loss by not getting what one might get, as well as a loss by parting with what one has.

TORTURE (s134, Criminal Justice Act 1988)

A public official or person acting in an official capacity (or a person at the instigation or with the consent of such an official) commits the offence of torture if he intentionally inflicts severe pain or suffering on another in the performance of his official duties. It is immaterial whether the pain or suffering is physical or mental and whether caused by an act or an omission. Penalty, life imprisonment. Defence to prove lawful authority, justification or excuse.

Chapter 25
Theft and other Matters connected with Property

THEFT

Basic definition of theft (Theft Act 1968, s1)

A person is guilty of theft if he dishonestly appropriates property belonging to another with the intention of permanently depriving the other of it; and 'thief' and 'steal' shall be construed accordingly.

It is immaterial whether the appropriation is made with a view to gain or is made for the thief's own benefit.

Dishonesty (s2)

A person's appropriation of property belonging to another is not to be regarded as dishonest:
  (a) if he appropriates the property in the belief that he has in law the right to deprive the other of it, on behalf of himself or of a third person; or
  (b) if he appropriates the property in the belief that he would have the other's consent if the other knew of the appropriation and the circumstances of it; or
  (c) (except where the property came to him as trustee or personal representative) if he appropriates the property in the belief that the person to whom the property belongs cannot be discovered by taking reasonable steps.

A person's appropriation of property belonging to another may be dishonest notwithstanding that he is willing to pay for the property.

Appropriates (s3)

Any assumption by a person of the rights of an owner amounts to an appropriation, and this includes, where he has come by the property (innocently or not) without stealing it, any later assumption of a right to it by keeping or dealing with it as owner.

Where property or a right or interest in property is or purports to be transferred for value to a person acting in good faith, no later assumption by him of rights which he believed himself to be acquiring shall, by reason of any defect in the transferor's title, amount to theft of property.

Property (s4)

Property includes money and all other property, real or personal, including things in action and other intangible property.

A person cannot steal land, or things forming part of land and severed from it by him or by his directions, except in the following cases, that is to say:

(a) when he is a trustee or personal representative, or is authorised by power of attorney, or as liquidator of a company, or otherwise, to sell or dispose of land belonging to another, and he appropriates the land or anything forming part of it by dealing with it in breach of the confidence reposed by him; or

(b) when he is not in possession of the land and appropriates anything forming part of the land by severing it or causing it to be severed, or after it has been severed; or

(c) when, being in possession of the land under a tenancy, he appropriates the whole or part of any fixture or structure let to be used with the land.

A person who picks mushrooms growing *wild on any land,* or who picks flowers, fruit or foliage from a plant growing wild on any land, does not (although not in possession of the land) steal what he picks unless he does it for reward or for sale or other commercial purpose.

For purposes of this subsection 'mushrooms' includes any fungus, and 'plant' includes any shrub or tree.

Wild creatures, tamed or untamed, shall be regarded as property; but a person cannot steal a wild creature not tamed nor ordinarily kept in captivity, or the carcass of any such creature, unless either it has been reduced into possession by or on behalf of another person and possession of it has not since been lost or abandoned, or another person is in course of reducing it into possession.

Belonging to another (s5)

Property shall be regarded as belonging to any person having possession or control of it, or having in it any proprietary right or interest (not being an equitable interest arising only from an agreement to transfer or grant an interest).

Where property is subject to a trust, the persons to whom it belongs shall be regarded as including any person having a right to enforce the trust, and an intention to defeat the trust shall be regarded accordingly as an intention to deprive of the property any person having that right.

Where a person receives property from or on account of another, and is under an obligation to the other to retain and deal with that property or its proceeds in a particular way, the property or proceeds shall be regarded (as against him) as belonging to the other.

Where a person gets property by another's mistake, and is under an obligation to make restoration (in whole or in part) of the property or its proceeds or of the value thereof, then to the extent of that obligation the property or proceeds shall be regarded (as against him) as belonging to the person entitled to restoration, and an intention not to make restoration shall be regarded accordingly as an intention to deprive that person of the property or proceeds.

With the intention of permanently depriving the other of it (s6)

A person appropriating property belonging to another without meaning the other permanently to lose the thing itself is nevertheless to be regarded as having the intention of permanently depriving the other of it if his intention is to treat the thing as his own to dispose of regardless of the other's rights; and a borrowing or lending of it may amount to so treating it if, but only if, the borrowing or lending is for a period in circumstances making it equivalent to an outright taking or disposal.

Without prejudice to the generality of subsection (1) above, where a person having possession or control (lawfully or not) of property belonging to another, parts with the property under a condition as to its return which he may not be able to perform, this (if done for purposes of his own and without the other's authority) amounts to treating the property as his own to dispose of regardless of the other's rights.

Penalty (s7)

Theft is punishable on indictment by 7 years' imprisonment and is therefore an arrestable offence.

THEFT OF MAILS IN TRANSMISSION (Theft Act 1968, s14)

Where a person steals or attempts to steal a mail bag or postal packet, or its contents, in the course of transmission as such between places in the

British postal area, or in doing so, or with intent to do so, commits any robbery, attempted robbery, or assault with intent to rob, then, notwithstanding that he does so outside England and Wales, he will be guilty of committing, or attempting to commit, the offence under the Theft Act, and can be prosecuted, tried and punished in England and Wales without proof that the offence was committed there.

British postal area includes England and Wales, Scotland, Northern Ireland, the Isle of Man and the Channel Islands.

OFFENCE OF TAKING FISH (Theft Act 1968, Sch 1)

Unlawfully taking or destroying or attempting to take or destroy any fish in private waters, or in waters where there is a private right of fishery.

ROBBERY (Theft Act 1968, s8)

A person is guilty of robbery if he steals, and immediately before or at the time of doing so, and in order to do so, he uses force on any person or puts or seeks to put any person in fear of being then and there subjected to force.

A person guilty of robbery or of an assault with intent to rob, shall on conviction on indictment be liable to imprisonment for life.

BURGLARY (Theft Act 1968, s9)

A person is guilty of burglary if:
  (1) he enters any building or part of a building as a trespasser and with *intent* to:
       (i)   steal anything in the building or part of a building in question, or
       (ii) inflict on any person therein any grievous bodily harm, or
       (iii) rape any woman therein, or
       (iv) do unlawful damage to the building or anything therein,
       or
  (2) Having entered any building or part of a building as a trespasser he steals or attempts to steal anything in the building or that part of it, or inflicts or attempts to inflict on any person therein any grievous bodily harm.
  (3) Reference to a building and a building which is a dwelling, shall apply also to an inhabited vehicle or vessel and shall apply to any such vehicle or vessel at times when the person having a habitation in it is not there as well as at times when he is. Penalty for burglary

- 14 years' imprisonment where committed in respect of a building or part of a building which is a dwelling; in any other case 10 years.

AGGRAVATED BURGLARY (Theft Act 1968, s10)

A person is guilty of aggravated burglary if he commits any burglary and at the time has with him any firearm or imitation firearm, any weapon of offence or any explosive; and for this purpose:
  (a) 'firearm' includes an airgun or air pistol, and 'imitation firearm' means anything which has the appearance of being a firearm, whether capable of being discharged or not; and
  (b) 'weapon of offence' means any article made or adapted for use for causing injury to or incapacitating a person, or intended by the person having it with him for such use; and
  (c) 'explosive' means any article manufactured for the purpose of producing a practical effect by explosion, or intended by the person having it with him for that purpose.
A person guilty of aggravated burglary shall on conviction on indictment be liable to life imprisonment.

REMOVAL OF ARTICLES FROM PLACES OPEN TO THE PUBLIC (Theft Act 1968, s11)

Where the public have access to a building in order to view the building or part of it, or a collection or part of a collection housed in it, any person who without lawful authority removes from the building or its grounds the whole or any part of any article displayed or kept for display to the public in the building or its grounds, shall be guilty of an offence.

For this purpose 'collection' includes a collection got together for a temporary purpose, but references in this section to a collection do not apply to a collection made or exhibited for the purpose of effecting sales or other commercial dealings.

It is immaterial that access is limited to a particular period or particular occasion; but where anything removed is there otherwise than forming part of a collection intended for permanent exhibition, there is no offence unless it is removed on a day when the public have access.

A person does not commit the offence under the section if he believes that he has lawful authority for the removal of the thing, or that he would have it if the person entitled to give it knew of the removal and the circumstances of it.

(Penalty - five years' imprisonment - arrestable offence.)

HARASSMENT OF TENANTS (Protection from Eviction Act 1977, s1)

Committed by a person who, with intent to cause the residential occupier of premises to give up occupation, does acts calculated to interfere with the peace or comfort of the occupier, or persistently withdraws or withholds services reasonably required for occupation of the premises as a residence.

TAKING MOTOR VEHICLES OR OTHER CONVEYANCES WITHOUT AUTHORITY (Theft Act 1968, s12)

A person shall be guilty of an offence if, without having the consent of the owner or other lawful authority, he takes any conveyance for his own or another's use or, knowing that any conveyance has been taken without such authority, drives it or allows himself to be carried in or on it.

A person guilty of this offence shall be liable to a fine not exceeding £2,000, or 6 months' imprisonment. Summary only.

An arrestable offence.

If on the trial of an indictment for theft the jury are not satisfied that the accused committed theft, he may be convicted of taking without authority.

The above shall not apply in relation to pedal cycles; but a person who, without having the consent of the owner or other lawful authority, takes a pedal cycle for his own or another's use, or rides a pedal cycle knowing it to have been taken without such authority, shall on summary conviction be liable to a fine not exceeding £50.

A person does not commit an offence under this section by anything done in the belief that he has lawful authority to do it or that he would have the owner's consent if the owner knew of his doing it and the circumstances of it.

'Conveyance' means any conveyance constructed or adapted for the carriage of a person or persons whether by land, water or air, except that it does not include a conveyance constructed or adapted for use only under the control of a person not carried in or on it, and 'drive' shall be construed accordingly.

'Owner' in relation to conveyance which is the subject of a hiring agreement or hire-purchase agreement, means the person in possession of the conveyance under that agreement.

Note that there does not have to be any propulsion in the conveyance's own element, eg a boat may be taken on the roof of a car; but there must be some movement.

This offence relates only to the 'borrowing' of a conveyance. If there is evidence of an intention to permanently deprive the owner the proper charge is theft.

AGGRAVATED VEHICLE-TAKING (Theft Act 1968, s 12A)

A person is guilty of aggravated taking of a vehicle if:
- (a) he commits an offence under s12(1) above in relation to a mechanically propelled vehicle; and
- (b) it is proved that, at any time after the vehicle was unlawfully taken (whether by him or another) and before it was recovered, the vehicle was driven, or injury or damage was caused in one or more of the following circumstances:
  - (i) the vehicle was driven dangerously on a road or other public place;
  - (ii) owing to the driving of the vehicle, an accident occurred by which injury was caused to any person;
  - (iii) owing to the driving of the vehicle, an accident occurred by which damage was caused to any property, other than the vehicle;
  - (iv) damage was caused to the vehicle.

A vehicle is driven dangerously if it is driven in a way which falls far below what would be expected of a competent and careful driver, and it would be obvious to a competent and careful driver that driving the vehicle in that way would be dangerous.

The penalty on conviction on indictment is imprisonment for not exceeding 2 years, or if death is caused as a result of an accident, 5 years.

(Note that this section was not in force at the time of writing.)

ABSTRACTING ELECTRICITY (Theft Act 1968, s13)

A person who dishonestly uses without due authority, or dishonestly causes to be wasted or diverted, any electricity, shall on conviction on indictment be liable to five years' imprisonment (arrestable offence).

(Section 42 of the Telecommunications Act 1984 contains a similar offence, ie to dishonestly obtain a licensed telecommunications system with intent to avoid payment of any charge.)

CRIMINAL DECEPTION

Obtaining property by deception (Theft Act 1968, s15)

(1) A person who by any deception dishonestly obtains property belonging to another with the intention of permanently depriving the other of it, shall on conviction on indictment be liable to ten years' imprisonment. (Arrestable offence.)

(2) A person is to be treated as obtaining property if he obtains ownership, possession or control of it, and 'obtain' includes obtaining for another or enabling another to obtain or to retain.

Deception means any deception whether deliberate or reckless by words or conduct as to fact or law, including a deception as to the present intentions of the person using the deception or any other person.

Note: There may be a conviction for theft even though the facts would also justify a conviction for criminal deception.

Obtaining pecuniary advantage by deception (Theft Act 1968, s 16)

(1) A person who by any deception dishonestly obtains for himself or another any pecuniary advantage shall on conviction on indictment be liable to imprisonment for a term not exceeding five years. (Arrestable offence.)

(2) The cases in which a pecuniary advantage within the meaning of this section is to be regarded as obtained for a person are cases where:

  (a) he is allowed to borrow by way of overdraft, or to take out any policy of insurance or annuity contract, or obtains an improvement of the terms on which he is allowed to do so; or

  (b) he is given the opportunity to earn remuneration or greater remuneration in an office or employment or to win money by betting.

Obtaining services by deception (Theft Act 1978, s1)

A person who by any deception dishonestly obtains services from another shall be guilty of an offence. It is an obtaining of services where the other is induced to confer a benefit by doing some act, or causing or permitting some act to be done, on the understanding that the benefit has been or will be paid for. Penalty, five years' imprisonment - arrestable offence.

Evasion of liability by deception (Theft Act 1978, s2)

Where a person by any deception:

  (a) dishonestly secures the remission of the whole or part of any existing liability to make a payment, whether his own liability or another's; or

  (b) with intent to make permanent default in whole or in part on any existing liability to make a payment or with intent to let another do so, dishonestly induces the creditor or any person claiming payment on behalf of the creditor to wait for payment (whether or not the due date for payment is deferred) or to forgo payment; or

(c) dishonestly obtains any exemption from or abatement of liability to make a payment,

he shall be guilty of an offence. Penalty, five years' imprisonment - arrestable offence.

Making off without payment (Theft Act 1978, s3)

A person who, knowing that payment on the spot for goods supplied or services done is required or expected from him, dishonestly makes off without having paid as required or expected and with intent to avoid payment of the amount due shall be guilty of an offence.

'Payment on the spot' includes payment at the time of collecting goods on which work has been done or in respect of which service has been provided. The above shall not apply where the supply of goods or the doing of the service is contrary to law, or where the service done is such that payment is not legally enforceable. Penalty, two years' imprisonment.

Any person may arrest without warrant anyone who is or whom he, with reasonable cause, suspects to be, committing or attempting to commit this offence. Note, however, that the police are advised to use this power of arrest only where the general powers exist under s25 of the Police and Criminal Evidence Act 1984.

FALSE ACCOUNTING (Theft Act 1968, s17)

(1) Where a person dishonestly, with a view to gain for himself or another or with intent to cause loss to another:
   (a) destroys, defaces, conceals or falsifies any account or any record or document made or required for any accounting purpose; or
   (b) in furnishing information for any purpose produces or makes use of any account, or any such record or document as aforesaid, which to his knowledge is or may be misleading, false or deceptive in a material particular.
(2) For purposes of this section a person who makes or concurs in making in an account or other document an entry which is or may be misleading, false or deceptive in a material particular, or who omits or concurs in omitting a material particular from an account or other document is to be treated as falsifying the account or document.

(Penalty, seven years' imprisonment - arrestable offence.)

HANDLING STOLEN GOODS (Theft Act 1968, s22)

A person handles stolen goods if (otherwise than in the course of stealing) knowing or believing them to be stolen goods he dishonestly receives the goods or dishonestly undertakes or assists in their retention, removal, disposal or realisation by or for the benefit of another person, or if he arranges to do so. Punishment: 14 years' imprisonment on indictment (arrestable offence).

In every case of handling, there is invariably a 'dishonest appropriation of property, belonging to another, with the intention of permanently depriving the other of it', and therefore an offence of theft.

Scope of offences relating to stolen goods

Reference to stolen goods relates to goods which have been stolen in England or Wales or elsewhere either by theft, blackmail or by deception. It includes goods whether in their original state or not, and other goods which represent the stolen goods in the hands of the thief, also any other goods which represent the stolen goods in the hands of the handler.

No goods shall be regarded as 'stolen goods' if they have been restored to the person from whom they were stolen, or other lawful possession or custody eg the police.

Special evidence

The following may be given to prove guilty knowledge in a case of handling stolen goods:
  (a) that he had in his possession, or dealt with in a way defined in handling, stolen goods from any theft during the previous 12 months; or
  (b) that he has within the preceding five years been convicted of theft or of handling stolen goods (seven days' notice in writing must be given of intention to prove the conviction).

ADVERTISING REWARDS FOR RETURN OF GOODS STOLEN OR LOST (Theft Act 1968, s23)

Where any public advertisement of a reward for the return of any goods which have been stolen or lost uses any words to the effect that no questions will be asked, or that the person producing the goods will be safe from apprehension or inquiry, or that any money paid for the purchase of the goods or advanced by way of loan on them will be repaid, the person advertising the reward and any person who prints or publishes the advertisement shall on summary conviction be liable to a fine.

GOING EQUIPPED FOR STEALING, ETC (Theft Act 1968, s25)

A person shall be guilty of an offence if, when not at his place of abode, he has with him any article for use in the course of or in connection with any burglary, theft or cheat.

Where a person is charged with an offence under this section, proof that he had with him any article made or adapted for use in committing a burglary, theft or cheat shall be evidence that he had it with him for such use.

An arrestable offence.

For purposes of this section an offence under s12(1) of taking a conveyance shall be treated as theft, and 'cheat' means an offence under s15.

POLICE (PROPERTY) ACT 1897 AND POLICE (DISPOSAL OF PROPERTY) REGULATIONS 1975

Under s1 of this Act, where property has come into the possession of the police in connection with any criminal charge a court of summary jurisdiction, on application by a police officer or a claimant to the property, may make an order for the delivery of the property, to the person appearing to the court to be the owner. If the owner cannot be ascertained, the court may make such order in respect of the property as it thinks fit.

Any person aggrieved by an order made by the court may, within six months from the date of the order, take legal proceedings for the recovery of the property against any person in possession by virtue of the order but otherwise his rights are extinguished.

Disposal of property

Where the owner has not been established and no court order has been made in respect of the property, it should be dealt with as follows:

(a) when such property is a perishable article, or its custody involves unreasonable expense or inconvenience, the same shall be sold as soon as conveniently possible after coming into the possession of the police;

(b) when such property consists of money, it shall be kept in the possession of the police for one year and then dealt with in the same manner as the proceeds of sales of property (c);

(c) in the case of any other property, it shall be retained in the possession of the police for one year and then sold.

The proceeds of sales and money held by the police, are paid to the treasurer of the police fund or to the chief officer of police, as may be directed by the police authority, and may be invested. The money standing to the credit of this fund can be used as follows:

(a) to defray expenses incurred in conveyance, storage, advertising for the owner, and sale of property;

(b) to pay reasonable compensation to persons by whom the property has been delivered to the police; and

(c) for any purpose which the Home Secretary may from time to time authorise.

Payments may also be made, at the discretion of the police authority, for the benefit of discharged prisoners, persons dependent on prisoners or discharged prisoners, either directly or by contributions to the funds of any discharged prisoners' aid society, the magistrates' court mission or the magistrates' court poor box.

RESTITUTION OF PROPERTY AND COMPENSATION

Theft Act 1968, s28

This section provides that where a person is convicted of an offence, under the Theft Act, the court may order restoration of the goods or their proceeds to any person entitled to recover them. The court may also order payment of compensation, out of any money taken from the offender's possession on his apprehension, to the owner of the goods if they are not restored to him or to any person who, having bona fide bought the goods or lent money on them, is required to restore them to the owner. Restitution orders will be made only when title to the property is clear from facts emerging in the criminal proceedings.

Powers of Criminal Courts Act 1973, s35

A court by or before which a person is convicted of an offence, instead of or in addition to dealing with him in any other way, may, on application or otherwise, make an order requiring him to pay compensation for any personal injury, loss or damage resulting from that offence or any offence taken into consideration. (Does not apply to accidents arising out of the presence of motor vehicles on roads.)

POWERS OF SEARCH (Theft Act 1968, s26)

Where there is reasonable cause to believe that any person has in his custody or possession, or on his premises, any stolen goods a justice on information on oath may grant a warrant to search for and seize the same. Any person may lay the information, but only a constable may execute the warrant.

Where under this section a person is authorised to search premises for stolen goods he may seize any goods he believes to be stolen goods.

INTERPRETATION

Section 34 of the Theft Act 1968 has already been mentioned in connection with blackmail, but, as it applies to the whole of the Theft Act, it is repeated here.

For the purpose of the Act:

(a) 'gain' and 'loss' are to be construed as extending only to gain or loss in money or other property, but as extending to any such gain or loss whether temporary or permanent; and
   (i) 'gain' includes a gain by keeping what one has, as well as gain by getting what one has not; and
   (ii) 'loss' includes a loss by not getting what one might get, as well as a loss by parting with what one has;
(b) 'goods', except in so far as the context otherwise requires, includes money and every other description of property except land, and includes things severed from the land by stealing.

ENTERING AND REMAINING ON PROPERTY (Criminal Law Act 1977)

A constable in uniform may arrest without warrant any person reasonably suspected of committing the following offences:

Without lawful authority using or threatening violence to enter property on which a person opposed to the entry is present (s6).

Failing to leave premises on which he is trespassing when required to do so by or on behalf of a displaced residential occupier or a protected intending occupier (s7).

Trespassing on premises and having with him a weapon of offence without lawful authority or reasonable excuse (s8).

Trespassing on any premises of a diplomatic mission, consular premises, the private residence of a diplomatic agent, etc (s9).

Resisting or intentionally obstructing a court officer engaged in executing an order for the recovery of possession of premises (s10).

'Premises' means any building, any part of a building under separate occupation, any land ancillary to a building, the site comprising any building or buildings together with land ancillary thereto, and also any movable structure, vehicle or vessel designed or adapted for residential use.

A 'displaced residential occupier' is any person who was occupying any premises as a residence immediately before being excluded from occupation by anyone who entered these premises as a trespasser.

A 'protected intending occupier' is a person who has purchased a freehold or leasehold interest in the premises which has not less than 21 years to run, who requires the premises for his own occupation as a residence, and holds a written statement to that effect attested by a justice of the peace or commissioner for oaths; or a person who has been authorised to occupy premises by a local authority, the Housing Corporation or a housing association.

'Weapon of offence' means any article made or adapted for use for causing injury to or incapacitating a person, or intended by the person having it with him for such use.

(Power of arrest preserved by Sch 2 to the Police and Criminal Evidence Act 1984.)

Chapter 26
Criminal Damage to Property

CRIMINAL DAMAGE ACT 1971

Property

For the purpose of the Criminal Damage Act 1971, 'property' is defined as 'property of a tangible nature, whether real or personal, including money', and:

    (a) including wild creatures which have been tamed or are ordinarily kept in captivity, and any other wild creatures or their carcasses if, but only if, they have been reduced into possession which has not been lost or abandoned or are in the course of being reduced into possession; but

    (b) not including mushrooms growing wild on any land or flowers, fruit or foliage of a plant growing wild on any land. 'Mushroom' includes any fungus and 'plant' includes any shrubs or trees.

Offences

Destroying or damaging property (s1)

    (1) A person who without lawful excuse destroys or damages any property belonging to another intending to destroy or damage any such property or being reckless as to whether any such property would be destroyed or damaged shall be guilty of an offence.

    (2) A person who without lawful excuse destroys or damages any property, whether belonging to himself or another:

        (a) intending to destroy or damage any property or being reckless as to whether any property would be destroyed or damaged, and

(b) intending by the destruction or damage to endanger the life of another or being reckless as to whether the life of another would be thereby endangered shall be guilty of an offence.

(3) An offence committed under this section by destroying or damaging property by fire shall be charged as arson.

Threats to destroy or damage property (s2)

A person who without lawful excuse makes to another a threat, intending that the other would fear it would be carried out:

(a) to destroy or damage any property belonging to that other or a third person, or

(b) to destroy or damage his own property in a way which he knows is likely to endanger the life of that other or a third person,

shall be guilty of an offence.

Possessing anything with intent to destroy or damage property (s3)

A person who has anything in his custody or under his control intending without lawful excuse to use it or cause or permit another to use it:

(a) to destroy or damage any property belonging to some other person, or

(b) to destroy or damage his own or the user's property in a way he knows is likely to endanger the life of some other person,

shall be guilty of an offence.

Statutory defence

It is a lawful excuse if:

(a) he honestly believed at the time that the person(s) having authority over the property had consented or would have consented if they had known of the circumstances; or

(b) he honestly believed at the time of the destruction or damage or threats that such action was immediately necessary to protect his own or another's property or interests and was reasonable in the circumstances.

(Note that this defence only applies to offences under ss 1(1), 2(1) and 3(1).)

Penalties and police powers

The penalty for arson or causing damage whereby life is endangered under ss 1(2) and 1(3) is life imprisonment. Any other offence - ten years' imprisonment. All offences under the Act are 'arrestable offences'.

Offences under s1 of this Act (excluding arson) involving property to the value of £2,000 or less are triable only summarily (Magistrates' Courts Act 1980, s22 and Sch 2, as amended).

Search warrant

If a justice receives information on oath that a person has in his custody or under his control or on his premises anything which there is reasonable cause to believe has been or is likely to be used to cause damage to another's property - or to any property in a way likely to endanger the life of another - the justice may issue a warrant authorising a constable to enter the premises, by force if necessary, and seize any such articles.

ENDANGERING LIFE OR PROPERTY BY THE USE OF EXPLOSIVES

Explosive Substances Act 1883

Section 2: causing explosion likely to endanger life or property - Any person who unlawfully and maliciously causes an explosion of a nature likely to endanger life, or to cause serious injury to property, whether any injury to person or property has been actually caused or not, shall be guilty of an offence. Penalty - life imprisonment.

Section 3: attempt to cause explosions or making or keeping explosives with intent to endanger life or property - Any person who unlawfully and maliciously:
  (a) does any act with intent to cause an explosion of a nature likely to endanger life or to cause serious injury to property; or
  (b) makes or has in his possession or under his control any explosive substance with intent by means thereof to endanger life or to cause serious injury to property shall, whether any explosion takes place or not, and whether any injury to person or property has been caused or not, be guilty of an offence.
  Penalty - 20 years' imprisonment.

Section 4: making or possessing explosives under suspicious circumstances - Any person who makes or *knowingly* has in his possession or under his control any explosive substance shall, unless he can show that he made it or had it in his possession or under his control for a lawful object, be guilty of an offence. Penalty - imprisonment for 14 years.

Explosive substance

Means any materials for making any explosive substance, also any apparatus, machine, implement, or materials used, or intended to be used, or adapted for causing, or aiding in causing, any explosion in or with any explosive substance, also any such part of any such apparatus, machine or implement.

Offences against the Person Act 1861

Section 28 - causing bodily harm, disfiguring, etc by explosive substance.

Section 29 - using explosives, corrosives, etc in a manner with intent to cause grievous bodily harm, etc whether bodily injury effected or not.

Section 30 - placing explosives near buildings or ships with intent to do bodily injury to any person, whether caused or not.

Section 64 - knowingly having in possession or making any gunpowder or explosive substance, machine, etc with intent to commit any indictable offence under the Act.

Control of Explosives Regulations 1991

These Regulations deal with the grant of explosives certificates to fit persons who are not of unsound mind or intemperate habit. Application must be made to the chief officer of police of the relevant area and aggrieved persons may appeal to the crown court within 21 days of a refusal. No person may acquire or keep any explosives without a valid certificate and, with certain exceptions, no person may keep explosives for private use.

OTHER OFFENCES RELATING TO DAMAGE (Malicious Damage Act 1861)

This Act was repealed by the Criminal Damage Act 1971 *except* for the following:

Section 35 - Obstructing railways with intent, etc
Whosoever shall *unlawfully and maliciously* put, place, cast or throw upon or across any railway, any wood, stone or other matter or thing, or shall

unlawfully and maliciously take up, remove, or displace any rail, sleeper, or other matter or thing, belonging to any railway, or shall *unlawfully and maliciously* turn, move, or divert any points or other machinery belonging to any railway, or shall *unlawfully and maliciously* do or cause to be done any other matter or thing, with intent, in any of the cases, aforesaid, to obstruct, upset, overthrow, injure, or destroy any engine, tender, carriage, or truck using such railway - life imprisonment.

(Similar offences under ss 32 and 33 of the Offences against the Person Act 1861.)

Section 36 - Obstructing railway rolling stock
Whosoever, by any unlawful act, or by any wilful omission or neglect, shall obstruct or cause to be obstructed, any engine, or carriage using any railway, or shall aid or assist therein, shall be guilty of an offence. Penalty - two years' imprisonment.

(Stone throwing on railways is dealt with under s56 of the British Transport Commission Act 1949.)

Section 47 - Causing danger to shipping
Whosoever shall unlawfully mask, alter or remove any light or signal, or unlawfully exhibit any false light or signal with intent to bring any ship or vessel, or boat, into danger, or shall *unlawfully and maliciously* do anything tending to the immediate loss or destruction of ship, vessel, or boat - life imprisonment.

Section 48 - Casting adrift boats, etc
Whosoever shall *unlawfully and maliciously* cut away, cast adrift, remove, alter, deface, sink or destroy, or shall unlawfully and maliciously do any act with intent to cut away, cast adrift, remove, alter, deface, sink or destroy, or shall in any other manner *unlawfully and maliciously* injure or conceal any boat, buoy, buoy-rope, perch, or mark used or intended for the guidance of seamen, for the purpose of navigation - seven years' imprisonment.

Chapter 27
Forgery, Counterfeiting and Official Secrets

FORGERY

The offence of forgery

This subject is covered by the Forgery and Counterfeiting Act 1981.

A person is guilty of forgery if he makes a false instrument with the intention that he or another shall use it to induce somebody to accept it as genuine, and by reason of so accepting it to do or not to do some act to his own or any other person's prejudice (s1).

(The common law maxim 'The document must be false; it must not merely tell a lie but tell a lie about itself', is still relevant. The word 'instrument' must be substituted for 'document' and this means that the instrument itself must be false and it is not enough that it contains a falsity.)

Meaning of terms

'Instrument' means:
  (a) any document, whether of a formal or informal character;
  (b) any stamp issued or sold by the Post Office;
  (c) any Inland Revenue stamp;
  (d) any disc, tape, sound track or other device on or in which information is recorded or stored by mechanical, electronic or other means.
A currency note is not an instrument. A mark denoting payment of postage authorised to be used instead of an adhesive stamp is to be treated as if it were a stamp issued by the Post Office.

'False'. An instrument is false if it purports to have been:
  (a) made in the form in which it is made by a person who did not in fact make it in that form;
  (b) made in the form in which it is made on the authority of a person who did not in fact authorise its making in that form;

(c) made in the terms in which it is made by a person who did not in fact make it in those terms;

(d) made in the terms in which it is made on the authority of a person who did not in fact authorise its making in those terms;

(e) altered in any respect by a person who did not in fact alter it in that respect;

(f) altered in any respect on the authority of a person who did not in fact authorise the alteration in that respect;

(g) made or altered on a date on which, or at a place at which, or otherwise in circumstances in which, it was not in fact made or altered;

(h) made or altered by an existing person but who did not in fact exist.

A person is to be treated as making a false instrument if he alters an instrument so as to make it false in any respect (whether or not it is false in some other respect apart from that alteration).

Note that the above list is comprehensive and an instrument will *not* be false unless it purports to have been made or altered as described.

'Prejudice' and 'Induce'. An act or omission intended to be induced is to a person's prejudice if, and only if, it is one which, if it occurs:

(a) will result in his:
   (i) temporary or permanent loss of property;
   (ii) being deprived of an opportunity to earn remuneration or greater remuneration;
   (iii) being deprived of an opportunity to gain a financial advantage otherwise than by way of remuneration; or

(b) will result in somebody being given an opportunity to:
   (i) earn remuneration or greater remuneration from him;
   (ii) gain a financial advantage from him otherwise than by way of remuneration; or

(c) will be the result of his having accepted a false instrument as genuine, or a copy of a false instrument as a copy of a genuine one, in connection with his performance of any duty.

An act which a person has an enforceable duty to do, and an omission to do any act which a person is not entitled to do, shall be disregarded.

References to inducing somebody to accept a false instrument as genuine, or a copy of a false instrument as a copy of a genuine one, include references to inducing a machine to respond to the instrument or copy as if it were genuine or a copy of a genuine one. Where this applies, the act or omission to be induced by the machine responding to the instrument or copy shall be treated as an act or omission to a person's prejudice.

'Loss' includes getting what one might get as well as parting with what one has.

Kindred offences

Copying a false instrument (s2).
It is an offence for a person to make a copy of an instrument which is, and which he knows or believes to be, a false instrument, with the intention that he or another shall use it to induce somebody to accept it as a copy of a genuine instrument, and by reason of so accepting it to do or not to do some act to his own or any other person's prejudice.

Using a false instrument (s3).
It is an offence for a person to use an instrument which is, and which he knows or believes to be, false, with the intention of inducing somebody to accept it as genuine, and by reason of so accepting it to do or not to do some act to his own or any other person's prejudice.

Using a copy of a false instrument (s4).
It is an offence for a person to use a copy of an instrument which is, and which he knows or believes to be, a false instrument, with the intention of inducing somebody to accept it as a copy of a genuine instrument, and by reason of so accepting it to do or not to do some act to his own or any other person's prejudice.

Offences relating to money orders, share certificates, passports, etc (s5).

(1)   *Having custody or control of a false instrument with intent*
It is an offence for a person to have in his custody or under his control an instrument to which this section applies which is, and which he knows or believes to be, false, with the intention that he or another shall use it to induce somebody to accept it as genuine, and by reason of so accepting it to do or not to do some act to his own or any other person's prejudice.

(2)   *Having custody or control of a false instrument*
It is an offence for a person to have in his custody or under his control, without lawful authority or excuse, an instrument to which this section applies which is, and which he knows or believes to be, false.

(3)   *Having custody or control of a machine or implement for making a false instrument*
It is an offence for a person to make or have in his custody or under his control a machine or implement, or paper or any other material, which to his knowledge is, or has been, specially designed or adapted for the making of an instrument to which this section

applies which is false and that he or another shall use the instrument to induce somebody to accept it as genuine, and by reason of so accepting it, to do or not to do some act to his own or any other person's prejudice.

(4)   *Having custody or control of a machine or implement*
It is an offence for a person to make or have in his custody or under his control any such machine, implement, paper or material, without lawful authority or excuse.

The instruments to which this section applies are: money orders; postal orders; United Kingdom postage stamps; Inland Revenue stamps; share certificates; passports and document which can be used instead of passports; cheques; travellers' cheques; cheque cards; credit cards; certified copies relating to an entry in a register of births, adoptions, marriages or deaths; certificates relating to entries in such registers.

Penalties

A person guilty of a forgery offence under this Part of the Forgery and Counterfeiting Act 1981 shall be liable on summary conviction to a fine not exceeding the statutory maximum, or to imprisonment for not exceeding six months, or to both.

A person guilty of an offence under ss 1, 2, 3, 4, 5(1) and 5(3), shall be liable on conviction on indictment to imprisonment for a term not exceeding ten years. These are, therefore, arrestable offences.

A person guilty of an offence under s 5(2) or 5(4) shall be liable on conviction on indictment to imprisonment for not exceeding two years.

Offences under other Acts

Apart from the foregoing offences under the Forgery and Counterfeiting Act 1981, certain other statutes also create forgery. These include:

Forgery Act 1861. Acknowledging any recognisance or other instrument before any court or authorised person in the name of any other person, without lawful authority or excuse (s36); and destroying, injuring, falsifying, etc any official records of births, baptisms, marriages, deaths or burials (s36).

Vehicles (Excise) Act 1971. Forgery of vehicle excise licences or registration marks, etc (s26).

Road Traffic Act 1988. Forgery of various documents relating to motor vehicles (s173).

Criminal Justice Act 1925. Forgery of a passport or knowingly making a false statement to obtain a passport.

COUNTERFEITING

Legislation and meaning of 'counterfeit', etc

Offences of counterfeiting notes and coins are dealt with under the Forgery and Counterfeiting Act 1981.

The term 'counterfeit' is defined in s28 of the Act as follows:

(a) A thing is a counterfeit of a currency note or of a protected coin:
  (i) if it is not a currency note or a protected coin but resembles a currency note or protected coin (whether on one side only or on both) to such an extent that it is reasonably capable of passing for a currency note or protected coin of that description; or
  (ii) if it is a currency note or protected coin which has been so altered that it is reasonably capable of passing for a currency note or protected coin of some other description.
(b) (i) A thing consisting of one side only of a currency note, with or without the addition of other material, is a counterfeit of such a note;
  (ii) A thing consisting of parts of two or more currency notes, or of parts of a currency note, or of parts of two or more currency notes, with the addition of other materials, is capable of being a counterfeit of a currency note.

'Currency note' means:

(a) any note which has been lawfully issued in England and Wales, Scotland, Northern Ireland, or any of the Channel Islands, the Isle of Man or the Republic of Ireland, and is or has been customarily used as money in the country where it was issued, and is payable on demand; or
(b) any note which has been lawfully issued in some country other than those mentioned above, and is customarily used as money in that country.

'British currency note' means any note which has been lawfully issued in England and Wales, Scotland or Northern Ireland, and is or has been customarily used as money in the country where it was issued, and is payable on demand.

'Protected coin' means any coin which is customarily used as money in any country, or is specified in an order made by the Treasury for the purpose of this Part of this Act.

'British coin' means any coin which is legal tender in any part of the United Kingdom.

'Imitation British coin' means any thing which resembles a British coin in shape, size and the substance of which it is made.

Counterfeiting notes and coins

It is an offence for a person to make a counterfeit of a currency note or of a protected coin, *intending* that he or another shall pass or tender it as genuine (s14(1)).

It is an offence for a person to make a counterfeit of a currency note or of a protected coin without lawful authority or excuse (s14(2)).

(Note that the difference between these two offences lies in the intention of the counterfeiter.)

Other offences

Passing, etc counterfeit notes and coins (s15(1))
It is an offence for a person:
  (a) to pass or tender as genuine any thing which is, and which he knows or believes to be, a counterfeit of a currency note or of a protected coin, or
  (b) to deliver to another any thing which is, and which he knows or believes to be, such a counterfeit, intending that the person to whom it is delivered or another shall pass or tender it as genuine.

Delivering counterfeit notes and coins to another (s15(2))
It is an offence for a person to deliver to another without lawful authority or excuse, any thing which is, and which he knows or believes to be, a counterfeit of a currency note or of a protected coin.

Custody or control of counterfeit notes and coins (s16)
  (1) It is an offence for a person to have in his custody or under his control any thing which is, and which he knows or believes to be, a counterfeit of a currency note or of a protected coin, intending either to pass or tender it as genuine or to deliver it to another with the intention that he or another shall pass or tender it as genuine.
  (2) It is an offence for a person to have in his custody or under his control, without lawful authority or excuse, any thing which is, and

which he knows or believes to be, a counterfeit of a currency note or of a protected coin.

Making or having custody or control of counterfeiting materials (s17)

(1) It is an offence for a person to make, or have in his custody or under his control, anything which he intends to use, or to permit any other person to use, for the purpose of making a counterfeit of a currency note or of a protected coin with the intention that it can be passed or tendered as genuine.

(2) It is an offence for a person without lawful authority or excuse, to make, or to have in his custody or under his control, anything which, to his knowledge, is or has been specially designed or adapted for the making of a counterfeit of a currency note.

(3) It is an offence for a person to make, or to have in his custody or under his control any implement which, to his knowledge, is capable of imparting to any thing a resemblance to the whole or part of either side of a protected coin, or to the whole or part of the reverse of the image on either side of a protected coin.

It is a defence for a person charged with an offence under subsection (3) to show that he made the implement or had it in his custody or under his control with the written consent of the Treasury, or that he had lawful excuse, otherwise than by virtue of the foregoing, or a lawful excuse for making it or having it in his custody or under his control.

Reproducing British currency notes (s18)

It is an offence for any person, unless the relevant authority has previously consented in writing, to reproduce on any substance whatsoever, and whether or not on the correct scale, any British currency note or any part of a British currency note.

Making, etc imitation British coins (s19)

It is an offence for a person:

(a) to make an imitation British coin in connection with a scheme intended to promote the sale of any product or the making of contracts for the supply of any service; or

(b) to sell or distribute imitation British coins in connection with any such scheme, or to have imitation British coins in his custody or under his control with a view to such sale or distribution, unless the Treasury have previously consented in writing to the sale or distribution of such imitation British coins in connection with that scheme.

Penalties

The penalties for offences under ss14 (1), 15(1), 16(1) and 17(1) are: on summary conviction a fine not exceeding the statutory maximum, imprisonment for not exceeding six months, or both; and on conviction on indictment a fine, imprisonment for not exceeding ten years, or both. These are therefore arrestable offences.

The penalties for offences under ss14(2), 15(2), 16(2), 17(2) and 17(3) are: on summary conviction a fine not exceeding the statutory maximum, imprisonment for not exceeding six months, or both; and on conviction on indictment a fine, imprisonment for not exceeding two years, or both.

Persons guilty of offences under ss 18 or 19 are liable on summary conviction to a fine not exceeding the statutory maximum, and on conviction on indictment to a fine.

OFFICIAL SECRETS

The Official Secrets Acts 1911 and 1920 deal with matters prejudicial to the safety or interests of the State. All offences under these Acts are arrestable offences regardless of the penalties.

Spying (1911 Act, s1)

A person is guilty of an offence if he, for any purpose prejudicial to the safety or interests of the State:
- (a) enters, approaches, inspects, or passes over a prohibited place;
- (b) makes a sketch, model, plan or note directly or indirectly useful to an enemy;
- (c) obtains, records or communicates a secret code or password, sketch, plan or model useful to an enemy. Penalty - 14 years.

Prohibited place means any place:
- (a) Belonging to or occupied by or on behalf of Her Majesty the Queen,
    - (i)   for defence, or naval or air force purposes (arsenals, docks, camps, stores, etc) or;
    - (ii) being a ship or aircraft; or
    - (iii) for getting metals, oils or minerals of use in war.
- (b) Whether owned or occupied by or for HM the Queen or not, if munitions of war (or sketches, models, etc of them) are made or kept therein.
- (c) Specially declared by the Secretary of State to be a prohibited place.

Accommodation addresses (Official Secrets Act 1920, s5)

This section relates to persons who carry on the business of receiving for reward letters, telegrams or other postal packets for delivery or forwarding to persons for whom intended.

Offences
  (a) Failing to notify the Chief Officer of Police of the address of the
       business premises, or change of address, or any change of informa-
       tion affecting register.
  (b) Failing to enter any of the particulars required to be entered in a
       book kept for that purpose, ie:
       (i)   name and address of each person for whom packet is received,
             or who makes request for use of facilities,
       (ii) instructions received as to delivery or forwarding,
       (iii) place from which packet came, date of postmark and of
             receipt, name and address of sender, if shown, and if regis-
             tered, the registration number,
       (iv) date of delivery, and to whom delivered,
       (v)   if forwarded, date and name and address of person.
  (c) Delivering a packet except against receipt in the book.
  (d) Handing packet to a person other than the one to whom addressed,
       unless written instructions signed by addressee permit this.
This does not apply to postal packets addressed to newspapers, jour-
nals, in reply to an advertisement in them. Books, postal packets and
instructions re delivery to be open to inspection by a constable at all
reasonable times.

Chapter 28
Offences against Public Justice

PERJURY

Perjury is a misdemeanour at common law. It is also dealt with by the Perjury Act 1911.

Section 1 of the Act states that perjury is committed by a person lawfully sworn as a witness or interpreter in a judicial proceeding who wilfully makes a statement material in that proceeding which he knows to be false or which he does not believe to be true.

(Penalty seven years' imprisonment - arrestable offence.)

'Lawfully sworn' includes affirmation and declaration as well as any oath, administered without objection by the person sworn.

'Judicial proceeding' includes a proceeding before any court, tribunal or person having by law power to hear, receive and examine evidence on oath.

'Material statement' is one such as might affect the decision of the court, tribunal or person, and the trial judge will decide whether the statement is or is not material.

Note: The perjury must be deliberate and not merely carelessness or mistake.

There are six points to prove in a case of perjury. These are as follows:

(a) must be a witness or interpreter;
(b) must be lawfully sworn;
(c) must be a judicial proceeding;
(d) must make the statement wilfully and with intent to mislead;
(e) must be material to the proceedings;
(f) the falsity of the statement or the belief that it is not true.

In addition corroboration is necessary to secure conviction for any offence against the Perjury Act, as the evidence of one witness alone as to the falsity of the statement will not be regarded as sufficient.

Subornation of perjury

It is a common law misdemeanour to procure another to commit perjury. It is also an offence under s7 of the Perjury Act to aid, abet, counsel, procure, incite or attempt to procure another person to commit an offence against the Act.

Unsworn evidence of a child

Where a child of tender years is allowed by a court to give unsworn evidence and he wilfully gives false evidence, he will be guilty of a summary offence (Children and Young Persons Act 1933, s38).

False statements tendered in evidence

Where written statements are admitted in evidence in committal or criminal proceedings any person who wilfully makes a statement material in those proceedings which he knows to be false or does not believe to be true, commits an offence under s89 of the Criminal Justice Act 1967. The Perjury Act 1911 shall have effect as if this offence were contained in it.

Other offences under the Perjury Act 1911

(a) Section 2 deals with false statements on oath made otherwise than in a judicial proceeding, eg naturalisation of an alien.

(b) Section 3 concerns false statements with reference to marriage, eg making false declarations to procure a marriage, or giving false particulars for the registrar, etc.

(c) Section 4 refers to false statements as to births and deaths.

(d) Section 5 deals with false statutory declarations otherwise than on oath.

(e) Section 6 - false declarations with intent to obtain registration. The section applies to registers kept under the Medical Act, Dentists' Act, Midwives' Act, Pharmacy Act, etc.

ESCAPE

It is an offence at common law for a prisoner, whether innocent or guilty, to escape from lawful custody. If a prisoner makes a voluntary escape by consent or connivance of his custodian, the custodian will also be guilty of an offence.

Any constable or other person who has a prisoner lawfully in custody and who negligently suffers him to go at large commits a misdemeanour at common law.

Prison breach

Prison breach is escape by force from lawful imprisonment by means of some actual breaking of the prison or place of custody. An unsuccessful attempt to break out of prison or any conspiracy to effect breach is an offence at common law.

Rescue

Rescue is the forcible liberation of a prisoner from lawful custody. A person who resists or wilfully obstructs a constable in the execution of his duty or a person assisting a constable in the execution of his duty shall be guilty of an offence (Police Act 1964, s57).

It is an offence to assault any person with intent to resist or prevent the lawful apprehension or detention of himself or of any other person for any offence (Offences against the Person Act 1961, s38). An attempted rescue of a prisoner may be dealt with summarily as assaulting, obstructing or resisting the police.

Chapter 29
Firearms

Definitions contained in the Firearms Act 1968

(a) *Firearm:* A lethal barrelled weapon of any description from which any shot, bullet, or other missile can be discharged; it includes any prohibited weapon whether it is such a lethal weapon or not, any component part of such lethal or prohibited weapon and any accessory to such weapon designed or adapted to diminish the noise or flash caused by firing the weapon.

(b) *Ammunition:* Ammunition for any firearm, including grenades, bombs and other like missiles, whether capable of use with such a firearm or not, and prohibited ammunition.

(c) *Imitation firearm*: Anything which has the appearance of a firearm (except certain prohibited weapons) whether capable of discharging shot, bullet or other missile or not.

(d) *Prohibited weapon:*

    (a) any firearm which is so designed or adapted that two or more missiles can be successively discharged without repeated pressure on the trigger;

    (ab) any self-loading or pump-action rifle other than one which is chambered for .22 rim-fire ammunition;

    (ac) any self-loading or pump-action smooth bore gun which is not chambered for .22 rim-fire cartridges and either has a barrel less than 24 inches in length or (excluding any detachable, folding, retractable or other movable butt-stock) is less than 40 inches long overall;

    (ad) any smooth bore revolver gun other than one which is chambered for 9mm rim-fire cartridges or loaded at the muzzle end of each chamber;

    (ae) any rocket launcher, or any mortar, for projecting a stabilised missile, other than a launcher or mortar designed for line-throwing or pyrotechnic purposes or signalling apparatus;

(b) any weapon of whatever description designed or adapted for the discharge of any noxious liquid, gas or other thing; and

(c) any cartridge with a bullet designed to explode on or immediately before impact, any ammunition containing or designed or adapted to contain any noxious thing and, if capable of being used with a firearm of any description, any grenade, bomb (or other like missile), or rocket or shell designed to explode as aforesaid.

(e) *Firearms dealer* : Means a person who by way of trade or business, manufactures, sells, transfers, repairs, tests or proves firearms or ammunition to which s1 applies, or shotguns.

(f) *Public place* : Includes any highway and any premises or place to which at the material time the public have access whether on payment or otherwise.

(g) *Shot gun*: A smooth bore gun (not being an airgun) which (i) has a barrel not less than 24 inches in length and does not have any barrel with a bore exceeding 2 inches in diameter; (ii) either has no magazine or has a non-detachable magazine incapable of holding more than two cartridges; and (iii) is not a revolver gun.

Firearms Act 1968, s1

Section 1 of the Firearms Act 1968, as amended, applies to every firearm except - (a) a shot gun; and (b) an air weapon (ie an air rifle, air gun or air pistol not of a type declared to be specially dangerous).

Firearm certificate (s1)

Before a person can have possession of a firearm or ammunition to which s1 of the Act applies he must hold a firearms certificate or be exempt. Certificates are granted by the chief officer of police where applicant resides. An applicant must have good reason for requiring and be a fit person and not prohibited from possessing a firearm. A certificate lasts for three years, or less. Conditions may be imposed at discretion of chief constable and are specified in the certificate.

Shot gun certificate (s28)

Before a person can have possession of a shot gun he must hold a shot gun certificate, or be exempt. Certificates are granted by the chief officer of police where applicant resides. The certificate shall be granted unless the applicant is prohibited or cannot possess without danger to public safety or peace. It is issued or renewed subject to any prescribed conditions which are specified in the certificate.

Exemptions from the need for a certificate

The following persons may possess a section 1 firearm or ammunition, or a shot gun without possessing a certificate:

(a) a person who has obtained a permit in the prescribed form from the chief officer of police (s7);

(b) a registered firearms dealer or his servant in the ordinary course of his business (s8);

(c) an auctioneer, carrier or warehouseman in the ordinary course of his business (s9);

(d) a licensed slaughterman in possession of a slaughtering instrument in the slaughterhouse or knacker's yard in which he is employed (s10(1));

(e) the proprietor of a slaughterhouse or knacker's yard or person appointed by him may have charge of a slaughtering instrument (s10(2));

(f) a person carrying a firearm or ammunition belonging to a certificate holder for sporting purposes only (s11(1));

(g) a person at an athletics meeting for the purpose of starting races (s11(2));

(h) a member of a cadet corps when engaged as a member or in connection with drill or target practice (s11(3));

(i) a person carrying on a miniature rifle range or shooting gallery using only air weapons or miniature rifles not exceeding .23 inch calibre (s11(4));

(j) a person borrowing a shot gun from the occupier of private premises and using it on those premises in the occupier's presence (s11(5));

(k) a person using a shot gun for shooting at artificial targets approved by the chief officer of police (s11(6));

(l) a person taking part in a theatrical performance or rehearsal, or in the production of a cinematograph film, but Secretary of State's authority required for use of a prohibited weapon (s12);

(m) a person possessing a firearm or ammunition on board a ship, or signalling apparatus on an aircraft or at an aerodrome, as part of the equipment of the ship, aircraft or aerodrome (s13);

(n) a person who has been in Great Britain for not more than 30 days in the preceding 12 months may possess a shot gun (s14);

(o) a person holding a Northern Ireland firearm certificate may possess a shot gun (s15);

(p) a person of or over 17 may borrow a rifle from the occupier of private premises and use it on those premises in the presence of the occupier (s16(1), Firearms (Amendment) Act 1988);

(q) the holder of a visitor's firearm permit or visitor's shotgun permit may possess, purchase or acquire such weapons (s17, Firearms (Amendment) Act 1988).

Trophies of war

Persons retaining trophies of war must hold firearms certificates, although no fee is payable. The person must be of good repute and the firearm (without ammunition) must be a personal memento used, carried or captured by him on active service. This does not apply to Government property, ie weapons issued or captured during the 1939-45 war, or in the Falklands Campaign in 1982.

Police powers (s48)

Any constable may demand from any person whom he believes to be in possession of a shot gun, or a firearm or ammunition to which s1 of the Act applies, the production of his certificate. If such person fails to produce the certificate or allow it to be read, or fails to prove he is exempt, the weapon or ammunition may be seized and the person's name and address demanded.

Firearms dealers

Firearms dealers must be registered with police. They may be removed from the register by a court after conviction or by the chief officer of police for failure to comply with conditions. All transactions must be entered in dealers' registers within 24 hours. The register and stock may be inspected by a police officer authorised in writing.

Firearms Rules 1989

A firearms certificate shall be granted or renewed subject to the following conditions:

(i) the holder must, on receipt, sign it in ink with his usual signature;

(ii) the holder must inform the chief officer of police by whom the certificate was granted of the theft or loss of any firearm or

ammunition to which it relates;
(iii) the holder must, without undue delay, inform the chief officer of police of any change in his permanent address;
(iv) the firearms and ammunition to which the certificate relates must at all times be stored securely so as to prevent, so far as reasonably practicable, access to them by an unauthorised person.
Similar provisions are made in respect of shotgun certificates.

AGES IN CONNECTION WITH FIREARMS

Under 17 years

(a) No person under the age of 17 years shall purchase or hire *any firearm* or ammunition (s22(1)).
(b) No person shall sell or hire *any firearm* or ammunition to a person under 17 years (s24(1)).

Between 14 and 17 years

(a) A person between 14 and 17 years may accept a *section 1 firearm* as a gift or loan, provided a certificate is held by each party to the transaction.
(b) A person between 14 and 17 years shall not have in his possession in a public place *any air weapon* except:
(i) an air gun or air rifle (not an air pistol) which is securely fastened in a gun cover so that it cannot be fired; or
(ii) at a rifle club or cadet corps; or
(iii) at a shooting gallery.

Under 15 years

(a) No person under 15 years shall possess an assembled *shot gun* unless:
(i) under supervision of a person 21 years or over; or
(ii) if the gun is in a securely fastened cover so that it cannot be fired (s22(3)).
(b) No person shall make a gift of any *shot gun* or ammunition to any person under the age of 15 years (s24(3)).

Under 14 years

(a) No person under 14 years shall have in his possession any *section 1 firearm* or ammunition (s22(2)) except when:
    (i) carrying for the holder of a certificate for sporting purposes; or
    (ii) at a rifle club or cadet corps; or
    (iii) at a shooting gallery.

(b) No person shall give or lend a person under 14 years any *section 1 firearm* or ammunition(s24(2)).

(c) No person under 14 years shall possess any *air weapon* or ammunition except:
    (i) when supervised by a person 21 or over on private premises; (the supervisor must not allow the discharge of missiles beyond those premises).
    (ii) at a rifle club/cadet corps; or
    (iii) at a shooting gallery; or
    (iv) in regard to an air gun or air rifle (not an air pistol) or ammunition in a public place provided:
        (a) under the supervision of a person 21 years or over; and
        (b) weapon securely fastened in gun cover so that it cannot be fired.

(d) No person shall make a *gift of any weapons or ammunition for an air weapon* to any person under the age of 14 years.

CRIMINAL USE OF FIREARMS

It is an offence under the Firearms Act 1968 for a person to:

(a) Have in his possession any firearm or ammunition with intent by means thereof to endanger life or to enable anyone else to do so whether injury to person has been caused or not (s16, penalty life imprisonment).

(b) Use or attempt to use a firearm or imitation firearm with intent to resist or prevent lawful arrest of himself or other person (s17(1), penalty life imprisonment).

(c) Possess at the time of committing or when arrested for any offence in Sch 1 to the Firearms Act (unless he proves possession for lawful object) (s17(2), penalty 14 years).

    Schedule of offences includes criminal damage, wounding, laying explosives to building, endangering railway passengers, assaults with intent to resist arrest or commit actual bodily harm, child-stealing and abduction, theft, burglary, blackmail, taking conveyance, police assault, rape, abduction of women, and attempting to commit such offences.

(d) Have with him a firearm or imitation firearm with intent to commit an indictable offence or to resist or prevent the arrest of himself or any other person (s18(1), penalty 14 years).

(e) Have with him in any public place, without lawful authority or reasonable excuse (proof on accused):
   (i)   any *loaded* shot gun, or
   (ii) any *loaded* air weapon, or
   (iii) any other firearm (loaded or not), together with ammunition for it (s19, penalty 5 years).

(f) Enter or be in any building, part of a building or land (includes land covered with water) as a trespasser, without reasonable excuse (proof on accused), when in possession of a firearm (s20, penalty 5 years).

Police powers to stop and search (s47)

A constable may:

(a) Require any person he suspects of having a firearm in a public place or to be committing or about to commit any of the foregoing offences under this Act elsewhere than in a public place, to hand over the firearm and any ammunition for examination. Any person who fails to do so commits an offence.

(b) Search a person and detain him for searching in such circumstances.

(c) Stop and search a vehicle he suspects of carrying a firearm in a public place, or search any vehicle which he suspects is being used, or is about to be used in connection with the commission of an offence under the foregoing provisions of this Act elsewhere than in a public place.

The following are arrestable offences under s24 of the Police and Criminal Evidence Act 1984:

(a) unlawfully shortening the barrel of a smooth bore shotgun to less than 24 inches (s4);

(b) possessing or distributing prohibited weapons or ammunition (s5);

(c) possessing firearm with intent to endanger life or injure property (s16);

(d) use of firearm to resist arrest (s17(1));

(e) possession of firearm or imitation firearm whilst committing or at the time of arrest for Sch 1 offence (s17(2));

(f) possession of firearm or imitation firearm with intent to commit an indictable offence (s18);

(g) carrying a loaded firearm (not an air weapon) in a public place (s19);

(h) trespassing with a firearm in a building (not on land) (s20(1)).

For the purpose of exercising these powers, a constable may enter any place and may seize and detain any firearm or ammunition which may be the subject of a court order for forfeiture.

Forfeiture and disposal of firearms (s52(1))

Where a person:

(a) is convicted of an offence under the Act (except in relation to a person under 15 years of age having with him an assembled shot gun or in relation to air weapon), or of a crime for which he is sentenced to imprisonment, borstal training or detention in a detention centre; or

(b) is bound over to keep the peace or be of good behaviour, with a condition that he shall not possess a firearm; or

(c) is the subject of a probation order with such a condition,

the court may order forfeiture of any firearm or ammunition found in his possession and cancel any firearm or shot gun certificate he holds; and a constable may seize and detain any firearm or ammunition which is the subject of such an order for forfeiture.

Chapter 30
Crime Prevention, Investigation and Detection

CRIME PREVENTION

The duties of a crime prevention officer

The Committee on the Prevention and Detection of Crime considered that the duties of a crime prevention officer should include:

    (a) the cultivation of a working two-way relationship between beat and patrol officers and the crime prevention officer, and encouragement of beat constables to report matters of crime prevention interest;

    (b) the collection, co-ordination and dissemination of crime prevention information and information on current trends of crime;

    (c) the acquiring of a thorough knowledge of technical aids to security, by study of appropriate journals and visits to manufacturers of locks, safes etc;

    (d) the inspection of property where there are special or difficult security features; the keeping of records of such visits to enable follow-up visits to be made at appropriate times;

    (e) maintaining a firm relationship with local bank managers, local authorities, and all other bodies to whom advice can be given on crime prevention;

    (f) the giving of talks, whenever the opportunity arises, to local bodies on crime prevention;

    (g) ensuring that crime prevention literature is used to its best effect and displayed or distributed on all appropriate occasions; the crime prevention officer should always have available a collection of locks and possibly burglar alarms for selective display;

    (h) the regular giving of lectures at probationer and refresher courses and the issue of a crime booklet for the guidance of all members of the force;

(i)   the co-operation and liaison with children where the force operates a Juvenile Liaison Scheme; with the Fire Service to ensure that security standards do not conflict with fire safety requirements; with nightwatchmen in those parts of the country where Nightwatchmen Mutual Aid Schemes have been introduced and with burglar alarm companies on matters in respect of the installation of alarms.

It should, of course, be remembered that all police officers, apart from those appointed as CPOs, are engaged in crime prevention work.

Scientific aids and forensic science laboratories

Eight forensic science laboratories are in operation throughout the country. The main objects of the laboratories are to assist police forces as follows:

(a)   in the practical application of scientific aids to police work in the investigation of all offences;

(b)   in the instruction and training of police officers in this branch of police work, covering especially the nature of the assistance the expert can render, the methods of searching for traces which can be put to good use by the expert, and the handling and packing of such materials as may be found so as to ensure their being preserved in a proper condition for scientific investigation; and

(c)   in the development, in collaboration with police officers, of fresh applications of science to police work by laboratory research.

The Home Office publish a booklet 'Scientific Aids to Criminal Investigation' which is available to all police officers on application to HMSO by Chief Officers.

Careful packing and labelling of materials submitted to a laboratory is essential for the following reasons:

(a)   to prevent the materials themselves becoming damaged or contaminated, or traces which are present being obliterated; and

(b)   to safeguard their integrity and give satisfactory proof of any exhibits that may be produced in court.

OFFENCES TAKEN INTO CONSIDERATION

Offences which are not included in the indictment may be taken into consideration:

(a)   if the prosecutor consents;

(b)   if the prisoner consents;

(c)   if the prisoner admits them;

(d) if the court has jurisdiction;

(e) if the offence is in the same general class as that for which the prisoner is indicted.

Only criminal charges can be dealt with in this way and the procedure to be followed is briefly as follows:

(a) If the prisoner is in custody in another police area:

    (i)   the prosecutor should be seen and his consent obtained to the offence being taken into consideration;

    (ii) a report and warrant (if one exists) should be sent to the police force holding the prisoner.

(b) If the prisoner is in custody in the Force area:

    (i)   prepare lists of outstanding offences;

    (ii)   supply one to the prisoner and obtain his receipt;

    (iii) mention them after his conviction at the trial;

    (iv)   have the lists available for the court.

STATUTORY PREVENTIVE MEASURES

Several Acts of Parliament give the police powers to deal with persons who, although not actually having committed crime, are found under such circumstances as to give rise to the belief that their intention is to commit crime. The main ones are given here.

Interference with vehicles

Under s9 of the Criminal Attempts Act 1981 a person is guilty of the offence of vehicle interference if he interferes with a motor vehicle or trailer, or with anything carried in or on a motor vehicle or trailer, with the intention that he or some other person will commit an offence of:

(a) theft of the motor vehicle or trailer or part of it;

(b) theft of anything carried in or on the motor vehicle or trailer; or

(c) an offence of taking a conveyance without consent; and if it is shown that a person accused of such an offence intended that one of those offences should be committed, it is immaterial that it cannot be shown which it was.

Enclosed premises (Vagrancy Act 1824, s4)

Any person may arrest without warrant any person found in or upon any dwelling house, warehouse, coach-house, stable or outhouse, or in any enclosed yard, garden or area for any unlawful purpose.

The unlawful purpose must be a criminal offence and not merely an act which is morally wrong. The yard, garden or area need only be enclosed on three sides.

(See Chapter 5 re general powers of arrest.)

Offensive weapons (Prevention of Crime Act 1953, s1, as amended, and Criminal Justice Act 1988, ss139 and 141)

This offence may be committed at any time by any person having in his possession any offensive weapon, without lawful authority or excuse (the proof of which lies on the accused), in any public place.

'Public place' includes any highway and any premises or place to which the public have access.

'Offensive weapon' means any article made or adapted for use for causing injury to the person, or intended by the person carrying it for such use by him, or by some other person.

Under s139 of the Criminal Justice Act 1988 any person who has any article which has a blade or is sharply pointed, except a folding pocket knife if the cutting edge of its blade is under 3 inches, is guilty of an offence. Defence to prove good reason or lawful authority, ie for use at work, religious reasons, or as part of national costume.

Section 141 of the 1988 Act also makes it an offence to manufacture, sell, hire, offer for sale, etc certain specified weapons listed in the Criminal Justice Act 1988 (Offensive Weapons) Order 1988, ie knuckledusters, swordsticks, beltbuckle knives, etc.

(See general power of arrest in Chapter 5.)

Restriction of Offensive Weapons Acts 1959 and 1961

Offences are committed by any person who imports or manufactures, sells or hires or offers for sale or hire, or exposes or has in his possession for the purpose of selling or hiring to any person, or lends or gives to any person, any knife commonly known as a 'flick knife', 'flick gun' or 'gravity knife'.

CROSSBOWS (Crossbows Act 1987)

This Act does not apply to crossbows with a draw weight of less than 1.4 kg.

Offences

A person who sells or lets on hire a crossbow or part of a crossbow to a person under the age of 17 is guilty of an offence unless he believes him to be 17 or older and has reasonable ground for the belief (s1).

A person under the age of 17 who buys or hires a crossbow or part of a crossbow is guilty of an offence (s2).

A person under the age of 17 who has with him - (i) a crossbow which is capable of discharging a missile, or (ii) parts of a crossbow which together (and without any other parts) can be assembled to form a crossbow capable of discharging a missile, is guilty of an offence unless he is under the supervision of a person who is 21 years of age or older (s3).

Powers of search and seizure

If a constable suspects with reasonable cause that a person is committing or has committed an offence under s3, he may:

(a)   search that person for a crossbow or part of a crossbow;

(b)   search any vehicle, or anything in or on a vehicle, in or on which he suspects with reasonable cause there is a crossbow, or part of a crossbow, connected with the offence.

A constable may detain a person or vehicle for the purposes of such a search and may seize and retain anything discovered which appears to be a crossbow or part of a crossbow. For the purpose of exercising these powers a constable may enter any land other than a dwelling house.

Other preventive measures

Note also the offence of going equipped for stealing (Theft Act 1968, s25); and trespassing on land with a firearm (Firearms Act 1968, s20). Both of these offences have been dealt with earlier.

NOTIFICATION OF CONVICTIONS TO CERTAIN PROFESSIONAL BODIES

The police are required to notify the appropriate authority of convictions of certain categories of persons, as follows:

(a)   Offences listed in the schedule of finger-printable offences:

   (i)   Pensioners of the Royal Irish Constabulary; the Home Office.

   (ii)   Registered Medical Practitioners; the General Medical Council.

   (iii)   Registered Dental Practitioners; the General Dental Council.

   (iv)   State Certified Midwives; the Central Midwives Board.

   (v)   State registered nurses, enrolled assistant nurses, student nurses and pupil assistant nurses; the General Nursing Council for England and Wales.

(b) Offences rendering a person unfit to teach or have charge of children:
   (i) A teacher in any school, a person employed in the care of children in a residential school, remand home, approved school, probation hostel, or home and the resident proprietor of a private school; the Home Office (Children's Department).
   (ii) A youth leader; the Home Office (Children's Department).
   (iii) A minister of religion; the Home Office (Children's Department).
(c) Offences relating to fitness to drive, or sexual offences: PSV drivers and conductors; the Traffic Commissioners.
(d) Offences relevant to fitness to fly: the holder of an air crew licence; the Board of Trade.
(e) Offences involving dishonesty or moral turpitude: barristers; the Home Office for transmission to Attorney General.
(f) Offences involving money or property: solicitors or solicitors' clerk; the Law Society.
(g) Any offences: Justice of the Peace; the Lord Chancellor.
(h) Any offences (other than minor traffic offences): civil servants or employees of the Atomic Energy Authority; Civil Service Department.

MODUS OPERANDI

The system

The 'modus operandi' (or 'MO') of a criminal means his method of working or how his crime was committed.

The methods and peculiarities of criminals are recorded so that they may be compared with subsequent crimes. Thus, when a crime is committed in a particular manner, comparison of the records of the 'MO' system, by process of elimination, may lead to the detection of the offender. All crimes are therefore indexed under as many as possible of the ten points of the system.

The ten points

(a) Classword - the class of person or property attacked.
(b) Entry - the actual point of entry into the premises.
(c) Means - the method adopted by the criminal in effecting his entry.
(d) Object - the motive for the crime, or the property stolen.

(e) Time - the hour, day and date, and also the occasion, such as twilight, meal time, on a race-day, during school hours, etc.

(f) Style - the criminal's *alleged* trade or profession.

(g) Tale - the criminal's story of himself in the locality accounting for his presence there.

(h) Pal - whether there is more than one person engaged in the crime.

(i) Transport - whether any vehicle was used in connection with the crime.

(j) Trade Mark - anything peculiar or unusual done at the scene of the crime.

Part 4
General Police Duties

Chapter 31
Police and Associated Organisations

MAINTENANCE AND CONTROL OF POLICE FORCES

Maintenance of police forces

Section 1(1) of the Police Act 1964, as amended by the Local Government Act 1972, provides that a police force shall be maintained for every county in England and Wales which is not comprised in the combined area constituted by an amalgamation scheme, and for every combined area constituted by such a scheme.

Function and powers of the Home Office

The most important provisions concerning the functions and powers of the Home Office in relation to the police are as follows:
  (a) the making of regulations as to the administration and conditions of service of police forces, including regulations with respect to appointment and promotion; probation; retirement; discipline; suspension; the maintenance of personal records; hours of duty, leave, pay and allowances; and the issue, use and return of police clothing, personal equipment etc;
  (b) the making of regulations as to the administration and conditions of service of special constables;
  (c) the making of regulations as to the government administration and conditions of service of police cadets;
  (d) the making of regulations as to pensions;
  (e) the making of regulations requiring police equipment to satisfy prescribed standards of design and performance;
  (f) the power to require the chief constable to submit a report to him on a matter connected with the policing of his area;

(g) the power to direct two or more chief constables to make collaboration agreements or provide assistance to one another;

(h) the power to approve voluntary schemes or make compulsory schemes for the amalgamation of two or more police areas;

(i) the power to make grants in respect of expenses incurred for police purposes by police authorities;

(j) the power to cause a local inquiry to be held by a person appointed by the Home Secretary into any matter connected with the policing of any area;

(k) recommending to the Queen who should be appointed as Her Majesty's Inspectors of Constabulary;

(l) the power to provide and maintain or to contribute towards the provisions or maintenance of common police services;

(m) the power to direct a chief officer of police to request the chief officer of another area to provide an officer of his force to carry out an investigation into a complaint from a member of the public;

(n) the power to call for statistics relating to offences, offenders, criminal proceedings and the state of crime in police areas, from chief officers of police;

(o) the making of regulations prescribing the constitution and proceedings of the Police Federation.

Constitution and functions of police authorities

Section 2 of the Police Act 1964, as amended, provides that the police authority of a county is the Police Committee. The number of members required to form these committees is determined by the Council concerned but:

(a) two-thirds must be councillors;

(b) one-third must be magistrates.

The committee appoints its own chairman. The clerk of the County Council acts as clerk to a police committee which usually meets every quarter.

A police authority may exercise its administrative authority quite independently of its council and is obliged to seek approval of or confirmation by the council only on matters of discretionary police expenditure.

The duties of a police authority are:

(a) To maintain an adequate and efficient Police Force for its area.

(b) To appoint the Chief Constable, subject to Home Office approval.

(c) To appoint the Deputy and Assistant Chief Constable after consultation with the Chief Constable, subject to Home Office approval.

(d) To determine and authorise the number of persons of all ranks which constitutes the establishment of the force and the number of divisions etc necessary for effective policing, subject to Home Office approval.

(e) To provide and maintain necessary buildings, subject to Home Office approval.

(f) To provide and maintain vehicles, apparatus, clothing and equipment.

(g) To approve provisions of pay, allowances, clothing, pensions, housing, accommodation, etc as laid down in Police Regulations.

A police authority has the following powers:

(a) With the approval of the Home Secretary it may require the resignation of the Chief Constable and Deputy or Assistant Chief Constables, in the interests of efficiency.

(b) In addition to the statutory annual report it may also require the Chief Constable to submit a written report on any matter connected with the policing of the area.

(c) To employ civilians for police purposes and to provide for an appropriate contributory superannuation fund.

(d) To keep itself informed of the manner in which complaints from members of the force are dealt with.

(e) To approve collaborative agreements.

Appointments to and removal from office

Appointments below the rank of Assistant Chief Constable are the sole responsibility of the Chief Constable (s7).

The services of a constable may be dispensed with at any time during his probationary period on the grounds that he is not fitted physically or mentally to perform the duties of his office, or that he is unlikely to become an efficient officer. There is no right of appeal against such dismissal. The constable may resign instead provided he does so before the date on which his services would have been dispensed with.

Jurisdiction of constables

A police officer has all the powers and privileges of a constable throughout England and Wales (s 19).

SPECIAL CONSTABLES

Special constables are enrolled to render assistance to regular members of police forces. They are appointed for the preservation of the public peace and for the protection of the inhabitants and the security of property in the police district concerned. Under s19 of the Police Act 1964 they have all the powers and privileges of a constable for the police areas in which they are appointed and in certain surrounding areas. Private detectives or enquiry agents, bailiffs, members of private police forces, licensees or managers of licensed premises, magistrates, clerks of courts and members of police authorities should not be appointed as special constables.

Special constables act in the execution of their duty under the direction and control of the chief officer of police of the district for which they are appointed. The Special Constabulary Regulations 1965 as amended, provide that a special constable must be at least 18 years of age, of good character and in good health. They are unpaid but may be reimbursed out-of-pocket expenses, and may receive certain allowances and sick pay.

The Police Pensions Regulations apply to special constables by virtue of the Special Constables (Pensions) Orders 1962 and 1964, in the event of permanent incapacity from following ordinary employment arising from police duty, or where a person dies as a result of an injury in the execution of his duty as a special constable.

COMMON SERVICES

Section 41 of the Police Act 1964 provides that the Home Office may provide and maintain certain common services to promote the efficiency of the police service. They are financed by the Crown Services Fund to which police authorities contribute according to the strength of the force.

The common services are:
- (a) the police college;
- (b) district training centres;
- (c) crime prevention courses;
- (d) central recruiting publicity;
- (e) standard entrance tests;
- (f) centralised promotion examinations and the Promotion Board;
- (g) forensic science laboratories;
- (h) wireless depots;
- (i) central organisation of regional crime squads (The National Coordinator);
- (j) Interpol attendance;
- (k) the Police Negotiating Board;
- (l) the Police National computer.

CENTRAL SERVICE

Section 43 of the Police Act 1964, as amended by the Police Officers (Central Service) Act 1989, provides that police officers engaged on temporary service with the Crown on common services are to be regarded as being on central service and not as members of their forces during that temporary service (except for the purposes of s19, 44, 47 and 52). On return to the force an officer reverts to his former rank, or rank to which he was promoted during his absence. Discipline regulations do not apply during central service, but offenders can be returned to their own forces to be dealt with.

COMPLAINTS—INVESTIGATION AND PROCEDURE

Section 84 of the Police and Criminal Evidence Act 1984 provides that any complaint by a member of the public against a police officer must be recorded immediately by the Chief Officer of Police and investigated by a senior officer under the supervision of the Police Complaints Authority. A copy of the complaint, and later a report of the investigation, shall be supplied to the Authority.

When a complaint or allegation is made of a breach of discipline there must be compliance with the rules of procedure at the hearing. The rules are set out in the Regulations, and the hearing of the charge is on judicial lines. If there is allegation of a criminal charge a report must be sent to the DPP before proceedings are taken. Minor matters may be dealt with by informal resolution.

The Police Complaints Authority may over-rule the Chief Officer's findings and direct that a tribunal shall be held. The Chief Officer will chair such a tribunal with two members of the Authority sitting with him. The finding will be by majority decision but punishment is a matter for the Chief Officer.

The Police Complaints Authority shall consist of a chairman appointed by HM the Queen and not less than eight members, appointed by the Home Secretary. A person who is, or has been, a constable in the UK is barred from being a member.

The Police (Complaints) (General) Regulations 1985 deal with procedural matters.

POLICE (DISCIPLINE) REGULATIONS

The Police (Discipline) Regulations 1985 (or the Police (Discipline) (Senior Officers) Regulations 1985 in the case of ranks over chief superintendent) lay down a discipline code, which is a list of offences that a police officer may commit, and the procedure for dealing with such offences. The chief officer of police is the discipline authority and offences may be punished by dismissal, requirement to resign, reduction in rank or rate of pay, a fine, reprimand or caution. An appeal may be made to the Secretary of State against a finding of guilt and punishment (the Commissioner in the Metropolitan Police).

The disciplinary offences are:

(1) Discreditable conduct, ie acting in a disorderly manner, a manner prejudicial to discipline or likely to bring discredit on the force.

(2) Misconduct towards a member of a police force, ie oppressive or abusive conduct, or assaulting a member of the force.

(3) Disobedience to orders, ie disobeying, omitting or neglecting to carry out any lawful order, or contravening a provision of Police Regulations.

(4) Neglect of duty, ie neglecting or omitting to perform duty, failing to work a beat or leaving a place of duty.

(5) Falsehood or prevarication, ie making a false, misleading or inaccurate statement or entry in an official document; destroying, mutilating, altering or erasing any official document; making a false statement in connection with appointment.

(6) Improper disclosure of information, ie without authority communicating information obtained as a member of a police force; making an anonymous communication to a police authority or member of the force; or canvassing a member of the police authority or council.

(7) Corrupt or improper practices, ie failing to account for money or property received; soliciting or receiving any gratuity, present or testimonial; placing himself under a pecuniary obligation to any person; improperly using his position for private advantage; writing, signing or giving any testimonial or recommendation.

(8) Abuse of authority, ie making an arrest without good cause; using unnecessary violence to a prisoner; being uncivil to a member of the public.

(9) Racially discriminatory behaviour, ie abuse of authority on the grounds of another person's colour, race, nationality or ethnic or national origins, or in any other way treating a person improperly on those grounds.

(10) Neglect of health, ie neglecting to carry out the instructions of a medical officer, or committing an act likely to retard a return to duty when sick.

(11) Improper dress or untidiness, ie being improperly dressed or untidy while wearing uniform, on or off duty.

(12) Damage to police property, ie wilfully or carelessly causing any waste, loss or damage to police property (but not when an officer has been required to pay for the loss or damage); failing to report any such loss or damage.

(13) Drunkenness, ie being unfit through drink for duties which he is or may be required to perform.

(14) Drinking on duty or soliciting drink, ie drinking or receiving any intoxicating liquor while on duty; or demanding or persuading any person to supply him with intoxicating liquor.

(15) Entering licensed premises, ie without good and sufficient cause entering any premises licensed for the sale of liquor, betting and gaming, or entertainment, while on duty, or while off duty but wearing uniform.

(16) Criminal conduct, ie having been found guilty by a court of law of a criminal offence.

(17) Being an accessory to a disciplinary offence, ie conniving at or knowingly being an accessory to an offence against discipline.

(Note that most of these disciplinary offences contain the phrase 'without good and sufficient cause'.)

Liability for wrongful acts of constables

A constable is responsible under the law for his own acts and can be proceeded against in the courts for any illegal act done outside the limits of his authority, eg illegal arrest, assault, trespass. In addition s48 of the Police Act 1964 provides that a chief officer of police shall be jointly liable in respect of the torts committed by his constables in the performance of their duties, in the same way as a master is liable for the torts of his servants (vicarious liability). Any damages awarded against a chief officer of police *shall* be paid out of the Police Fund. The constable who commits such an act may, however, have to pay damages himself.

POLICE REPRESENTATIVE INSTITUTIONS

Police Federation

Section 44 of the Police Act 1964 provides that there shall be a Police Federation for England and Wales for the purpose of representing members of police forces in all matters affecting their welfare and efficiency, other than questions of discipline or promotion affecting individuals. The Federation acts through local and central representative bodies; and is entirely independent of, and unassociated with, any body or person outside the police service, but may employ persons outside the police service in an administrative capacity.

The Police Federation Regulations 1969 make provision for the assistance of the Federation in injury claims by members. Federation funds may be used to provide legal advice and assistance to members charged with traffic offences, except drink/driving offences. These funds may also be used to assist members in taking civil proceedings for defamation.

Police Negotiating Board for the United Kingdom

The Police Negotiating Board was established to consider questions of leave, pay, hours of duty, allowances, pensions, clothing and equipment. It consists of an official side and a staff side.

The Police Negotiating Board has five standing committees:

'A' for considering matters (other than pensions) peculiarly affecting ranks above that of chief superintendent;

'B' for considering matters (other than pensions) peculiarly affecting the ranks of chief superintendent and superintendent;

'C' for considering matters (other than pensions) peculiarly affecting ranks below that of superintendent, or affecting police cadets;

'D' for considering matters (other than pensions) which do not fall to any of the previous committees because of the range of ranks affected; and

'E' for considering pension matters.

OFFENCES UNDER THE POLICE ACT 1964

Assaults on constables (s51)

(1) It is an offence to assault a constable in the execution of his duty, or a person assisting such constable. (Power of arrest at common law.)

(2) It is an offence for any person to resist or wilfully obstruct a constable in the execution of his duty, or a person assisting a constable in the execution of his duty.

Impersonation (s52)

(1) Any person who with intent to deceive impersonates any member of a police force or special constable or makes any statement or does any act calculated falsely to suggest that he is such a member or constable.

(2) Wearing any article of police uniform calculated to deceive, etc.

(3) Unlawful possession of any article of police clothing.

Causing disaffection (s53)

Any person who causes, or attempts to cause, or does any act calculated to cause, disaffection amongst the members of the Police Force, etc.

THE POLICE REGULATIONS

Section 33 of the Police Act 1964 authorises the Secretary of State for Home Affairs to make regulations from time to time for the government of all the police forces in England and Wales. The current regulations are the Police Regulations 1987, as amended.

The main objects of these regulations are:

(a) To ensure uniformity of conditions of service throughout the police service.

(b) To ensure a uniform standard of discipline.

(c) To standardise procedure for dealing with disciplinary offences.

Some of the more important Regulations are summarised here:

Restrictions on private life of members (reg 10 and Sch 2)

A police officer:

(a) shall at all times abstain from any activity which is likely to interfere with the impartial discharge of his duties or which is likely to give rise to the impression amongst members of the public that it may so interfere and in particular a constable shall not take any active part in politics;

(b) shall obtain the approval of the chief officer of police to the place where he resides;

(c) shall not, without the previous consent of the chief officer of police, receive a lodger in a house or quarters with which he is provided by the police authority or sub-let any part of the house or quarters;

(d) shall not, unless he has previously given written notice to the chief officer of police receive a lodger in a house in which he resides and in respect of which he receives a rent allowance or sub-let any part of such a house;

(e) shall not wilfully refuse or neglect to discharge any lawful debt.

Incompatible business interests (reg 11)

The 'business interests' covered by the regulation are:

(i) having any office or employment for hire or gain or carrying on any business; or

(ii)   residing where a member of his family carries on a shop or like business: or

(iii) having a spouse (not being separated) who carries on a shop or other like business in that force area; or

(iv)   having a relative in his family living with him who holds (or has any pecuniary interest in) any licence or permit granted under any enactment relating to intoxicating liquor, betting or gaming, or entertainment in that force area.

'Relative' includes his spouse, parent, son, daughter, brother or sister.

In the case of a police officer having such a business interest: the officer must forthwith notify the chief officer of police in writing, unless he had disclosed the interest on his appointment. The chief officer must decide whether or not he considers the interest incompatible with continued service and notify the officer accordingly, in writing. The officer has ten days in which to appeal to the Police Authority against an adverse decision by notice in writing to the Authority. If appeal fails, or is not pursued, and the officer continues to have the interest the chief officer may, if the police authority approves, dispense with his services.

Business interests precluding appointment (reg 12)

Save in so far as the chief officer may allow, a person shall not be eligible for appointment to a police force, if he or a relative has a business interest as in reg 12.

Qualification for appointment (reg 13)

Applicants for appointment must have attained the age of 18 years. Satisfactory references as to character are required and physical and educational examinations must be passed.

Probationary service (reg 16)

The first two years' service as a constable in a force is a period of probation. This does not apply to a transfer from another force where probation has been completed. Exceptions also may apply to constables joining or rejoining a force after previous service in that or any other force, as follows:

(a)   where the period of probation previously served is at least one year then the probation is one year, but the Chief Constable can reduce this to a period which makes an aggregate of not less than two years;

(b) where the full period of probation was completed in previous service, the Chief Constable can dispense with the probation period.

Personal records (regs 19-21)

A Chief Constable must keep a personal record of each member of his force. This must include particulars of:

(a) Personal Description including place and date of birth.
(b) Marriage and children.
(c) Other service - armed forces, civil service, and transfers from one force to another.
(d) Examinations for promotion.
(e) Force record, ie promotions, postings, removals, injuries, illnesses, commendations, rewards, punishments other than cautions, date of leaving force (with reason, cause or manner).

A right of inspection of his own personal record is given to any police officer who makes the request. On transfer to another force the records are sent to that other force.

Punishment of a fine or reprimand is expunged after 3 years free from punishment other than a caution, and after 5 years in any other case.

Fingerprints (reg 22)

Every member of a police force shall have his fingerprints taken. These must be kept separate from other fingerprints and destroyed on his ceasing to be a member of a police force.

Duty to carry out lawful orders (reg 23)

Every police officer is required to carry out lawful orders and, punctually and promptly, to perform all appointed duties and attend to all matters within the scope of his office.

Normal daily period of duty (reg 26)

The normal period of duty (including the period for refreshments) is eight hours. So far as the exigencies of duty permit, this must be performed in one tour and an interval of 45 minutes allowed for refreshments. Where a member is required to perform duty in more than one tour and does not go home in between, an interval for refreshment shall be included at the beginning or end of one of the tours.

Rostering of duties (reg 27)

An annual duty roster must be published showing rest days, public holidays on which duty may have to be performed, and the time of daily periods of duty. Rosters must make provision for an interval of not less than eight hours between periods of duty, and not more than seven days between rostered rest days.

Overtime (reg 28)

Overtime is worked by remaining on duty after a tour has ended, or by being recalled between two tours of duty. It is compensated by payment at a rate of time and a third for each complete period of 15 minutes worked in a week. Time off may be elected in lieu and must be granted within 3 months.

No account is taken of any period of less than 30 minutes overtime, other than a period of 15 minutes of which warning was given at the beginning of a tour of duty.

Where an officer is recalled to duty between two rostered tours for less than four hours, he shall be entitled to reckon four hours overtime, plus any travelling time under regulation 31.

Where an officer is engaged on casual escort duty, account is only taken of:

- (a) time during which he is in charge of the prisoner,
- (b) time spent in travelling to or from the place where he takes charge of or hands over the prisoner, and
- (c) any other time allowed by the chief officer, who may exclude a period not exceeding eight hours in proper sleeping accommodation when he is charge of the prisoner.

Public holidays and rest days (reg 29)

Officers below the rank of superintendent must, so far as the exigencies of duty permit, be allowed a day's leave on each public holiday and be granted two rest days each week. ('Week' means a period of seven days beginning with such day as fixed by the chief officer.)

An officer required to do duty on a rostered rest day must be granted:

(a) where less than eight days' notice was given, an allowance at the rate of time and a half, plus another day off in lieu;

(b) where at least eight days' but less than 29 days' notice was given, an allowance at the rate of time and a half;

(c) in any other case, another rest day in lieu.

An officer required to do duty on a public holiday must be granted:

(a) where less than eight days' notice was given, an allowance at the rate of double time, plus another day off in lieu, which shall be treated as a public holiday;

(b) in any other case, an allowance at the rate of double time.

Alternatively, an officer may elect within 28 days to have time off equal to double time in the case of a public holiday and time and a half in the case of a rostered rest day. This must be granted, subject to the exigencies of duty, within three months.

A period of less than four hours worked on a public holiday or rostered rest day shall be treated as though it were a period of four hours. The period of duty shall include the time occupied in going to and returing from the place of duty, unless the total period exceeds six hours or is treated as a period of duty under reg 29.

Travelling time treated as duty (reg 31)

Where an officer is required to perform his normal daily period of duty in more than one tour, or is recalled to duty between two tours, the time occupied in travelling to and from his home shall be treated as a period of duty. Travelling expenses shall be treated as expenses incurred in the execution of duty and must be reimbursed.

Annual leave (reg 33 and Sch 3)

Annual leave is additional to rest days and public holidays. An officer below the rank of superintendent must, so far as the exigencies of duty permit, be allowed to take his annual leave in one period continuous with days falling within the period on which he is not required to perform duty.

Annual leave may be taken, subject to the exigencies of duty, as a single period, as single days, in periods of more than one day, or as half days. Not more than three days shall be taken as half days, which are periods of four hours without any entitlement to any interval for refreshments.

An officer recalled to duty from annual leave must be given additional compensatory leave of two days for each of the first two days, and $1\frac{1}{2}$ days for every subsequent day.

Sick leave (reg 34)

An officer must not be absent from duty on account of injury or illness unless a registered medical practitioner has certified him unfit, provided that he may be absent without a certificate where the period of unfitness does not exceed seven days, including any day on which he would not have been required to perform duty.

A medical practitioner approved by the police authority may countermand the certificate of unfitness for duty after consultation with a third doctor.

Subsistence, refreshment and lodging allowance (reg 58)

A member of or below the rank of superintendent retained on duty beyond his normal daily period, or engaged away from his usual place of duty, who certifies that he has been unable to obtain a meal in his usual way and has incurred additional expenditure, shall be paid:

(a) a refreshment allowance if he is retained or engaged for between 2 and 5 hours;

(b) a subsistence allowance if the period exceeds 5 hours.

A lodging allowance may also be payable.

THE POLICE (PROMOTION) REGULATIONS 1979, as amended

Qualifications for promotion (1991 Rules)

Part I of the qualifying examination consists of a single multiple choice paper and candidates must achieve a minimum of 75%. After passing Part I candidates must take Part II at the first opportunity, ie within 12 months. This part consists of a series of practical exercises over a period of 90 minutes. In order to pass a score must be achieved which predicts competence in the next rank.

The examination to the rank of sergeant is restricted to constables who have completed not less than 2 years' service and the required probationary period by 30th November of the year in which Part I is taken. Part I will normally be held in March and Part II during October and November of the same year.

The examination to the rank of inspector is restricted to sergeants who are of substantive rank on 1st July of the year in which Part I is taken. Part I will normally be held in October and Part II during April and May of the following year.

Police Staff College Accelerated Promotion Courses

A constable selected to attend an AP(S) course will be promoted temporarily to the rank of sergeant from the commencement date of the course. If successful he will automatically become a substantive sergeant even though he may be supernumerary to his force establishment, and will be promoted to the rank of inspector after completion of one year as a sergeant to the satisfaction of his chief officer.

A sergeant selected for an AP(I) course will be promoted to the rank of inspector for a probationary period from the start of the course.

TRAINING

Probationer constables attend an initial course at a District Training Centre on joining. This is designed to prepare them for operational duties, by teaching first aid, life-saving and self-defence, in addition to law subjects and practical police duties. In the second year of service there is a continuation course.

Apart from central training, the continued instruction of probationers is the responsibility of Force Training Schools. Refresher courses are also run for constables (the recommendation of the Working Party on Training being a three or four week course at five-yearly intervals).

Courses are recommended for newly promoted officers in their duties and responsibilities. Most forces also hold courses for promotion study, management and retirement. Courses for specialists such as detectives, dog handlers and traffic patrol are also dealt with by individual forces, as also is driver training.

Higher training is the responsibility of the Police Staff College at Bramshill.

CADETS

Police cadets are employees of the police authority. Actual appointments are made by the chief officer of police or an assistant commissioner in the Metropolitan Police, and cadets are under his control and subject to dismissal by him. The Police (Cadets) Regulations 1968 provide for the administration and conditions of service of police cadets.

Training of cadets was reviewed by a Working Party in 1965 which recommended that cadet training should be full-time for the first two years with the emphasis on all-round education, games, physical training and 'mind-broadening' activities, including social and constitutional studies.

'Adventure training' was recommended as a means of developing qualities of initiative and self-reliance. Vocational training 'on the job' should be kept to the third and last year of cadetship and direct involvement in police work should be avoided until a cadet is at least 18 years old.

A majority of ex-cadets in a force was held to be undesirable and a maximum proportion of 30 to 40% was suggested as an annual recruit intake.

BROADCASTING

Broadcast messages originated by the police must be restricted to requests for witnesses of accidents, missing persons, and danger to life, eg lost drugs, escaping wild animals, etc.

Messages to assist the free flow of road traffic may also be broadcast. These are in three categories: forseeable traffic congestion; unforseeable traffic congestion; and road conditions, and general notes of interest.

POLICE PENSIONS (Police Pensions Act 1976 and Police Pensions Regulations 1987)

Under these regulations provision is made for a policeman's ordinary pension, short service award, ill-health award, injury award, or deferred pension. A half rate pension is payable after 25 years' service and a two-thirds pensions after 30 years' service. Up to a quarter of a pension may be commuted for a cash sum. The rate of contribution payable is curently 11% for a man and 8% for a woman.

Compulsory retirement ages are-
  (a) commissioner or assistant commissioner in the City of London, chief constable, deputy chief constable or assistant chief constable - 65 years;
  (b) metropolitan assistant commissioner, or superintendent or inspector in any other force - 60 years;
  (c) metropolitan deputy assistant commissioner or commander - 57 years;
  (d) sergeant or constable, or any metropolitan rank below commander - 55 years.

Officers entitled to receive a pensions of two-thirds of pay may be required to retire on grounds of efficiency of the force.

POLICE INJURY BENEFIT (Police (Injury Benefit) Regulations 1987)

Provision is made for enhanced benefits in case of death or total disablement resulting from an injury received by a police officer in the execution of duty. This is in the form of a gratuity payable to a member, or in the case of death to a dependent relative.

Chapter 32
Poisons and Drugs.
Betting, Gaming and Lotteries

POISONS

The Pharmacy and Poisons Act 1933, as amended by the Pharmacy and Medicines Act 1941 and the Pharmacy Act 1954, together with the Poisons Rules 1972, deal with the registration of chemists and the sale and supply of poisons.

A list of substances which are treated as poisons (the 'Poisons List') is prepared and approved by the Secretary of State. This list is divided into two parts:

(a) Part 1 poisons may only be sold under the supervision of a registered pharmacist and on registered premises. A record must be made of all sales in the Poison Register, of the name and address of the purchaser, the person authorising the sale, and the date, quantity and purpose for which required. (The requirement to sign the register does not apply in the case of medicine supplied or dispensed by a doctor, dentist or veterinary surgeon.)

(b) Part 2 poisons (which are mainly solutions containing poison) may only be sold by an authorised seller or a person whose name is on the local authority's list.

Police action re poisons is usually restricted to notifying any breach of the Acts and Regulations to the local authority.

DRUGS

The purpose of the law relating to drugs, in the Misuse of Drugs Act 1971 and the Misuse of Drugs Regulations 1985, is to prevent the abuse of certain drugs and traffic in them.

Controlled drugs are graded into three groups ('A', 'B' and 'C') according to their relative harmfulness and the prevalence of their misuse.

Penalties for offences vary according to the class of drugs (eg the penalty for production, supply and possession with intent to supply a Class A drug is life imprisonment; Class B, 14 years; and Class C, 5 years).

Possession

The following persons have a general authority to possess controlled drugs:
(a) a constable when acting in the course of his duty as such;
(b) a person engaged in the business of a carrier when acting in the course of that business;
(c) a person engaged in the business of the Post Office when acting in the course of that business;
(d) an officer of customs and excise when acting in the course of his duty as such;
(e) a person engaged in the work of any laboratory to which the drug has been for forensic examination when acting in the course of his duty as a person so engaged;
(f) a person engaged in conveying the drug to a person authorised by these Regulations to have it in his possession.

In addition, other persons such as doctors, dentists, veterinary surgeons, pharmacists, etc may supply and possess controlled drugs. Persons who have controlled drugs lawfully prescribed may also be in possession. (Note that this does not apply to cannabis and LSD, as they cannot be prescribed.)

The main offences

These are:
(a) Unlawful production or supply to another of controlled drugs: s4.
(b) Unlawful possession of controlled drugs, and possession with intent to supply to another: s5.
(c) Unlawfully cultivating a cannabis plant: s6.
(d) Occupiers or managers of premises knowingly using, permitting or suffering the smoking of cannabis or cannabis resin: s8.
(e) Smoking or using prepared opium: s9.

A person charged with unlawful possession has a statutory defence, if he has taken possession of the controlled drug in order to prevent someone else from committing an offence, and either destroyed it or handed it to someone lawfully entitled to take custody.

Power to arrest, search and seize

All the offences listed are arrestable offences under s24 of the Police and Criminal Evidence Act 1984, with the exception of possession of a Class C drug.

A constable may, if he reasonably suspects a person to be unlawfully in possession of a controlled drug, detain and search that person or a suspected vehicle and seize anything which may be evidence of an offence (s23).

Any constable may enter the premises of a person carrying on business as a producer or supplier of controlled drugs and inspect books or documents (s23).

Definitions

The following definitions are used in the Act:

'Controlled drug' means any substance or product for the time being specified in Sch 2 to the Act. They are divided into:

Class 'A' drugs, which include morphine, opium, heroin, cocaine, LSD and injectable amphetamines;

Class 'B' drugs, which include amphetamines, codeine, cannabis and cannabis resin;

Class 'C' drugs, which include milder drugs such as mandrax and pipradol.

'Cannabis' (except in the expression 'cannabis resin') means any plant of the genus *Cannabis* or any part of any such plant (by whatever name designated) except that it does not include cannabis resin or any of the following products after separation from the rest of the plant, namely:

(a)   mature stalk of any such plant,

(b)   fibre produced from mature stalk of any such plant, and

(c)   seed of any such plant.

'Cannabis resin' means the separated resin, whether crude or purified, obtained from any plant of the genus *Cannabis.*

'Prepared opium' means opium prepared for smoking and includes dross and any other residues remaining after opium has been smoked.

'Possession', for the purpose of this Act, means the things which a person has in his possession shall be taken to include anything subject to his control which is in the custody of another.

BETTING, GAMING AND LOTTERIES

BETTING (Betting, Gaming and Lotteries Act 1963)

Betting is the staking of money or other valuable thing on the event of a doubtful issue. A bet does not include any bet made or stake hazarded in the course of, or incidental to, any gaming.

Betting is not unlawful in itself, but becomes so when persons:
(a) loiter in or frequent streets or public places to bet; or
(b) use, cause or permit to be used premises for the purpose of betting with persons resorting thereto; except when persons using the premises and persons with whom betting transactions are effected either reside or work on those premises; or a 'betting office licence' is in force for the premises; on approved race-courses when horse racing takes place; on tracks on any day when book making may lawfully take place; on club premises where all members are holders of a bookmaker's permit or betting agency permit.

Street betting (s8)

Any person frequenting or loitering in streets or public places, either on his own behalf or on behalf of any other person, for the purpose of bookmaking, or betting or agreeing to bet, or paying or receiving or settling bets, commits an offence.

Betting with young persons (s21)

It is an offence for any person to have any betting transaction with a young person, or to employ a young person in the effecting of a betting transaction or in a licensed betting office, or to receive or negotiate any bet through a young person.

Licensed betting offices (ss 9,10 and Sch 4)

Licences may be granted to the holder of a bookmaker's permit, or holder of a betting agency permit, or the Horserace Totalisator Board. A licence holder must comply with the following conditions regarding the conduct of his premises:
(a) Must be closed on Sundays, Christmas Day and Good Friday, and on any other day between 6.30 pm and 7.00 am.
(b) No person apparently under 18 years of age to be admitted.

(c) The betting office licence must be displayed.

(d) No television or radio to be provided.

(e) The holder of the licence must not encourage any person to bet.

(f) No refreshments to be served on the premises.

(g) No music, dancing or other entertainment.

The licensee and his servant or agent may refuse to admit, or expel from the premises, any person who is drunk, violent, quarrelsome, or whose presence would subject the licensee to a penalty.

A constable *may,* on request, help to expel from a licensed betting office any person whom he has a reasonable cause to believe to be liable to be expelled therefrom, and he may use such force as may be required for that purpose.

(Note the word 'may'- not 'must' as in the Licensing Act.)

GAMING (Gaming Act 1968. Betting, Gaming and Lotteries Act 1963)

Definitions

'Gaming' means the playing of a game of chance for winnings in money or money's worth, whether any person playing the game is at risk of losing any money or money's worth or not.

'Game of chance' includes a game of chance and skill combined and a pretended game of chance or of chance and skill combined, but does not include any athletic game or sport.

Control of gaming

Gaming is not in itself unlawful, but may become unlawful if it is carried on otherwise than in the place and under the conditions which have been laid down for it.

The Gaming Act 1968 created 'The Gaming Board for Great Britain' to control gaming. The Board has been given wise powers as to the inspection and approval of premises, persons, etc; and works closely with the 'Licensing Authority' which consists of local magistrates sitting at 'Bookmakers, etc Licensing Sessions'. Inspectors are appointed by the Gaming Board to enforce the various conditions imposed by the Act.

Premises cannot be licensed or registered until a prior certificate of approval and consent has been granted by the Gaming Board; and the licensing authority must take into account any advice given to them by the Gaming Board.

In England and Wales no gaming may take place on Sunday between 4 am and 2 pm on any premises in respect of which a licence is in force.

Premises

Subject to certain conditions, gaming may be lawfully conducted in the following premises:
(a) Uncontrolled premises, ie private dwelling-houses on a domestic occasion; or hostels, halls of residence, etc, when the players are wholly or mainly persons who are resident there.
(b) Controlled premises, ie miners' welfare institutes; licensed club premises; clubs registered for gaming; and clubs registered for gaming by machines.

Gaming in public places (s5)

It is an offence for any person to take part in gaming in any street, or other place to which, whether on payment or otherwise, the public have access.

Gaming in licensed premises (s6)

Dominoes, cribbage and any other game approved by the licensing justices may be played on premises in respect of which a Justices 'On' Licence has been granted, provided that the game is not for high stakes, and the playing of the game does not constitute a primary inducement to persons to attend the premises. Gaming by persons under 18 years in licensed premises is absolutely forbidden.

Amusements with prizes (s16)

Gaming in the form of 'amusements with prizes' is lawful, under certain conditions, at either:
(a) Non-commercial entertainments. Where gaming is carried on at an entertainment which has been organised for purposes other than private gain, ie bazaars, sales of work, fetes, dinners, dances, sporting or athletic events or events of a similar character, or
(b) Commercial entertainments. Where gaming is held on premises for which a permit authorising such an 'amusement' has been issued by the Local Rating Authority; or at any pleasure fair, provided by travelling showmen, which is held on premises that

have not been previously used for more than 27 days in that year for the holding of such a fair.

The aggregate amount taken must not exceed £20. Amount paid to participate and money prize must not exceed 30p.

Gaming at small parties, etc (s41)

Gaming may be lawfully carried on at an entertainment to raise money *otherwise than for private gain,* provided that:

(i)   there is one payment only (not exceeding £2.50) for entrance fee, stakes or otherwise to take part in all the games at the entertainment;

(ii) the total value of all the prizes awarded for all the games at any one entertainment must not exceed £250;

(iii) the whole of the proceeds (less expenses) must be applied for purposes other than private gain;

(iv) the expenses deducted must not exceed the reasonable cost of the facilities provided.

GAMING BY MACHINE

The use of machines for gaming is permitted only on premises which are licensed or registered under the Act, with the exception of gaming machines for amusement with prizes.

BINGO

The commercial playing of bingo is governed by s20 and s21 of the Gaming Act 1968. No gaming may take place in bingo club premises except between 10 am and midnight on Saturday, 2 pm and 11 pm on Sunday, and 10 am and 11 pm on other days. The Gaming (Bingo) Act 1985 permits games to be played jointly on different premises in certain circumstances.

LOTTERIES (Lotteries and Amusements Act 1976)

A lottery is a distribution of prizes by lot or change which does not constitute gaming. In order to establish a lottery three elements are required: a distribution of prizes, an element of pure chance, and a contribution by the participant towards the chance.

Section 1 of the Lotteries and Amusements Act 1976 states that all lotteries which do not constitute gaming are unlawful, except as provided by this Act.

The following lotteries are lawful:

Small lotteries incidental to exempt entertainments - s3

(a) Exempt entertainment means a bazaar, sale of work, fete, dinner, dance, sporting or athletic event or entertainment of a similar character, whether limited to one day or extending over two or more days.

(b) The whole proceeds of the entertainment, less expenses of the entertainment, the printing of tickets and not more than £50 for the purchase of prizes, shall be devoted to purposes other than private gain.

(c) None of the prizes shall be money prizes.

(d) Tickets or chances to be sold or issued and the result to be declared on the premises where the entertainment takes place and during the progress of the entertainment.

(e) The lottery shall not be the only, or the only substantial, inducement for persons to attend the entertainment.

Private lotteries - s4

(a) Private lottery means a lottery which is promoted for, and in which the sale of tickets or chances is confined to, members of one society not connected with gaming, betting or lotteries; or persons who all work on the same premises or reside on the same premises.

(b) The whole proceeds, less expenses for printing and stationery, shall be devoted to the provision of prizes; or purposes of the society; or part to prizes and the remainder to such purposes.

(c) There shall not be any advertisement other than on the premises or contained in the ticket.

(d) The price of every ticket or chance shall be the same and shall be stated on the ticket.

(e) Tickets must bear the name and address of the promoter and a statement regarding the restriction on sale and winnings.

(f) No ticket or chance shall be issued except on receipt of full price and no money received shall be returned.

(g) No tickets shall be sent through the post.

Societies' lotteries - s5

(a) Society's lottery means a lottery promoted on behalf of a society which is established and conducted wholly or mainly for charitable purposes; participation in or support of athletic or games or cultural activities; other purposes which are neither purposes of private gain nor purposes of any commercial undertaking.

(b) Must be promoted in Great Britain.

(c) The society must be registered with the local authority.

(d) Must be promoted in accordance with a scheme approved by the society.

(e) Either the total value of tickets or chances to be sold must be (i) £10,000 or less; or (ii) the scheme must be registered with the Board before any tickets or chances are sold.

(f) The whole proceeds, less deductions for lawful expenses or the provision of prizes, shall be applied to purposes of the society (see rules below).

Local lotteries - s6

(a) Local lottery means a lottery promoted by a local authority. It may be promoted for any purpose for which the local authority has power to incur expenditure.

(b) Must be promoted in Great Britain.

(c) Be promoted in accordance with a scheme approved by the local authority.

(d) Be registered with the Board before any tickets or chances are sold (see rules below).

Rules for authorised lotteries

(a) In the case of a society's lottery the promoter shall be a member of the society; and every ticket, notice and advertisement shall specify the name of the society, name and address of the promoter and date of the lottery.

(b) No ticket or chance in a society's or local lottery to exceed £1.00.

(c) The prize of every ticket or chance to be the same, and stated on the ticket.

(d) Tickets or chances must be purchased at full price and no money received to be refunded.

(e) No prize in a society's lottery, where the total value of tickets sold is £10,000 or less, to exceed £2000 in amount or value.

(f) No prize in a society's lottery which is registered with the Board, or in a local lottery, shall exceed £2000 for a short-term lottery, £3000 for a medium-term lottery and £4000 for any other lottery.

(g) The total value of tickets or chances sold in a society's lottery which is registered with the Board, or in local lottery, shall not exceed £20,000 for a short-term lottery, £40,000 for a medium-term lottery, and £80,000 for any other lottery.

(h) A short-term lottery is one held less than one month after a previous lottery. A medium-term lottery is one where less than three months but not less than one month has passed after a previous lottery.

(i) The amount of the proceeds of a society's or a local lottery appropriated for prizes shall not exceed half of the whole proceeds.

(j) The amount of the proceeds of a society's or a local lottery appropriated on account of expenses (exclusive of prizes) shall not exceed whichever is the less of:
   (i) the expenses actually incurred ; and
   (ii) 25% where the whole proceeds do not exceed £10,000; or 15% if over £10,000 or such larger percentage (not exceeding 25%) as the Board may authorise.

Frequency of lotteries

No society or local authority shall hold more than 52 lotteries in any period of 12 months, except in certain circumstances.

Offences (s2)

Subject to the provisions of this section, it is an offence for any person to do any of the following acts:
   (a) Print any tickets for use in the lottery; or
   (b) sell, distribute, offer, advertise or have possession of any ticket or chance for sale or distribution;
   (c) print, publish, or distribute any advertisement, any list of winners or any matter tending to induce persons to take part in a lottery; or
   (d) bring or invite any person to send into Great Britain any ticket in or advertisement of the lottery; or
   (e) send or attempt to send into Great Britain any proceeds from the sale of tickets or any record of the sale of tickets; or
   (f) use any premises or knowingly permit any premises to be used in connection with a lottery; or
   (g) cause, procure or attempt to procure any person to do any of the above acts.

In any proceedings it shall be a defence to prove either that the lottery was not unlawful; that it was a society's or a local lottery and the person charged believed that it was being conducted in accordance with the Act; or that the lottery was not promoted wholly or partly outside Great Britain and constitutes gaming as well as a lottery.

PRIZE COMPETITIONS (s14)

It is unlawful to conduct in or through any newspaper, or in connection with any trade or business or the sale of any article to the public:
  (a) any competition in which prizes are offered for forecasts of the result of a future event, or of a past event the result of which is not yet ascertained or not yet generally known;
  (b) any other competition in which success does not depend to a substantial degree on the exercise of skill.

Chapter 33
Community Legislation

IMMIGRANTS

The Immigration Act 1971, as amended

This Act is concerned with persons who have the right of abode in the United Kingdom, and who shall be free to live in the UK and to come and go without let or hindrance.

A person has the right of abode in the United Kingdom if he is:

(a) a British citizen; or

(b) a Commonwealth citizen, who immediately before the commencement of the British Nationality Act 1981 was a Commonwealth citizen having the right of abode, and has not ceased to be a Commonwealth citizen.

Landing and registration

A non-British citizen (ie a person who does not have the right of abode) who wishes to enter the United Kingdom must seek the permission of an immigration officer before doing so. The owners of aircraft or ships if carrying passengers for reward may only land non-British passengers at certain designated ports or airports.

Restrictions may be placed on non-British citizens regarding employment or occupation or they may be subject to conditions requiring registration with the police.

Preserved powers of arrest (ss 24 and 25)

A constable or immigration officer may arrest without warrant anyone who has, or whom he has reasonable cause to suspect has, committed or attempted to commit any of the following offences:

(a) entering the UK without leave or in breach of deportation order;
(b) having entered, remaining beyond the time, or failing to observe conditions;
(c) without reasonable cause failing to notify change of residence or failing to report to the police or immigration officer if so required.

A constable or immigration officer may also arrest without warrant any person who has or is reasonably suspected of securing or facilitating the entry into the UK of anyone known or reasonably suspected of being an illegal entrant.

Hotel records (Immigration (Hotel Records) Order 1974)

Where the keeper of the premises provides a lodging or sleeping accommodation for reward a register of all persons aged 16 years or more staying one or more nights shall be kept.

All persons shall give name and nationality, if alien, particulars of passport, and upon leaving details of next destination.

Aliens

An alien is a person who is neither a Commonwealth citizen, nor a British protected person, nor a citizen of the Republic of Ireland.

Under the Immigration (Registration with Police) Regulations 1972, aliens are required to register with the police, notify changes of address and absences from home of over two months (regs 5, 6 and 7).

On demand by a constable or immigration officer an alien must produce his registration certificate or give a satisfactory reason for failing to produce it. Where he fails to produce it on demand the alien may be required to produce it within 48 hours at a police station specified by the constable or immigration officer (reg 11).

PEDLARS (Pedlars Act 1871)

A pedlar is a hawker, petty chapman, tinker, caster of metals, mender of chairs, or other person who, without horse or other beast bearing or drawing burden, travels and trades on foot and goes from town to town or to other men's houses, carrying to sell or exposing for sale any goods, wares or merchandise immediately to be delivered or offering for sale his skill in handicraft.

A pedlar's certificate is issued by a chief officer of police; remains in force one year from date of issue; and authorises trading in any part of the

United Kingdom. It is not transferable.

To obtain the grant of a certificate the applicant must have resided in the district for at least one month; be 17 years of age or over; be a person of good character and intend in good faith to carry on trade as a pedlar.

Production of certificate

A pedlar must produce his certificate at all times on demand to a justice; a police officer; a person to whom he offers his goods for sale; and any person in whose private grounds or premises he is found.

Commercial travellers, book agents with written authority of publishers, sellers of vegetables, fish, fruit or victuals, and sellers in legally established markets or fairs are exempt from the need for a pedlar's certificate.

Inspection of pack

Any police constable may open and inspect any pack, box, trunk or case in which a pedlar carries his goods. If he refuses or prevents inspection he commits an offence.

SCRAP METAL DEALERS (Scrap Metal Dealers Act 1964)

A scrap metal dealer includes anyone who carries on a business which consists wholly or partly of buying and selling scrap metal whether the scrap metal is sold in the form in which it was bought or otherwise.

An itinerant collector means a person regularly engaged in collecting waste materials and old, broken, worn out or defaced articles by means of visits from house to house.

Conditions

Every scrap metal dealer must:
  (a) register his name and address and each place of business with the local authority;
  (b) notify any change within 28 days and renew registration every three years;
  (c) keep a record in a bound book of all scrap metal received, showing date and time of receipt, the full name and address of the seller, and description, weight of metal, price paid, and if delivered by motor

vehicle its registration mark. Similar records must be kept when the metal is processed or despatched.

Itinerant collectors may be exempted from condition (c) but they must keep receipts of sale of scrap metal for two years.

When a scrap metal dealer is convicted of contravening the above conditions or of any offence involving dishonesty, the court may make an order lasting not more than two years, to the effect that any scrap metal received must remain unaltered for 72 hours and no metal shall be received between 6.00 pm and 8.00 am the following day.

Other offences

Apart from the above offences it is an offence for a scrap metal dealer to acquire any scrap metal from a person apparently under the age of 16 years, or for any person to sell scrap metal to a dealer and give a false name or address.

Police powers

Any constable has a right to enter and inspect, at all reasonable times, any place for the time being entered in the register of scrap metal dealers kept by the local authority.

Any constable may require the production of, and inspect, any scrap metal kept at that place and any book which the dealer is required to keep and to take copies of or extracts from any such book or receipt.

VAGRANCY

The Vagrancy Act 1824 arranges offenders in three categories:
(a) Idle and disorderly persons (s3).
(b) Rogues and vagabonds (s4).
(c) Incorrigible rogues (s5).

The following are some of the offences under the Act:
(a) Begging (s3). Every person wandering abroad or placing himself in a public place, street, court or passage to beg or gather alms, or causing or procuring or encouraging any child or children to beg.
(b) Exposing wounds to gather alms (s4). Every person wandering abroad and endeavouring by the exposure of wounds or deformities to obtain or gather alms.
(c) Sleeping out (s4). Every person wandering abroad and lodging in any barn or outhouse or in any deserted or unoccupied building, or

in the open air, or in any tent, cart, or waggon (in which he does not travel) and not giving a good account of himself, provided he declines any reasonably accessible free shelter, or persistently sleeps out, or causes or is likely to cause damage or infection or other offensive consequence to property.
(d) Fraudulent collections (s4). Every person going about as a gatherer or collector of alms, or endeavouring to procure charitable contributions of any nature or kind, under any false or fraudulent pretence.
Other vagrancy offences have been dealt with earlier.

LATE NIGHT REFRESHMENT HOUSES (Late Night Refreshment Houses Act 1969)

A late night refreshment house is any house, room, shop or building kept open for public refreshment, resort and entertainment at any time between the hours of 10 o'clock at night and 5 o'clock the following morning, other than a house, room, shop or building which is licensed for the sale of beer, cider, wine or spirits.

A licence issued by the local authority is required if the premises are open for sale of refreshments between 10 o'clock and 5 o'clock.

The following offences may be committed by the proprietor:
(a) Knowingly allowing gaming on the premises.
(b) Knowingly allowing prostitutes, thieves and drunken persons to assemble on the premises.
(c) Refusing to admit a constable on duty.

Police officers may enter licensed refreshment houses at any time, and must help to expel drunken or disorderly persons on request of the keeper.

STREET AND HOUSE TO HOUSE COLLECTIONS

Street collections

Section 5 of the Police, Factories, etc (Miscellaneous Provisions) Act 1916 gives power to a police authority to make regulations with respect to the places and the conditions in which persons may be permitted to sell articles or collect money for charitable purposes.

These regulations may vary slightly in different areas, but usually require:
(a) a permit from the Chief Officer of Police;
(b) the issue of a written authority to each collecter;
(c) the use of closed and sealed receptacles for money;

(d) that no person is paid for services rendered;
(e) that a financial statement be tendered;
(f) that no obstruction or annoyance be caused;
(g) the wearing of badges by collectors;
(h) a minimum age of 16 years for collectors except members of recognised youth organisations.

House to house collections

The House to House Collections Act 1939 deals with collections from the public for charity by visits to houses and business premises; it directs that no such charitable collection be made without authority under the Act. (A house to house collection may be combined with a street collection in the same appeal.)

A person may be authorised to hold a house to house collection in the following ways:

(a) by licence granted by the local authority for periods up to 18 months;
(b) by an order of exemption granted by the Secretary of State (national collections);
(c) by a certificate of exemption granted by a Chief Officer of Police (local collections of short duration).

Under the House to House Collections Regulations 1947 the holder of a licence, or order or certificate of exemption, must comply with the following requirements:

(a) each collector must have a certificate of authority;
(b) each collector must have a badge showing the purpose of the collection;
(c) each collector must have a collecting box or a receipt book. The purpose of the collection and a distinguishing number must be on the wrapper of each box;
(d) each collector must sign his name on his certificate of authority and on his badge and wear the badge in a prominent position;
(e) the minimum age for collectors of money is 16, except for members of recognised youth organisations.

The unauthorised use of badges or certificates is an offence.

Police powers

A police officer may require any person whom he believes to be acting as a collector to declare his name and address and to sign his name. He may also demand the production of a certificate of authority.

LITTER

The Litter Act 1958 makes it an offence for any person without proper authority to *throw down, drop* or otherwise *deposit* in, into or from any place in the open air to which the public are permitted to have access without payment, and *leave* anything whatsoever in such circumstances as to cause, contribute to, or tend to lead to, the defacement by litter of any place in the open air.

For this purpose any covered place open to the air on at least one side and available for public use shall be treated as being a place in the open air.

A court in sentencing may have regard to the risk of injury to persons or animals, or damage to property, that may be caused by the litter (Dangerous Litter Act 1971).

NOISE ABATEMENT

Section 62 of the Control of Pollution Act 1974 deals with noise in streets.

Subject to certain exceptions a loudspeaker in a street shall not be operated:

    (a) between the hours of *nine in the evening and eight the following morning, for any purpose;*

    (b) *at any other time,* for the purpose of *advertising any entertainment, trade or business;**

and any person who operates or permits the operation of a loudspeaker in contravention of this subsection shall be guilty of an offence.

'Street' means a highway and any other road, footway, square or court which is for the time being open to the public.

*Para (b) above shall not apply to the operation of a loudspeaker between the hours of noon and seven in the evening on the same day if the loudspeaker:

    (a) is fixed to a vehicle which is being used for the conveyance of a perishable commodity for human consumption; and

    (b) is operated solely for informing members of the public (otherwise than by means of words) that the commodity is on sale from the vehicle; and

    (c) is so operated as not to give reasonable cause for annoyance to persons in the vicinity.

The following uses are exempted from the above provisions:

    (a) police, fire brigade, or ambulance purposes, a water authority in the exercise of its functions, or by a local authority within its area;

    (b) communicating with persons on a vessel for the purpose of directing the movement of that or any other vessel;

    (c) if the loudspeaker forms part of a public telephone system;

(d) if the loudspeaker:
    (i)   is in or fixed to a vehicle, and
    (ii) is operated solely for the entertainment of or for communicating with the driver or a passenger of the vehicle or, where the loudspeaker is or forms part of the horn or similar warning instrument of the vehicle, solely for giving warning to other traffic, and
    (iii) is so operated as not to give reasonable cause for annoyance to persons in the vicinity;
(e) otherwise than on a highway, by persons employed in connection with a transport undertaking used by the public in a case where the loudspeaker is operated solely for making announcements to passengers or prospective passengers or to the persons so employed;
(f) by a travelling showman on land which is being used for the purpose of a pleasure fair;
(g) in case of emergency.

POSTAL OFFENCES

Offences connected with the postal services are dealt with by the Post Office Act 1953. Some of the offences contained in the Act are as follows:

Prohibition on sending certain articles by post (s11)

A person shall not send or attempt to send or procure to be sent a postal packet which:
(a) save as the Postmaster General may either generally or in any particular case allow, encloses any explosive, dangerous, noxious or deleterious substance, any filth, any sharp instrument not properly protected, any noxious living creature, or any creature, article or thing whatsoever which is likely to injure either other postal packets in course of conveyance or an officer of the Post Office; or
(b) contains any indecent or obscene print, painting, photograph, lithograph, engraving, cinematograph film, book, card or written communication, or any indecent or obscene article, whether similar to the above or not; or
(c) has on the packet, or on the cover thereof, any words, marks or designs, which are grossly offensive or of an indecent or obscene character.

Carelessness, negligence or misconduct of postal employees (s59)

Any person employed to convey or deliver mail bags or postal packets must not:

(a) without authority or whilst the mail bag or postal packet is in his custody or possession, leave it, or suffer any person, not being the person in charge thereof, to ride in the place appointed for the person in charge thereof in or upon any vehicle used for the conveyance thereof, or to ride in or upon a vehicle so used and not licensed to carry passengers, or upon a horse used for the conveyance on horseback thereof;

(b) be guilty of any act of drunkenness whilst so employed;

(c) be guilty of carelessness, negligence or other misconduct whereby the safety of the mail bag or postal packet is endangered;

(d) without authority collect, receive, convey or deliver a postal packet otherwise than in the ordinary course of post;

(e) give any false information of an assault or attempt at robbery upon him; or

(f) loiter on the road or passage, or wilfully misspend his time so as to retard the progress or delay the arrival of a mail bag or postal packet in the course of transmission by post, or fail to use due care and diligence safely to convey a mail bag or postal packet at the due rate of speed.

Placing of injurious substances in or on a letter box (s60)

A person shall not place or attempt to place in or against any post office letter box or telephone kiosk or cabinet any fire, match, light, explosive substance, dangerous substance, filth, noxious or deleterious substance, or fluid, and shall not commit a nuisance in or against any post office letter box or telephone kiosk or cabinet and shall not do or attempt to do anything likely to injure the box, kiosk or cabinet or its appurtenances or contents.

Disfiguring letter boxes (s61)

A person shall not without due authority affix or attempt to affix any placard, advertisement, notice, list, document, board or thing in or on, or paint or tar, any post office, post office letter box, telegraph post or other property belonging to or used by or on behalf of the Postmaster General, and shall not in any way disfigure any such office, box, post or property.

Obstructing or molesting postmen (s65)

Wilfully obstructing or molesting or inciting anyone to obstruct or molest, an officer of the Post Office in the execution of his duty, or whilst in any post office or within any premises belonging to any post office or used therewith obstruct the course of business of the Post Office.

Note that it is also an offence to assault or obstruct a person engaged in public telecommunications, under s46 of the Telecommunications Act 1984.

MENTAL HEALTH

The Mental Health Act 1983 provides for the treatment and care of mentally disordered persons. The following parts of the Act are of interest to police officers:

Return of mental patients who are absent without leave (s138)

Any constable and certain other persons may take into custody any mentally disordered person who has absented himself from hospital without leave, or failed to return after leave, and return him to the hospital.

Mentally disordered persons found in public places (s136)

A constable who finds a person in a public place who appears to be suffering from mental disorder and to be in need of care or control, may remove him to a place of safety. He may be detained there for not more than 72 hours for the purpose of examination and interview.

Definitions

'Mental disorder' means mental illness, arrested or incomplete development of mind, psychopathic disorder, and any other disorder or disability of mind.

'Severe mental impairment' means a state of arrested or incomplete development of mind which includes severe impairment of intelligence and social functioning and is associated with abnormally aggressive or seriously irresponsible conduct on the part of the person concerned.

'Mental impairment' means a state of arrested or incomplete development of mind (not amounting to severe mental impairment) which includes significant impairment of intelligence and social functioning and is associated with abnormally aggressive or seriously irresponsible conduct on the part of the person concerned.

'Psychopathic disorder' means a persistent disorder or disability of mind (whether or not including significant impairment of intelligence) which results in abnormally aggressive or seriously irresponsible conduct on the part of the person concerned.

WIRELESS - OFFENCES IN CONNECTION WITH WIRELESS TELEGRAPHY

Wireless Telegraphy Act 1949

Section 1: It is an offence for any person to establish a wireless telegraphy station or use any wireless telegraphy apparatus without a licence.

Section 5(a) creates the offences of sending, or attempting to send, any false or misleading wireless messages, in particular any message falsely suggesting that a vessel or aircraft is in distress. It is an offence under 5(b) to listen to wireless messages without authority with intent to obtain information, or to disclose any information obtained. (These offences cover the use of radio scanners.)

Section 13 states that it is an offence to use any apparatus for interfering with wireless telegraphy.

A justice on sworn information may issue a search warrant authorising persons authorised by the Postmaster General to enter and inspect any premises, vehicles, vessels or aircraft and to test any apparatus found.

MALICIOUS COMMUNICATIONS ACT 1988

Any person who sends to another person:
- (a) a letter or other article which conveys a message which is indecent or grossly offensive; a threat; or information which is false and known or believed to be false by the sender; or
- (b) any other article which is, in whole or part, of an indecent or grossly offensive nature,

is guilty of an offence if his purpose is to cause distress or anxiety to the recipient or to any other person to whom he intends it should be communicated.

Chapter 34
Public Safety

THEATRES (Theatres Act 1968; Sunday Theatre Act 1972)

All premises used for public performance of any play must be licensed and comply with rules and conditions considered necessary in the interest of public safety or health. Public performances of a stage play may not take place on a Sunday at premises so licensed, between 2.00 am (3.00 am in the inner London area) and 2.00 pm.

'Play' is defined as:

(a) any dramatic piece whether involving improvisation or not, which is given wholly or in part by one or more persons actually present and performing and in which the whole or a major portion of what is done by the person or persons performing, whether by way of speech, singing or action, involves the playing of a role; and

(b) any ballet given wholly or in part by one or more persons actually present and performing, whether or not it falls within para (a).

The licensing authority for premises in Greater London is the Greater London Council; and for the remainder of England and Wales, the county council.

Obscene plays

There is no censorship of plays before performance, but it is an offence to present a play which is obscene or defamatory; or with intent to, or which is likely to, stir up racial hatred or occasion a breach of the peace.

The prohibitions on obscenity and defamation do not apply to a play given on a domestic occasion in a private dwelling. None of the provisions apply to rehearsals; or to enable records or films to be made by means of the performance or the performance to be broadcast or transmitted via a diffusion service.

Powers of entry

A police officer at all reasonable times may enter premises in respect of which a licence is in force and where he has reason to believe a play is being, or is about to be, performed in order to see that the conditions of the licence are being complied with. It is an offence to wilfully obstruct him.

CINEMAS (Cinemas Act 1985)

No premises shall be used for a film exhibition unless licensed for the purpose and complying with safety regulations. Licences are granted by local councils after consultation with the fire authority and the chief officer of police.

'Film exhibition' means any exhibition of moving pictures which is produced otherwise than by the simultaneous reception and exhibition of television programmes broadcast by the BBC or IBA, or programmes included in a cable programme service which is, or does not require to be, licensed under the Cable and Broadcasting Act 1984.

There are the following exemptions from the need for a licence:
(a) Exhibitions in private dwelling houses, to which the public are not admitted.
(b) Premises used not more than six days in a year, provided seven days' notice is given to the police and the licensing authority.
(c) Exhibitions to which the public are not admitted or are admitted without payment.
(d) Exhibitions whose sole or main purpose is to demonstrate any product, advertise goods or services, or provide information, education or instruction.

The Cinematograph (Safety) Regulations 1955 prescribe certain conditions with regard to safety which apply to the auditoriums and projection boxes of cinemas.

Children in Cinemas (Cinematograph (Children) (No 2) Regulations 1955)

If over 100 children attend an entertainment for children, given elsewhere than in a private dwelling house, there must be sufficient adult attendants to take safety precautions. The police have right of entry to such entertainments under the Children and Young Persons Act. A child is a person under 16.

No child apparently under five years of age must be admitted to any cinema performance unless accompanied by a person over 16 years of age.

No child apparently under 12 years of age to be admitted to any cinema performance after 7.00 pm unless accompanied by a person over 16 years, except where the film or portion of film has not been shown before 7.00 pm on that day.

At children's performances there must be at least one attendant for every 100 (or part of 100) children on the ground floor, and one attendant for every 50 (or part of 50) children on other floors; in any case there must be an attendant for each exit.

Police powers

A constable may at all reasonable times enter premises, licensed or not, where he has reason to believe that a cinematograph exhibition is being or is about to be given, to see that the law is being observed.

MUSIC, SINGING AND DANCING

Premises kept for public music, singing or dancing are licensed by the licensing justices or the local authority in certain areas (usually towns) where Part IV of the Public Health Acts Amendment Act 1890 has been adopted. Conditions are imposed regarding the hours of entertainment and conduct of the premises. Liquor licensed premises do not require a music, singing and dancing licence for recorded music or broadcast performances, or for live music by not more than two performers.

The practice of hypnotism in such licensed premises and elsewhere can be regulated by the local authorities under the Hypnotism Act 1952.

LIBRARIES (Libraries Offences Act 1898)

This Act provides penalties for disorderly conduct, the use of bad language and betting and gambling in libraries. It is also an offence to remain in a library after closing hours after having been requested to leave.

PRIVATE PLACES OF ENTERTAINMENT (LICENSING) ACT 1967

Where an entertainment is private but is promoted for private gain, premises (with certain exceptions) require to be licensed by the local authority in areas where the Act has been adopted. It may be a condition of the licence that police have right of entry.

RAILWAYS

The basic offences relating to railways are trespass upon railway property and throwing stones in a manner likely to cause damage. Both of these offences may be dealt with under the British Transport Commission Act 1949.

Wanton or malicious damage to railway property is an offence under s67 of the Transport Act 1972.

Other offences specifically relating to railways have been dealt with earlier in the section on the Malicious Damage Act 1861.

AIR TRANSPORT AND NAVIGATION

The Air Navigation Order 1985 deals with the following matters:

Part I	Registration and marking of aircraft
Part II	Air operator's certificates
Part III	Airworthiness and equipment of aircraft
Part IV	Aircraft crew and licensing
Part V	Operation of aircraft
Part VI	Fatigue of crew
Part VII	Documents and records
Part VIII	Control of air traffic
Part IX	Aerodromes, aeronautical lights and dangerous lights
Part X	General

Only a few of these subjects are of interest to the police and these are as follows:

Airworthiness

With certain exceptions, no aircraft registered in the United Kingdom shall fly unless there is in force in relation to it:
  (a) A certificate of airworthiness.
  (b) A certificate of maintenance, if used for public transport, etc.
  (c) A certificate of compliance, if any overhaul, repair, etc has been made.

Licensing of crew

Members of the flight crew of a registered aircraft (ie pilot, navigator, engineer and radio operator) must be of the number and description specified in the certificate of airworthiness, be of the required age, and each hold the necessary licence of competency according to his duties as a member of the crew and the type of aircraft. A person under 17 cannot be in sole control of an aircraft in motion, and a person under 16 cannot be in control of a glider. A licence must be signed forthwith in ink by the holder. A licence issued under the law of another country can be rendered valid for the UK by a certificate of validation issued by the CAA. Article 23 prohibits the giving of instruction in flying while in flight except by a fully qualified instructor.

Documents and records

Some or all of the following documents must be carried by British aircraft, except when a flight is solely within the United Kingdom and begins and ends at the same aerodrome:

- (a) Certificate of registration.
- (b) Certificate of airworthiness.
- (c) Licences of flight crew.
- (d) Wireless licence and current telecommunications log book.
- (e) Copy of certificate of maintenance.
- (f) Copy of load sheet - if cargo carried.
- (g) Technical log.
- (h) Operations manual.

Which documents are carried depends on the purpose or destination of the flight.

The commander of an aircraft must produce all documents required to be carried on an aircraft in flight, within a reasonable time of a request by an authorised person.

Offences relating to aircraft

- (a) Flying in such a manner as to be the cause of unnecessary danger to any person on property (Civil Aviation Act 1982, s81).
- (b) Flying over any congested area of a city, town or settlement at a height less than 1500 feet above the highest fixed object within 2000 feet, except a helicopter with the permission in writing of the CAA (Rule 5, Rules of the Air Regulations 1991).
- (c) The Rules of the Air also cover the conduct of passengers and create offences such as being drunk on an aircraft, acting in a manner likely to endanger the aircraft or stowing away.

Offences committed in aircraft in flight over the United Kingdom are dealt with in the same way as they would be if committed on land. This applies to any nationality of aircraft.

The Tokyo Convention Act 1967 permits any offence committed in a British aircraft elsewhere than over the United Kingdom, to be dealt with as if committed in the United Kingdom. The consent of the DPP is necessary to prosecute in these cases.

Police powers

Under article 84 of the Rules of the Air any authorised person (which includes a constable) is empowered to enter at all reasonable times any aerodrome, or any place where an aircraft is landed, for the purpose of inspecting:

  (a) the aerodrome,
  (b) any aircraft on the aerodrome or other place,
  (c) any document which he has power to demand under the Order.

MAJOR INCIDENT PROCEDURE

Major incidents may include a wide range of occurrences, such as train or aircraft crashes, motorway accidents, large fires, mine disasters, serious floodings, etc. All police forces have their own basic procedure for dealing with these incidents. It should be remembered that one of the main problems at the scene is obstruction by traffic and sightseers.

Aircraft in distress

If the police see an aircraft crash or in apparent distress, they should telephone their stations and the nearest fire and ambulance services, giving the following information:

  (a) type of aircraft or details which may identify it;
  (b) where crashed, or direction of flight and estimated height;
  (c) time seen;
  (d) nature of distress.

At the scene of a crashed aircraft, police action should be as follows:

  (a) All vehicles and personnel approach a crash from an up-wind and up-hill position. Keep the wind on your back and stay up-hill at all times if possible.
  (b) Onlookers must be kept up-hill and up-wind.
  (c) Nobody must be allowed to smoke in the vicinity of any crash.
  (d) Under no circumstances must persons remove any part of a crashed aircraft. The part taken may be required by the accident prevention officers to help them determine why the aircraft crashed.

   (e) Should the crash be in the vicinity of occupied property, steps should be taken to inform the inhabitants of the danger. They should be advised to shut all doors and windows and remove curtains, turn off gas and electricity at the mains, damp down coal fires and refrain from striking matches.

   (f) If it is thought advisable that the occupants should leave the property, they should do so by the doors or windows farthest from the incident.

   (g) All vehicles should be parked up-hill and up-wind of the aircraft.

In addition to the foregoing, in the case of military aircraft, the following procedure shall be adopted:

   (a) No one should touch bodies or wreckage until competent authorities arrive on the scene, *unless it is essential to do so.*

   (b) *If it is essential,* those doing so should photograph the body in situ, if possible, disturb the wreckage as little as possible and note everything they do or displace. A body which has to be moved may be taken to the nearest mortuary.

   (c) No clothing or equipment should be removed from the bodies except by an Air Force medical officer or pathologist.

   (d) Where fire or explosion occurs and the aircraft is believed to be carrying nuclear weapons, no attempt should be made to save lives or fight fires. If an approach is necessary it should be made from up-wind avoiding any smoke or fires. Any person who has been within 500 yards should be requested to remain until examined for presence of any radioactive substances. They should also be advised not to smoke, eat or drink.

   (e) Vehicles should be parked to the side of the aircraft and not too near. Care should be taken to see that they are not in line with guns, or rockets, or in front of or behind jet engines.

Chapter 35
Trade Disputes and Elections, etc

TRADE DISPUTES

Section 29 of the Trade Union and Labour Relations Act 1974 defines a trade dispute as a dispute between employers and workers, or between workers and workers, which is connected with terms and conditions of employment, allocation of work, matters of discipline and membership of unions, etc.

Intimidation and like offences

Section 7 of the Conspiracy and Protection of Property Act 1875 provides that the following shall be offences:

Every person who with a view to compel any other person to abstain from doing or to do any act, which such other person has a right to do or abstain from doing, wrongfully and without legal authority:

(a) uses violence to intimidate any other person or his wife or children, or injures his property; or

(b) persistently follows any other person about from place to place; or

(c) hides any tools, clothes or other property owned by such other person, or deprives him of or hinders him in the use thereof; or

(d) watches or besets the house or other place where such other person resides, or works or carries on business, or happens to be or the approach to such house or place; or

(e) follows such other person with two or more other persons in a disorderly manner in or through any street or road.

A constable may arrest without warrant anyone he reasonably suspects is committing an offence under this section.

Picketing

Section 15 of the Trade Union and Labour Relations Act 1974 defines peaceful picketing. It shall be lawful for one or more persons in contemplation or furtherance of a trade dispute to attend:
  (a) at or near his own place of work, or
  (b) if he is an official of a trade union, at or near the place of work of a member of that union whom he is accompanying and whom he represents,
for the purpose only of peacefully obtaining or communicating information or peacefully persuading any person to work or not to work.

This is the authority for picketing, but picketing only remains lawful so long as it is carried out in a peaceful manner. If there is any kind of intimidation an offence is committed under s7 of the Conspiracy and Protection of Property Act 1875.

The Act has not laid down any limit to the number of a picket, but where a crowd watching or besetting any works is so disproportionate in size to what is needed for lawful purposes as to exclude the idea of peaceful persuasion, the Act may cease to apply, and the person taking part in the demonstration would then become liable to be charged with watching or besetting. The Code of Practice on Picketing suggests a maximum of six persons.

(See Public Order Act 1986 in Chapter 22.)

ELECTIONS

The Representation of the People Act 1983 deals with the conduct of parliamentary and local government elections. The duties of the police at election times are to preserve law and order in the usual manner, and in addition to deal with public meetings and assist presiding officers at polling stations to prevent any misconduct.

Offences

Section 60 creates the offence of personation which is voting in the name of some other person whether living, dead or fictitious. Two witnesses are necessary to prove this offence.

Section 100 provides that no member of a police force may persuade any person to vote or not vote. This is known as illegal canvassing.

Section 113 is the offence of bribery or giving of consideration of value to induce a voter to vote or refrain from voting.

Section 114 deals with treating which is the providing or accepting of any meat, drink or entertainment to influence any person to vote or refrain from voting.

Section 115 is undue influence. This is using or threatening to use any force, restraint or threats to make a person vote or refrain from voting.

Disturbances at election meetings are dealt with under s97 in respect of political meetings held between the date of issue of a writ for the return of an MP and the date he is returned, or local government election meetings within three weeks of the election date.

It is an offence for a person at a lawful public meeting to act, or incite others to act, in a disorderly manner for the purpose of preventing the transaction of the business for which the meeting was called.

DISTURBING PUBLIC WORSHIP

Sections 2 and 3 of the Ecclesiastical Courts Jurisdiction Act 1860 make riotous, violent or indecent behaviour an offence in any place of religious worship at any time, or in any churchyard or burial ground.

TRESPASS

Trespass is a *civil* wrong. There are three main types:
   (a) Trespass to the person - includes assaults, batteries and false imprisonment.
   (b) Trespass to goods - involves interference with the possession of goods.
   (c) Trespass to land - involves entry on land or premises in the possession of another.

If called upon to assist in the ejection of a trespasser, a constable should act with caution, and if after proper enquiry the trespasser refuses to leave, he may give the necessary physical aid required. A constable in these circumstances is acting in the capacity of a private person aiding the occupier and he is not acting in the execution of his duty.

(See offences of entering and remaining on property in Chapter 25, and trespass offence on page 200).

Chapter 36
Children and Young Persons

CARE PROCEEDINGS

Care and supervision orders

Section 31 of the Children Act 1989 provides that on the application of any
local authority or authorised person, a court may make an order:
- (a) placing the child with respect to whom the application is made in
    the care of a designated local authority; or
- (b) putting him under the supervision of a designated local authority
    or of a probation officer.

A court may only make a care order or supervision order if it is satisfied:
- (a) that the child concerned is suffering, or is likely to suffer, signifi-
    cant harm; and
- (b) that the harm, or likelihood of harm, is attributable to - (i) the care
    being given to the child, or likely to be given to him if the order
    were not made, not being what it would be reasonable to expect a
    parent to give to him; or (ii) the child's being beyond parental
    control.

No care or supervision order may be made with respect to a child who
has reached the age of 17 (or 16, in the case of a child who is married).

'Authorised person' means:
- (a) the National Society for the Prevention of Cruelty to Children and
    any of its officers; and
- (b) any person authorised by order of the Secretary of State to bring
    proceedings under this section and any officer of a body which is
    so authorised.

'Harm' means ill-treatment or the impairment of health or development.

'Development' means physical, intellectual, emotional, social or
behavioural development.

'Health' means physical or mental health.

'Ill-treatment' includes sexual abuse and forms of ill-treatment which are not physical.

Police involvement in the Children Act 1989

Section 46 of the Children Act 1989 provides that where a constable has reasonable cause to believe that a child would otherwise be likely to suffer significant harm, he may remove the child to suitable accommodation and keep him there; or take such steps as are reasonable to ensure the child's removal from any hospital or other place in which he is then being accommodated is prevented.

A child with respect to whom a constable has exercised powers under this section is referred to as having been taken into police protection.

As soon as is reasonably practicable after taking a child into police protection, the constable concerned shall:

(a)   inform the local authority within whose area the child was found of the steps that have been, and are proposed to be, taken with respect to the child and the reason for taking them;

(b)   give details to the authority within whose area the child is ordinarily resident of the place at which the child is being accommodated;

(c)   inform the child (if he appears capable of understanding) of the steps that have been taken with respect to him and of the reasons for taking them; and of the further steps that may be taken with respect to him;

(d)   take such steps as are reasonably practicable to discover the wishes and feelings of the child;

(e)   secure that the case is inquired into by an officer designated for the purposes of this section by the chief officer of the police area concerned; and

(f)   where the child was taken into police protection by being removed to accommodation which is not provided by or on behalf of a local authority or as a refuge for children at risk, secure that he is moved to accommodation which is so provided.

As soon as is reasonably practicable after taking a child into police protection, the constable concerned shall take such steps as are reasonably practicable to inform:

(a)   the child's parents;

(b)   every person who is not a parent of his but who has parental responsibility for him; and

(c)   any other person with whom the child was living immediately before being taken into police protection,

of the steps that he has taken with respect to the child, the reasons for taking them and the further steps that may be taken with respect to him.

No child may be kept in police protection for more than 72 hours. While a child is being kept in police protection, the designated officer may apply on behalf of the appropriate authority for an emergency protection order to be made with respect to the child.

Where a child has been taken into police protection, the designated officer shall allow the following persons to have such contact (if any) with the child as, in his opinion, is both reasonable and in the child's best interests:

(a) the child's parents;
(b) any person who is not a parent of the child but who has parental responsibility for him;
(c) any person with whom the child was living immediately before he was taken into police protection;
(d) any person in whose favour a contact order is in force with respect to the child;
(e) any person who is allowed to have contact with the child by virtue of parental contact order; and
(f) any person acting on behalf of any of those persons.

Under s48 a warrant may be issued authorising a constable to assist persons attempting to exercise powers under emergency protection orders for the discovery of children who may be in such need.

By virtue of s50 a court may make a recovery order if there is reason to believe that a child has been abducted, or has run away or is staying away from a responsible person, or is missing. 'Authorised person' for this purpose includes any constable.

MISCELLANEOUS MATTERS

Some ages fixed by law

Under 5 years	Minding such children for reward from more than one household needs registration. Intoxicants must not be given.
5 years or over	Education compulsory.
Under 7 years	A person must not be drunk in charge of such a child in a public place.
Under 10 years	Not criminally responsible for his acts.
Under 12 years	Must not be trained in dangerous performances. Must not be sold an animal as a pet.
Under 13 years	Gunpowder must not be sold to such a child. May not be employed.
Under 14 years	If 10 years or over, is criminally responsible if proved to have sufficient capacity to know what he or she is

	doing is wrong. Rag dealer must not give child any article whatsoever. Boy cannot be convicted of rape or other offence involving sexual intercourse.
14 years or over	Criminally responsible for acts. Summary court may order his fingerprints and palmprints to be taken by the police.
Under 15 years	Not admitted to a knacker's yard.
Under 16 years	Alien need not register. Cigarettes must not be sold to, or smoked by, in public. Liqueur chocolates must not be sold to. Fireworks may not be supplied to. Marriage of person under 16 is void. May not drive any motor vehicle. Education compulsory if 5 or over.
Under 17 years	At a police station must be released on bail unless good reason to the contrary. Pedlar's certificate must not be issued to such person.

Employment

The Children and Young Persons Act 1933, s18, and the Children and Young Persons Act 1963, s34.

Generally no child shall be employed:

(a) Until his age is 13 years.

(b) Before the close of his day's school hours, but byelaws may allow a child to be employed for one hour before his day's school hours, eg newspaper boy.

(c) Before 7.00 am or after 7.00 pm for not more than two hours on any school days.

(d) On a Sunday for more than two hours.

(e) To lift, carry or move anything so heavy as to be likely to cause injury to him.

Section 18(2) empowers local authorities to make byelaws in respect of children. These byelaws may vary considerably between different local authorities. Subsection (3) provides that nothing in this section or any byelaw shall prevent a child from taking part in a performance licensed under this Act.

Street trading

Section 20 of the Children and Young Persons Act 1933 states that no person under the age of 17 years shall engage or be employed in street trading.

(Note that byelaws may permit young persons under the age of 17 years to be employed by their *parents* in street trading. Byelaws may also regulate or prohibit street trading by persons under the age of 18 years.)

Street trading means seeking business in the street, and does not include business between shop and customer in their home. It is not confined to trading on a person's own account, but includes the hawking of newspapers, matches, flowers, etc and playing musical instruments or singing in streets or public places. A person shall be deemed to be employed notwithstanding that he receives no payment for his work.

However, choristers taking part in a religious service or in choir practice for a religious service, whether for reward or not, shall *not* be deemed to be employed.

Dangerous performances

Section 23 of the 1933 Act provides that no person under the age of 16 years shall take part in a performance in which his life or limbs are endangered. This offence may be committed by any person who causes or procures such young persons to commit the act, or his parent or guardian by allowing it.

Section 24 states that no person under 12 years of age shall be trained to take part in a performance of a dangerous nature, and that persons between 12 and 16 years must be licensed by the local authority.

NEGLECT AND CRUELTY TO CHILDREN

The Children and Young Persons Act 1933, as amended, deals with offences in connection with children and young persons.

The offences created by the Act and the purpose for which they were enacted, fall roughly into three categories:
  (a) the prevention of physical cruelty;
  (b) the prevention of moral danger;
  (c) the prevention of injury other than by cruelty.

Definitions

A *child* is a person under the age of 14 years.

A *young person* is a person who has attained the age of 14 years and is under the age of 17 years.

An *adult* is a person who is, in the opinion of the court before which he is charged, of the age of 17 years or upwards.

The main offences under the 1933 Act

(a) Cruelty to persons under 16. Committed by persons of 16 years and over having responsibility for any child or young person under 16 years. It must be proved that the offender wilfully assaults, ill-treats, neglects, abandons or exposes in a manner likely to cause unnecessary suffering or injury to health (s1).

(b) Brothels. It is an offence for any person having responsibility for a juvenile between 4 and 16 years to allow the juvenile to reside in or frequent a brothel (s3).

(c) Begging. It is an offence to allow any person under 16 years to be in any street premises or place for the purpose of begging or getting alms (s4).

(d) Giving intoxicants. No person must give or cause to be given intoxicants to a child under the age of five years except on a doctor's order, or in the case of sickness or other urgent cause (s5).

(e) Sale of tobacco. It is an offence to sell tobacco or cigarette papers to a person under 16 years ('tobacco' includes cigarettes, tobacco substitute smoking mixtures, and any tobacco product for oral or nasal use), and a constable has a duty to seize any tobacco from a person under 16 found smoking in a street or public place (s7). Note that the penalty was increased by the Children and Young Persons (Protection from Tobacco) Act 1991.

(f) Exposure to risk of burning. A person of 16 or over who has responsibility for a child under 12 commits an offence by allowing the child to be in a room containing an open fire grate, or any heating appliance liable to cause injury by contact, without sufficient protection against the child being burned or scalded if the child is thereby killed or seriously injured (s11).

(g) Vagrants preventing children from receiving education. It is an offence for a person to habitually wander from place to place and take with him a person of compulsory school age, thus preventing that person from receiving efficient full-time education (s10).

(h) Entertainments. Failure to provide for the safety of children at entertainments is an offence. If more than 100 children, there must be attendants (s12).

Forms of cruelty for the purpose of s1

(a) Assaults - This does not preclude the right of parent or teacher to administer reasonable punishment.

(b) Ill-treats - Actual suffering is not necessary. Its likelihood is sufficient.

   (c) Neglects - Failure to provide adequate food, clothing, medical aid or lodging or take steps to get some provided through the Ministry of Social Security shall be deemed to be neglect.

      If the death of an infant under three is caused by suffocation through being overlain by a person of 16 years or over, who has gone to bed under the influence of drink, it is deemed to be neglect on the part of that person.

   (d) Abandons - To leave a child to its fate.

   (e) Exposes - Exposing to any possible danger (eg to physical injury or the effects of the weather). Intentional injury is not necessary.

Abandoning children

The Offences against the Person Act 1861, s27, makes it an offence to abandon or expose any child under two years whereby its life is endangered or its health is, or is likely to be, permanently injured. Persons under 16 years may be convicted under this Act. The penalty is five years' imprisonment, so this is an arrestable offence.

First Schedule offences

The offences listed in Sch 1 to the Children and Young Persons Act 1933 include:

      Murder or manslaughter of a child or young person.

      Infanticide.

      Abandoning or exposing a child under two so as to endanger life or health.

      Abduction of a girl under 16.

      Child stealing.

      Assaults, defilement and unnatural offences.

      Incest with a child or young person.

      Allowing a juvenile under 16 to take part in a dangerous public performance.

      Offences against ss1, 3, 4 or 11 of the 1933 Act.

      Seduction or prostitution.

      Offences under the Indecency with Children Act 1960.

      Any other offence involving bodily injury to a child or young person.

      Taking indecent photographs of children, etc.

      Inciting a girl under 16 to commit incest.

      Any other offence involving bodily injury to a child or young person.

Unauthorised removal of children from England and Wales

Immigration officers may prevent the departure from England and Wales of any child who, by order of the High Court, is a ward of court, or the subject of a custody order or an injunction which prohibits a child from being taken out of the jurisdiction.

Any constable called to assist an immigration officer must prevent such a child from embarking.

Fireworks (Fireworks (Safety) Regulations 1986)

No person shall supply, offer to supply or agree to supply any fireworks to any person apparently under the age of 16 years.

Chapter 37
Liquor Licensing Laws

The main Act covering liquor licensing is the Licensing Act 1964, as amended, but the Acts of 1872 and 1902 are still in use. The following applies to the 1964 Act unless otherwise stated.

Permitted hours and variations

Intoxicating liquor may only be sold, supplied, consumed in or taken away from licensed premises during certain hours (s53). These are known as the 'permitted hours' and are generally as follows -
  Weekdays: the hours from 11.00 am to 11.00 pm. Off-licence premises, 8.00 am until the end of permitted hours.
  Sundays, Christmas Day and Good Friday: the hours from 12 noon to 10.30 pm, with a break of 4 hours beginning at 3.00 pm.
  The licensing justices in any district, if they are satisfied that the requirements of the district make it desirable, may by order modify the weekday permitted hours so that they begin earlier but not before 10 am (s60).
  In addition to the permitted hours a further 20 minutes is allowed for consumption or taking away of intoxicating liquor (except in open vessels), after the end of permitted hours. This is increased to 30 minutes for persons taking meals where the liquor is ancillary to the meal (s63).
  Opening during permitted hours is not obligatory (s90).

Extension of permitted hours

An extension of one hour may be added to permitted hours in respect of premises which are structurally adapted and used for the regular supply of table meals in a part of the premises habitually set apart for this purpose.

On Sundays, Christmas Day and Good Friday the period between the first and second parts of permitted hours may be added (s68).

In licensed premises and registered clubs where an evening extension is in force if, in addition, live entertainment is provided, permitted hours may be extended until 1.00 am. This provision only applies on days when entertainment is provided and where the sale and supply of intoxicating liquor is ancillary to the refreshment and entertainment. (Intoxicants may not be supplied to persons admitted after midnight or less than half an hour before the entertainment is due to end (s70).)

Special hours certificate

A special hours certificate can be granted by the licensing justices to licensed premises or by magistrates to registered clubs where music and dancing is provided in addition to refreshment (liquor ancillary).

If granted, the permitted hours on a particular weekday shall extend to 2.00 am. If music and dancing is not provided after midnight, permitted hours finish at midnight. If music and dancing end at any time between midnight and 2.00 am the permitted hours must end at the same time (s76).

Exemption orders (s74)

A general order of exemption may be granted by a magistrates' court to the holder of an 'On' licence or the secretary of a registered club with premises near a public market, or a place where persons follow a trade or calling, if the magistrates are satisfied that it is desirable for the accommodation of a considerable number of persons. The order specifies the days and times at which the extension applies.

A special order of exemption may be granted by a magistrates' court to the holder of an 'On' licence or the secretary of a registered club authorising him to sell intoxicants outside permitted hours on his premises on a special occasion, eg a Christmas Eve dinner or dance.

Exceptions from prohibition of sale outside permitted hours (s 63)

Where any intoxicating liquor is supplied during the permitted hours, s59 does not prohibit or restrict :
(a) the consumption of any liquor on the premises during the first 20 minutes after the end of those hours, nor the taking of liquor from the premises unless in an open vessel;

(b) the consumption of liquor on the premises during the first half hour after the end of those hours, if it was supplied as an ancillary to a meal;

(c) sale, supply or consumption in premises where a person is residing;

(d) the ordering of intoxicating liquor to be consumed off the premises, or the despatch of liquor so ordered;

(e) the sale to a trader for the purposes of his trade, or to a registered club;

(f) the sale or supply to any canteen or mess;

(g) the taking of intoxicating liquor from the premises by a person residing there;

(h) the supply for consumption on the premises to any private friends of a person residing there who are entertained by him at his own expense;

(i) the supply for consumption on the premises to persons employed there, or the consumption of liquor so supplied at the expense of their employer.

In addition s59 does not apply at an airport approved under s22 of the Customs and Excise Management Act 1979 (international airports where hot and cold beverages other than intoxicating liquor are supplied).

Conduct of licensed premises

The Licensing Acts contain provisions for preserving order in licensed premises, controlling sales of intoxicating liquor and restricting sales of intoxicating liquor to young persons. A licensee may be held responsible for the conduct of his premises, even in his absence, but certain sections imply knowledge on the part of the licensee and note must be taken of words such as 'knowingly', 'allowing', 'suffering', 'permitting', etc.

In many licensing offences several persons may be involved under one set of circumstances. For instance, in the offence of consuming intoxicants after permitted hours, offences may be committed by the licensee (selling); the barman (supplying); and the customer (consuming). If there is insufficient evidence to establish a charge of supplying, the offence of aiding and abetting consumption may be considered.

The holder of a justices' licence must not :

(a) knowingly suffer to remain on the premises any constable on duty or supply intoxicating liquor to him (except by the authority of a superior officer), or bribe or attempt to bribe any constable (s178);

(b) knowingly allow his premises to be the habitual resort or meeting place of reputed prostitutes (s175);

(c) permit the premises to be a brothel (s176);

(d) permit drunkenness, violent, quarrelsome or disorderly conduct, or sell intoxicating liquor to a drunken person (s172);

(e) suffer any unlawful gaming on his premises (s177);

(f) supply intoxicating liquor on credit, except when consumed at a meal or by a resident (s169);

(g) sell or supply a measure of intoxicating liquor exceeding that required ('long pull') (s165);

(h) sell intoxicating liquor to a person under 18 or knowingly allow a person under 18 to consume (s169);

(i) sell or supply intoxicating liquor during non-permitted hours (s59).

Definition of bar

Many licensing offences may only be committed in a bar. A bar includes any place *exclusively or mainly used for the sale and consumption of intoxicating liquor;* but not when it is set apart for the service of table meals, and the supply of intoxicating liquor is confined to persons having table meals there (ss 201 and 171).

Other offences in licensed premises

(a) Persons under 18 shall not in licensed premises buy or attempt to buy any intoxicating liquor, nor consume intoxicating liquor in a *bar* (s169(2)).

(b) No person shall buy or attempt to buy intoxicating liquor in a *bar* of licensed premises, for consumption by a person under 18 (s 169(3)).

(Sale to or purchase by a person 16 years of age or over of beer, porter, cider or perry for consumption at a meal in a part of licensed premises usually set apart for the service of meals is permissible under s169(4), as such a place is not a bar. Any type of intoxicating liquor may be *consumed* by a person under 18 when not in a bar.)

(c) Selling or exposing for sale intoxicating liquor by retail without holding a justices' licence (s160).

(d) Consuming or taking from licensed premises or a registered club any intoxicating liquor during non-permitted hours (with exceptions) (s59).

(e) Licensee or his servant knowingly delivering intoxicating liquor to a person under 18 years (with exceptions) (s 169(5)).

(f) Knowingly sending a person under 18 for intoxicating liquor sold in licensed premises for consumption off the premises (s 169(6)).

(g) Procuring or attempting to procure intoxicating liquor in licensed premises for consumption by a drunken person or aiding such a person to do so (s163).

Delivery of intoxicants (s163)

Intoxicants shall not be delivered from a van, vehicle or basket unless ordered before despatch. Particulars must be entered in a delivery book or invoice carried by the person delivering, and in a day-book kept on his premises. No other intoxicants may be carried. A person shall not refuse to allow a constable to examine any van, vehicle, basket or document. (This does not apply to a trader for his trade or club for club purpose.)

DRUNKENNESS

Drunkenness is not an offence in itself and only becomes an offence when it is accompanied by circumstances laid down in certain statutes. There is no legal definition of drunkenness; the police officer on the spot has to decide whether a person is sufficiently drunk and the attendant circumstances are sufficient to justify a charge.

Offences

(a) Simple drunkenness (Licensing Act 1872, s12).
    Every person found drunk, in any highway or other public place (whether a building or not), or on licensed premises (when open to the public). (Licensing Act 1902, s1.)
(b) Drunk and disorderly (Criminal Justice Act 1967, s91).
    Any person who in any public place is guilty, while drunk, of disorderly behaviour. In this section public place includes any highway and any other premises or place to which at the material time the public have or are permitted to have access, whether on payment or otherwise.
(c) Drunk in charge of horse, cattle or carriage on a highway (Licensing Act 1872, s12).
    Carriage includes a pedal cycle.
(d) Drunk in possession of a loaded firearm (Licensing Act 1872, s12).
    This offence can take place anywhere public or private.
    There is no need to prove actual danger. An honest belief that offence is being committed is sufficient.

(e) Drunk in charge of a child under seven years (Licensing Act 1902, s2).

In any highway or public place, whether a building or not, or in licensed premises.

(f) Drunk, violent, quarrelsome or disorderly on licensed premises and refusing to leave when requested (Licensing Act 1964, s174). Power is given to a licensee to expel and for the police to assist. A constable must assist on request.

Definition of public place

Any place to which the public have access, whether on payment or not.

TYPES OF LICENCES AND PERMISSIONS

Sale of intoxicating liquor

'Intoxicating liquor' means spirits, wine, beer, cider or any other fermented, distilled or spirituous liquor, but does not include any liquor of an original gravity not exceeding 1016° and a strength not exceeding 1.2% perfumes, flavouring essences not intended for consumption, medicated spirits or wine intended for use as a medicine and not a beverage (s201).

Justices' licences (s1)

Intoxicating liquor may not be sold by retail unless a justices' licence has been granted. A justices' licence is granted by the licensing justices authorising sale by a specified person from specified premises.

The licensing justices are a committee of the local justices. They deal with the granting of licences and other licensing business at the 'General Annual Licensing Meetings', and not less than four transfer sessions in the 12 months beginning with February in every year (s26).

There are two categories of justices' licences:

(a) *On-Licence*. This authorises the retail sale of intoxicants for consumption both on and off the premises, but in the case of licence granted under Part IV of the Licensing Act 1964 special conditions apply as follows :

(i) Restaurant licence authorises sale and supply only to persons as an ancillary to the main mid-day and/or evening meal.

(ii) Residential licence authorises sale and supply only to persons residing in premises which supply a main meal in addition to breakfast. Residents may treat bona fide friends on premises. Residents may be supplied for off consumption with a packed meal.

   (iii) Combined restaurant and residential licence authorises sale and supply to both residents and persons taking table meals, in accordance with the above conditions.

  (b) *Off-Licence.* Authorises retail sale of intoxicants for consumption *off* the premises only.

Either of the above licences may be granted for one or more of the different classes of intoxicating liquor. Premises for which there is a justices' licence in force are known as 'licensed premises'. There are different types of licences according to the type of intoxicants sold.

A justices' licence is not necessary for sale of intoxicants in certain places, eg passenger vessels (including passenger trains, ships and aircraft) and properly authorised canteens.

Occasional licence (s180)

An occasional licence is granted by Justices of the Peace on application by the holder of a justices'on-licence and entitles him to sell and supply intoxicants on a special occasion elsewhere than on his licensed premises. 24 hours' notice must be given to the chief officer of police.

The maximum duration of an occasional licence is three weeks. It may not be granted for the sale of intoxicants on Christmas Day, Good Friday or any day of public thanksgiving or mourning. It may, however, be granted for such sale on a Sunday.

Such premises are licensed premises in respect of permitting drunkenness, keeping disorderly houses or brothels, harbouring constables, gaming, power to exclude drunkards, constable's power of entry, employment of and supply of intoxicants to persons under 18 years. They cease to be licensed premises at the expiration of the occasional licence.

Occasional permissions

The Licensing (Occasional Permissions) Act 1983 permits licensing justices to grant occasional permission to officers of organisations not carried on for the purpose of private gain. This will allow intoxicating liquor to be sold during any period not exceeding 24 hours at a function held by that organisation. The justices must be satisfied that the premises are suitable and that there will be no disturbance or annoyance of residents, or disorderly conduct, and other conditions may be attached to the permission. Not more than four occasional permissions may be granted in a year.

Sales to persons under 18 years are prohibited and drunkenness must not be permitted. A constable may enter the premises at any time specified in the occasional permission for the purpose of preventing and detecting offences.

POLICE POWERS

Any constable may, for the purpose of preventing or detecting the commission of any offence against the Licensing Act 1964, enter any licensed premises at any time during permitted hours and for half an hour afterwards. He may also enter at any time outside permitted hours when it is reasonably suspected that such an offence is being, or is about to be, committed.

In the case of an occasional licence the power of entry applies to the hours specified in the licence, and in the case of a special hours certificate between 11.00 pm and half an hour after the end of permitted hours. It is an offence to fail to admit a constable who demands entry (s186).

A constable *must,* when called upon, help to expel from licensed premises any person who is drunk, violent, quarrelsome or disorderly, or whose presence would subject the licensee to a penalty.

CHILDREN AND YOUNG PERSONS IN LICENSED PREMISES

The holder of a justices' licence must not allow a person under 14 years to be in the *bar* of his licensed premises during permitted hours, except:

(a) children of the licensee,
(b) children of residents but not if employed in the premises,
(c) children passing through the *bar* to other parts of the premises,
(d) in railway refreshment rooms, or other premises made to be used for any purpose to which the holder of a justices' licence is merely ancillary,

and no person shall cause or procure this. The licensee is guilty of an offence unless he proves that he exercised all due diligence to prevent the person under 14 from being admitted or he believes that the person has apparently attained the age of 14.

Children are also permitted in a place set aside for the service of table meals and not used for the sale or supply of intoxicating liquor otherwise than to a person having table meals there and for consumption by such a person as ancillary to his meal.

CLUBS

There is no statutory definition of the word 'club' but it denotes a voluntary association of a number of persons for a common object or purpose, eg recreation, art, science, politics, sport, or social welfare, etc.

There is no control over clubs as such, unless they wish to sell intoxicating liquor. Intoxicants may not be supplied on any club premises by or on behalf of the club except under the authority of either:

(a) Registration certificate - registered club.

(b) Justices' licence - licensed club.

Licensed clubs (s 55)

A club wishing to sell intoxicating liquor to its members (a 'proprietary club') must obtain a justices' licence and as such becomes licensed premises for all purposes of the law including right of entry by the police, permitted hours, and restrictions on the sale and supply of liquor to persons under 18 years.

The licensing justices may attach conditions to a club licence to include the prohibition or restriction of sales of liquor to non-members and relieve the licensee of the obligation to display a notice on the premises with his name and particulars of licence.

Registered clubs (ss 39 and 40)

A club requires to obtain a registration certificate from the magistrates' court for the petty sessional area, if it occupies premises habitually used as a club and intoxicating liquor is supplied therein to members and guests.

Before a registration certificate is granted, a club must satisfy the following conditions :

(a) There must be an interval of two days between application and admission as members.

(b) It must be conducted in good faith as a club and have not less than 25 members.

(c) The purchase and supply of intoxicants must be under the control of an elective committee.

(d) No person (apart from the club) shall receive any pecuniary benefit from the purchase or supply of intoxicants.

(e) The club must be managed by fit persons.

(f) The premises must not be disqualified.

(g) The club must not have any other club premises which are licensed whereby any abuse of permitted hours is likely.

Supply of intoxicants to members of registered clubs does not amount to a sale. There must not be any sale of liquor to non-members, except as provided in club rules. All liquor must be paid for at the time of supply, except when with a meal. Liquor must not be supplied for OFF consumption except to a member on the premises.

Note that there is no age restriction as there is in the case of 'licensed' premises.

Permitted hours for registered clubs (s62)

The permitted hours for registered clubs on week-days are the general licensing hours. On Sundays, Christmas Day and Good Friday the hours are as fixed by the rules of the club, but not longer than $5^1/_2$ hours between 12 noon and 10.30 pm, within a break of not less than 2 hours between 3.00pm and 5.00pm and not more than $3^1/_2$ hours after 5.00 pm.

These general licensing hours may be varied by Special Orders of Exemption, General Orders of Exemption and Extensions of Permitted Hours, as these may be granted to a registered club as they are granted to licensed premises.

Cancellation of registration certificate

The certificate may be cancelled by a magistrates'court on the complaint of the chief officer of police or the local authority on any of the following grounds :
  (a) Failure to comply with any of the conditions of registration above.
  (b) That the club is conducted in a disorderly manner or used for any unlawful purpose.
  (c) That the club is the resort of criminals or prostitutes.
  (d) It is used for indecent displays.
  (e) There is frequent drunkenness.
  (f) There have been illegal sales of intoxicants within the preceding 12 months.
  (g) The club rules are habitually disregarded in any material respect.

Police powers

On initial application for registration, club premises may be inspected by the police if special reasons exist which make it necessary.

Apart from this there is no power of entry without warrant into registered clubs, except when a special hours certificate is in force. Such premises are not licensed premises and the position is similar to a private house. This only applies to registered clubs, as clubs for which a justices' licence is in force are 'licensed premises' and the police have a power of entry. If, however, a special hours certificate is granted, the club premises are open to inspection by the police while it is in force.

SEARCH WARRANTS

(a) Licensing Act 1964, s187
   A search warrant may be granted on sworn information that intoxicating liquor is being sold or kept or exposed for sale by retail without a justices' licence. This type of warrant applies to any place, gives a power to seize liquor and a power of arrest if a name and address are refused.

(b) Licensing Act 1964, s54
   A search warrant may be granted on sworn information that there are reasonable grounds for believing that any registered club is so managed as to constitute grounds for cancelling a registration certificate held by the club, or that intoxicating liquor is sold or supplied or kept for sale or supply in club premises for which the club does not hold a registration certificate or a justices' licence. This applies to all clubs. There is no power to seize liquor or to arrest, but documents may be seized.

A police officer would be well advised when raiding a registered or licensed club to be in possession of both warrants as each gives different powers.

INTOXICATING SUBSTANCES (SUPPLY) ACT 1985

This Act prohibits the supply to persons under 18 years of age of substances, other than controlled drugs, which may cause intoxication if inhaled (eg glue and solvents).

Chapter 38
Armed Forces and Bomb Hoaxes

ABSENTEES AND DESERTERS

Definitions

An absentee is a member of HM Forces who is absent from his unit without leave and intends to return.

A deserter is one who is absent from his unit without leave and does not intend to return. A court of inquiry is usually held after an absence of 21 days before a man is declared to be a deserter.

Procedure

On reasonable suspicion that a person is a deserter or absentee any constable may arrest that person without warrant (preserved power). Women cannot be arrested as deserters - only as absentees. Members of the WRNS cannot be arrested on these charges. (Army Act 1955, s186; Air Force Act 1955, s186; Naval Discipline Act 1957, s105.)

The power of arrest does not entitle a police officer to force entrance to a dwelling house without a warrant.

Deserters or absentees who are arrested, except on a naval warrant, are taken before a court and can be remanded in custody for an escort. Deserters or absentees arrested on a naval warrant shall, as soon as practicable, be delivered into naval custody.

Deserters or absentees who surrender themselves may be handed over to a service escort without appearing before a court. If the officer in charge of a police station is satisfied that an escort is not necessary, they may be given rail warrants and allowed to return unaccompanied. In any case where the person so requests, he must be taken before a court.

OFFENCES IN REGARD TO UNIFORMS

It is an offence under the Uniforms Act 1894 for a person not in HM military or air forces to wear the uniform or dress having the appearance or distinctive marks of such uniform without HM permission (except in stage plays, etc).

It is an offence for a person not in HM Forces to wear naval, military or air force uniform or dress resembling it so as to be likely to bring it into contempt, or to employ another to so wear that uniform or dress.

The unauthorised use or wearing of any military decoration, medal or anything so nearly resembling as to deceive, or falsely pretending to be entitled to use or wear the same are also offences under this Act.

INCITEMENT TO MUTINY AND DISAFFECTION

(a) It is an indictable offence, punishable with life imprisonment, to maliciously try to incite any person serving in HM Forces from his duty and allegiance, or to incite such person to commit an act of mutiny or any traitorous or mutinous practice (Incitement to Mutiny Act 1797).

(b) It is an offence under the Incitement to Disaffection Act 1934, maliciously to attempt to incite any member of HM Forces from his duty or allegiance to the Crown, or with intent to commit the offence, to possess any document likely to induce such disaffection.

BOMB HOAXES

Section 51 of the Criminal Law Act 1977 provides that a person who places any article in any place whatever; or dispatches any article by post, rail or any other means whatever of sending things from one place to another, with the intention of inducing in some other person a belief that it is likely to explode or ignite and thereby cause personal injury or damage to property, is guilty of an offence. 'Article' means substance.

An offence is also committed by a person who communicates any information which he knows or believes to be false to another person, with the intention of inducing in him or any other person a false belief that a bomb or other thing liable to explode or ignite is present in any place or location.

The penalty for these offences is not exceeding five years' imprisonment; therefore they are arrestable offences.

Chapter 39
Animals, Birds, Fish and Plants

DISEASES OF ANIMALS

This subject is dealt with by the Animal Health Act 1981. For the purpose of this Act and the regulations and orders made under it, 'animal' means cattle, sheep, goats and all other ruminating animals, swine, horses, asses, mules and jennets. ('Cattle' means bulls, cows, oxen, heifers and calves, and a jennet is a small Spanish horse.)

Enforcement of the Act is the responsibility of:

- (a) the Ministry of Agriculture, Fisheries and Food, through divisional veterinary inspectors;
- (b) local authorities, through inspectors (who may be police officers); and
- (c) the police.

Notifiable diseases

Some diseases are 'notifiable', eg foot-and-mouth disease, cattle plague, sheep pox, swine fever, sheep scab, anthrax and glanders. Special provision is made for rabies.

Where one of these diseases exists, the Minister may declare an area or place to be infected and make an order prohibiting or regulating the movement of animals, persons, carcasses and materials within, into or out of that place or area. Orders may also prescribe or regulate the cleansing and disinfection of infected places and, in the case of some diseases, the slaughter of animals.

Offences

Failing, without lawful authority or excuse, to keep an animal separate so far as practicable, or to give notice of disease with all practicable speed (s15(7)).

Without lawful authority or excuse:

(a) throws, places, causes or suffers to be thrown or placed into any river, stream, canal, navigation or other water, or into the sea within 4.8 km of the shore, the carcass of an animal which has died of disease, or been slaughtered as diseased; or

(b) digs up or causes to be dug up, a carcass buried under the direction of the Minister or local authority (s35(4)).

Without lawful authority or excuse, refuses an inspector admission to any land, building, vehicle, etc; or otherwise obstructs or impedes him; or in any respect obstructs or impedes an inspector or constable in the execution of his duty (s66).

Without lawful authority or excuse, does anything in contravention of this Act, order or regulation; or failing to give, produce, observe or do any notice, licence, rule or thing which he is required to do (s73).

Without lawful authority or excuse, does or omits to do anything which is declared by this Act to be an offence, or does anything declared to be not lawful (s72).

Police powers

Under s60 of the Animal Health Act 1981 the police force of each police area must execute and enforce the Act and every order of the Minister. Where a person is seen or found committing, or is reasonably suspected of being engaged in committing, an offence against the Act, a constable may without warrant stop and detain him. The constable may, whether so stopping or detaining the person or not, stop, detain and examine any animal, vehicle, boat or thing to which the offence or suspected offence relates, and require it to be forthwith taken back to the place from which is was unlawfully removed.

If a person obstructs or impedes or assists in obstructing or impeding an officer other than a constable in the execution of this Act, order or regulation, a constable may without warrant apprehend the offender and take him before a justice with all practicable speed.

Powers in relation to rabies

Section 61 of the 1981 Act provides that, without prejudice to the powers of arrest conferred by s60, a constable may arrest without warrant any person whom he, with reasonable cause, suspects to be in the act of committing or to have committed an offence consisting of:

    (a) the landing or attempted landing of any animal in contravention of an order made for the purpose of preventing the introduction of rabies into Great Britain; or

    (b) the failure by the person having the charge or control of any vessel or boat to discharge any obligation imposed on him by such an order; or

    (c) the movement in contravention of an order of any animal into, within or out of a place or area declared to be infected with rabies.

For the purpose of arresting a person under this power, a constable may enter (if need be by force) and search any vessel, boat, hovercraft, aircraft or vehicle of any other description, in which that person is or in which the constable, with reasonable cause, suspects him to be.

For the purpose of exercising any power to seize an animal or cause an animal to be seized, a constable may enter (if need be by force) and search any vessel, boat, aircraft or vehicle of any other description, in which there is, or in which he with reasonable cause suspects that there is, an animal to which the power applies.

CRUELTY

Protection of Animals Act 1911

Section 1 states that if any person shall:

    (a) cruelly beat, kick, ill-treat, over-ride, over-drive, over-load, torture, infuriate, or terrify any animal, or cause or procure, or, being the owner, permit any animal to be so used, or by wantonly or unreasonably doing or omitting to do any act, or causing or procuring the commission or omission of any act, cause any unnecessary suffering, or being the owner, permit any unnecessary suffering to be so caused to any animal; or

    (b) convey or carry, or cause or procure, or, being the owner, permit to be conveyed or carried, any animal in such manner or position as to cause that animal any unnecessary suffering; or

    (c) cause, procure, or assist at the fighting or baiting of any animal; or keep, use, manage, or act or assist in the management of, any premises or place for the purpose, or partly for the purpose, of fighting or baiting any animal, or permit any premises or place to be so kept, managed, or used, or receive, or cause or procure any person to receive money for the admission of any person to such premises or place; or

    (d) wilfully, without any reasonable cause or excuse, administer, or cause or procure, or being the owner permit, such administration of, any poisonous or injurious drug or substance to any animal, or wilfully, without any reasonable cause or excuse, cause any such substance to be taken by any animal; or

(e)   subject, or cause or procure, or being the owner permit to be subjected, any animal to any operation which is performed without due care and humanity; or

(f)   tether any horse, ass or mule so as to cause unnecessary suffering;

he shall be guilty of an offence of cruelty.

'Animal' means any domestic or captive animal.

'Domestic animal' includes any animal of whatsoever species which is tame or which has been or is being sufficiently tamed to serve some purpose for the use of man.

'Captive animal' includes any animal (not being a domestic animal) of whatsoever kind or species, which is in captivity or confinement or which is maimed, pinioned, or subjected to any contrivance to prevent its escape.

An owner shall be deemed to have permitted cruelty if he has failed to exercise reasonable care and supervision in respect of the protection of the animal. The offence of cruelty does not apply to the destruction of animals as food for mankind, unless accompanied by the infliction of unnecessary suffering; or to the coursing or hunting of a captive animal, unless it is liberated in an injured, mutilated, or exhausted condition, or if it is coursed or hunted in an enclosed space from which it has no reasonable chance of escape.

A police constable may apprehend without warrant any person whom he has reason to believe is guilty of an offence under this Act which is punishable by imprisonment without the option of a fine, whether upon his own view or upon the complaint and information of any other person who shall declare his name and address. Where a person having charge of a vehicle or animal is apprehended, it shall be lawful for a constable to take charge of such vehicle or animal and deposit them in some place of safe custody. Reasonable costs of such detention and of veterinary treatment where required, are recoverable from the owner in the event of a conviction (s12).

(The Protection of Animals Act 1911 also deals with the use of poisoned grain and flesh (s8), and spring traps (s10), provides a power of entry to knackers' yards (s5), and empowers a constable to deal with injured animals (s11).)

Abandonment of Animals Act 1960

This Act makes it an offence to abandon any animal in circumstances likely to cause unnecessary suffering. Any person causing, permitting or procuring this offence shall be guilty of the offence of cruelty under s1 of the Protection of Animals Act 1911.

Pet Animals Act 1951

Every person carrying on a pet business at premises must have a licence issued by the local authority. The following conditions apply:
- (a) no person shall sell animals as pets in any street or public place, or at a stall or barrow in a market;
- (b) no person shall sell an animal as a pet to any person reasonably believed to be under 12 years of age.

Both of these offences carry three months' imprisonment.

'Animal' includes any description of vertebrate (mammals, birds, reptiles, amphibians and fishes).

Animal Boarding Establishments Act 1963

No person shall keep a boarding establishment for animals except under the authority of a licence granted by the local authority.

'Animal' for this purpose, means any dog or cat.

Cruelty to Animals Act 1876

This Act makes it an offence to perform on any living animal any experiment calculated to give it pain, except on licence and subject to certain restrictions. A search warrant may be granted in cases where it is believed that such experiments are being carried out unlawfully.

Cock Fighting Act 1952

It is an offence to possess any article for the purpose of using or permitting its use in cock fighting.

Performing Animals (Regulation) Act 1925

No person shall exhibit any performing animal at public entertainments or train any animal for such purpose unless he is registered with the local council.

Any constable may enter at all reasonable times and inspect any premises where performing animals are trained, exhibited or kept. He can inspect the animals found there and require the production of the certificate of registration. He is not, however, entitled to go on or behind the stage during any public performance.

DOGS

Wearing of collars

The Control of Dogs Order 1930 provides that every dog of any age in any highway or place of public resort must wear a collar with the owner's name and address thereon. Exceptions are provided for hounds, dogs being used for sporting purposes, dogs used for the destruction of vermin, and dogs used for tending cattle or sheep.

Stray dogs

Section 3 of the Dogs Act 1906, as amended, deals with the right of the police and authorised officers of a local authority to seize stray dogs, detain them for 7 days, and sell or destroy them if their owners are not traced. This does not apply to dogs found on land or premises other than a highway or place of public resort unless the owner consents.

Section 2 of the Dogs (Amendment) Act 1928 obliges the finder of a stray dog to either return it to its owner or take it to the nearest police station. In the latter case, the finder may keep the dog, provided he does so for at least one month, unless it is claimed by its owner. A register must be kept by the chief officer of police. Dog licence duty was abolished by the Local Government Act 1988, s38.

Dangerous dogs

The following are the main offences in respect of dangerous dogs:
  (a) Being in charge of a dog worrying livestock (Dogs Act 1906, s1, and the Dogs (Protection of Livestock) Act 1953, s1).
  (b) Failing to keep a dangerous dog under control after a complaint to that effect has been made (Dogs Act 1871, s2).
  (c) Suffering an unmuzzled ferocious dog to be at large (Town Police Clauses Act 1848, s28).
  (d) Keeping a dog bred for fighting, ie a pit bull terrier, a Japanese tosa, a dogo argentino, or a filo braziliero. Any such dog must not be in a public place without being muzzled and on a lead (Dangerous Dogs Act 1991, s1).
  (e) Allowing a dog to be dangerously out of control in a public place. Aggravated offence if any person is injured by an out-of-control dog (Dangerous Dogs Act 1991, s3).

Under s 2 of the Dogs Act 1871 a magistrates' court can, on receiving a complaint that a dog is dangerous and not kept under control, issue an order to the owner that the dog be kept under proper control or destroyed.

'Dangerous' includes dangerous to cattle or to poultry. An order may be made even if the dog is kept on private premises if other persons have access to them. Failure to comply with such an order is an offence and there is a daily penalty for failing to comply.

'Public place' means any street, road or other place (whether or not enclosed) to which the public have or are permitted to have access whether for payment or otherwise and includes the common parts of a building containing two or more separate dwellings.

Disqualification for keeping a dog

Under the Protection of Animals (Cruelty to Dogs) Act 1933, persons convicted of cruelty may be disqualified by a court from keeping a dog. A person is presumed to keep a dog if it is seen in that person's custody, charge or possession, or in his house or premises.

Unburied carcasses

It is an offence to permit carcasses of cattle to remain unburied in a field or other place to which dogs can gain access, if this is done knowingly and without reasonable excuse (Dogs Act 1906, s6, and the Dogs (Amendment) Act 1928).

Control of dogs on roads

By s27 of the Road Traffic Act 1988, a local authority may by order made after consultation with the police and confirmation by the Minister, designate a road. A person who causes or permits a dog to be on such a designated road unless on a lead commits an offence. Dogs used for driving sheep or cattle and sporting dogs under proper control are exempted.

Guard dogs

The Guard Dogs Act 1975 states that a person shall not use or permit the use of a guard dog at any premises unless a handler capable of controlling the dog is present on the premises *and* the dog is under the control of the handler at all times, except while it is secured so that it is not at liberty to go freely about the premises.

The handler of a guard dog must keep the dog under his control while it is being used as a guard dog, except while another handler has control of it or it is secured.

Warning notices must be displayed at all entrances to premises where guard dogs are used.

'Guard dog' means a dog which is used to protect premises, property kept on premises, or a person guarding the premises.

GAME LAWS

General

There are various definitions of 'game' but the principal birds are pheasants, partridges and grouse. Hares are also included and rabbits are game under certain statutes.

No person shall kill, pursue or take game, or use any dog, gun, net or other instrument for the purpose of taking or killing game or searching for game, without a licence. Even when such a licence is obtained, permission is required to take or pursue game on land. Game licences are obtainable at main post offices.

The owner of land or a person authorised by him can kill hares or rabbits on such land without a licence. Authority must be in writing (Ground Game Act 1880).

It is unlawful to kill game (including hares) on Sundays and Christmas Day and in the close seasons, which are:
- (a) Pheasants between 1st February and 1st October.
- (b) Partridges between 1st February and 1st September.
- (c) Grouse between 10th December and 12th August.

There is no close season for rabbits.

Poaching and trespass in pursuit of game

'Poaching' relates to a number of offences committed by persons who trespass on land in pursuit of game. These are:
- (a) Day trespass (Game Act 1831). Trespassing on land in pursuit of game in the daytime.
- (b) Night poaching (Night Poaching Acts 1828 and 1844). Unlawfully taking game or rabbits by night; entering on land by night with any instrument to take or destroy game; and three or more persons together by night entering or being on land to take game, any one of them being armed.

'Night' begins one hour after sunset and ends one hour before sunrise.

Police action

A constable may enter on land, with the exception of certain government property, if he has reasonable grounds for suspecting that a person is committing any offence of day trespass or night poaching. He may require any person committing the offence of day trespass to quit the land and give his name and address (Game Act 1831 and Game Laws (Amendment) Act 1960).

Under the Poaching Prevention Act 1862 any constable in any highway, street, or public place, may search any person he may have good cause to suspect of coming from land where he has been unlawfully in pursuit of game and having in his possession any game unlawfully obtained or any gun or other thing used for the killing or taking of game. He may also stop and search any conveyance in which he has cause to suspect game or guns, etc are being carried by any such person. Any game or gun, etc may be seized but not dogs or ferrets. No power of arrest is given to a constable by these Acts.

Deer

The Deer Act 1991 protects red deer, fallow deer, roe deer and sika deer by making it an offence to take or wilfully kill them during the close seasons. These are:

Roe deer buck	1st November to 31st March inclusive.
Buck and stags of other species	1st May to 31st July inclusive.
All hinds and doe	1st March to 31st October.

It is also an offence to take or wilfully kill deer in the night; or to set traps, snare or poisoned or stupefying bait; or use any such article, net, certain types of firearm or any arrow, spear or similar missile.

Under the Act it is an offence to enter any land without the consent of the owner or occupier in search or pursuit of deer, or while on any land to take, kill or injure any deer, or to search for or pursue deer with such intent.

Fish

The Salmon and Freshwater Fisheries Act 1975 regulates fishing for salmon, trout, freshwater fish and eels by means of a licensing system. Numerous offences are created by the Act. Any constable or water bailiff may require any person fishing to produce his licence and give his name and address.

(Remember that s32 and Sch 1 to the Theft Act 1968 deal with the unlawful taking or destroying of fish.)

WILD ANIMALS, BIRDS AND PLANTS

Dangerous wild animals

Section 1 of the Dangerous Wild Animals Act 1976 makes it an offence for a person to keep any dangerous wild animal of certain specified species, without a licence granted by a local authority. Where a licence is granted certain conditions as to the health and security of the animal must be complied with.

The provisions of this Act do not apply to dangerous wild animals kept in zoological gardens, circuses, licensed pet shops, and places registered for the purpose of performing experiments.

Badgers

The Badgers Act 1991 and the Badgers (Further Protection) Act 1991 create offences of wilfully killing, injuring or taking any badger (except as permitted by the Act), having in possession or under control a recently killed badger or its pelt, cruelly ill-treating a badger, using badger tongs, and digging for badgers. It is also an offence to intentionally or recklessly interfere with a badger sett by obstructing its entrance or allowing a dog to enter, except when blocked by loose material for the purpose of fox hunting if removed afterwards.

WILDLIFE AND COUNTRYSIDE ACT 1981

Wild animals

Under s9 and Sch 5 to the Act it is an offence to intentionally kill, injure or take any protected wild animal; to have in possession or control any such live or dead animal; to damage, destroy or obstruct any structure or place which any such animal uses for shelter; and to sell or offer for sale any such animal.

The protected animals include the adder, bottle-nosed dolphin, harbour or common porpoise, common dolphin, common otter, red squirrel, and various types of snakes, butterflies, moths, toads, newts and snails.

Wild birds

Section 1 of the Act makes it an offence to intentionally kill, injure or take *any* wild bird, or to intentionally take or destroy their eggs.

'Wild bird' means any bird of a kind which is ordinarily resident in or is a visitor to Great Britain in a wild state, but does not include poultry, or, except for certain purposes, any game bird.

Schedule 1 lists certain rare birds which are protected by special penalties, and Sch 2 lists birds which may be taken or killed outside the close season. Note, however, that for general purposes this Act applies to all wild birds.

Wild plants

Offences are created by s13 of intentionally uprooting any wild plant, or intentionally picking, uprooting or destroying any listed wild plant in Sch 8. There are also offences of selling or offering for sale any live or dead wild plants.

(It should not be forgotten that flowers, fruit and foliage growing wild are also protected by s4(3) of the Theft Act 1968.)

Police powers

A constable may stop and search any person suspected with reasonable cause of committing any offence under the Wildlife and Countryside Act 1981, and may seize and detain anything which may be evidence of the offence. For this purpose a constable may enter onto any land other than a dwelling house.

Index

Q

R